CHARLES V. CHAPIN, M.D.

* * * * * * *

CHARLES V. CHAPIN
AND THE
PUBLIC HEALTH MOVEMENT

* * * * * * *

James H. Cassedy

HARVARD UNIVERSITY PRESS

CAMBRIDGE, MASSACHUSETTS · 1962

* * * * * * *

Publication of this book has been aided
by a grant from the Ford Foundation

Library of Congress Catalog Card Number 62-13265

Printed in the United States of America

* * * * *

To the memory of my father
WILLIAM A. T. CASSEDY, II

* * * * *

ACKNOWLEDGMENTS

I GREATLY appreciate the opportunity to talk and correspond with many persons who knew Chapin personally or were familiar with public health work and its history. I was fortunate in having interviews, just before their deaths, with Dr. Haven Emerson and Prof. Murray P. Horwood. Mrs. C.-E. A. Winslow, Mrs. Wade Hampton Frost, and Mrs. Albert J. Chesley graciously furnished recollections both of their late husbands and of Dr. and Mrs. Chapin. Many other nationally prominent people were equally helpful and generous with their time. These include: Dr. Reginald Atwater, Dr. David Bodian, Dr. James A. Doull, Dr. Louis I. Dublin, Dr. John A. Ferrell, Dr. Edward S. Godfrey, Dr. John E. Gordon, Dr. Claude E. Heaton, Prof. Ira V. Hiscock, Prof. Margaret Merrell, Dr. Alton S. Pope, Prof. Samuel C. Prescott, Dr. Watson S. Rankin, Mr. Burt A. Rickard, Dr. Phillip E. Sartwell, Prof. Richard H. Shryock, Dr. Wilson G. Smillie, Dr. Henry F. Vaughan, Dr. Huntington Williams, Prof. E. B. Wilson, and Prof. Abel Wolman.

Providence people provided particularly valuable insights into Dr. Chapin's work and life. These included, in the medical profession, Dr. Alexander M. Burgess, Dr. Harold C. Calder, Dr. Halsey DeWolf, Dr. John Donley, Dr. Frank T. Fulton, Dr. William M. Muncy, Dr. Lester Round, Dr. Arthur Ruggles, and Dr. Elihu Wing, Sr. Among nonmedical persons, special help was given me by Rev. Arthur Bradford, Mr. William Alden Browne, Miss Grace P. Chapin, Mrs. Donald Cowell, Mr. Paul Gleeson, Mrs. Guy F. Strickler, and Prof. Charles A. Stuart.

Courteous assistance was given by the staffs of the libraries used during the course of preparing the book. These include particularly The Brown University Libraries, The Library of the Rhode Island Historical Society, The Library of the Rhode Island State Department of Health, The Welch Medical Library, and the Library of the Harvard Medical School. A special note of appreciation is given to Mrs. Helen DeJong and her staff at the Library of the Rhode Island Medical Society. Mrs. Margaret G. Barnaby of the Harvard School of Public Health, and Miss Helen Bayne, Archivist of the NYU-Bellevue Medical Center, both made many helpful suggestions, while Mr. Joseph Gordon, Director of Health Education of the Baltimore Department of Health also gave valuable assistance.

The Superintendent of Health of Providence, Dr. Joseph Smith, and his Deputy, Dr. Edwin Knights, were generous with both their time and recollections. Dr. Hilary Connor, Superintendent of Chapin Hospital, and Dr. Edgar J. Staff, Director of Laboratories of the Rhode Island State Department of Health, also took interest in the project.

The book owes a special debt to Dr. Clarence L. Scamman. His edition of *The Papers of Charles V. Chapin, M.D.* helped to define the problems for this study as well as to lighten the chores of bibliographical epidemiology. He gave his encouragement to this project, answered many questions, and drew deeply from his experience as a close associate of Chapin.

The Graduate School of Brown University provided fellowship assistance while this work was originally being prepared as a Ph.D. thesis. Williams College later made a grant toward clerical expenses.

Mrs. Barbara Snow Cassedy made many constructive observations on style. She also assisted in other ways, tangible and intangible.

Professor Donald Fleming, now at Harvard University but formerly at Brown University, suggested the importance of making a study of Dr. Chapin. Subsequently, both while advising the preparation of this work as a Ph.D. thesis and since, he has given to it encouragement and critical comment.

J.H.C.

* * * * *

CONTENTS

Frontispiece. Charles V. Chapin, M.D. Detail of a portrait in the Library of the Rhode Island Medical Society, Providence, painted in 1927 by William Cushing Loring (1879–1959). (Photograph courtesy of Brown University Library.)

* * * * *

PROLOGUE

T<small>HE</small> spectacular late-nineteenth-century breakthrough in medical knowledge was fashioned largely in Europe. Its consolidation in the field of public health during the half-century or so after 1876, however, owed much to American leaders. From their posts at the Johns Hopkins University William H. Welch and William Osler sparked an impulse which spread modern scientific medicine around the world, while men like Wade H. Frost helped to develop scientific epidemiology and other specialized disciplines. In Cuba, Walter Reed and his associates solved the riddle of yellow fever, while William C. Gorgas went on to gain the admiration of all nations by conquering the disease. In New York City and New York State, Hermann M. Biggs built up two of the world's finest health organizations, while he and William H. Park showed what a bacteriological laboratory could do in such organizations. In Massachusetts, the host of distinguished public health scientists working during many of these years included the pathologist-entomologist Theobald Smith, the sanitary administrator Henry P. Walcott, the epidemiologist and teacher William T. Sedgwick, the teacher-writer Milton J. Rosenau, and the all-around sanitarian C.-E. A. Winslow. These men, together with others like George Sternberg, Charles Stiles, George Kober, and Victor Vaughan, were the leaders of a generation which gave preventive medicine a substantial scientific basis for the first time and made the modern American public health movement the envy of the world.

Charles Value Chapin was one of this group of sanitary pioneers. His career spanned the entire half-century after 1876, while his work touched at innumerable points on that of many other leaders. Welch was his teacher and a source of inspiration; Gorgas was his classmate and life-long intimate. His career ran parallel in many respects to that of Biggs, and he kept up a constant interchange of ideas with Smith, Park, and Vaughan. He was an intimate associate of Sedgwick, Walcott, and Rosenau, and men like Winslow and Frost counted him as their teacher as well as their collaborator. Chapin had a quality of leadership which brought the friendship and cooperation of his peers, and which, with younger public health workers, inspired tremendous personal loyalty. The close rapport which he enjoyed with all of these men was an essential element in the success he obtained in his work.

From his position as Superintendent of Health of the City of Providence, Rhode Island, Chapin made a highly individual and lasting contribution to better health for all. More than a devoted and well-loved local health officer, he was an imaginative administrator, a demanding voice in his profession, and a tireless and constructive investigator. Using the tools of bacteriology and field epidemiology, he moved a decade or more ahead of his profession throughout his long career, both as prophet and as authoritative model whom other health officers followed in adjusting to the new scientific information.

Chapin's two great achievements are inseparable. First, he made an exhaustive study of the confused accumulation of ancient theory about the communicable diseases, and weighed his findings in the light of the new facts revealed by the laboratory investigator and the epidemiologist. The results were an unprecedented attack on outmoded sanitary dogma and the formulation of a new body of principles which provided the basis for the entire modern attitude toward these diseases. Chapin then transferred these principles into a system of standards and values for the guidance of the practicing health officer. This methodology brought an unheard-of discipline into public health administration at both state and local levels, and provided much of the impetus for the nation-wide spread of scientific public health benefits in the present century. Chapin's courage, vigorous action, and persuasive logic inspired a new generation of sanitarians to emulate him.

As a health officer in a moderate-sized city, Chapin came to know the broad aspects of public health work as few other men have. The public health problems he met in Providence were more typical of the problems of most cities than were those of New York, London, or Berlin. Likewise, the solutions he worked out were more practical for most other places than were the special solutions applicable to the great metropolises. Thus, the pattern of public health work which Chapin developed became the pattern adopted throughout the United States and in many respects around the world.

Since 1850 Providence has produced a succession of unusually gifted leaders for the American public health movement, persons like Edwin M. Snow, Frederic P. Gorham, Dennett L. Richardson, and Mary S. Gardner. Chapin was the most brilliant star in this galaxy. With these others he helped make his city into a laboratory for the development of public health knowledge and administrative techniques. At the same time, living in an old community beset by the vast effects of immigration, industrialization, and urbanization, he provided, for almost fifty years, a constructive spur to the often-dormant Yankee conscience in meeting these problems. Chapin became one of those of whom it can be said that his career was not only of immense ultimate benefit to mankind in general but of great immediate value to his own neighbors.

Chapin's contemporaries put his contributions to humanity, his advancement of the scientific spirit, and his insights into the communicable diseases on the same plane with the achievements of Louis Pasteur. They ranked his use and interpretation of vast amounts of routine cumulative data with William Farr's analyses of the Registrar General's records in Great Britain. They recognized him as "the foremost epidemiologist of a day when epidemiology was lucky to find some person who could spell it," as the peer of such great European investigators as Thomas Sydenham, Peter Panum, William Budd, and John Snow. They agreed with C.-E. A. Winslow that "Dr. Chapin's contributions to the philosophy and methodology of public health are greater than any living man. In the past only Frank, Chadwick, Simon, Shattuck, Sedgwick, and Biggs have perhaps made an equal impress upon public health practice throughout the world." [1] Public health workers since Chapin's time have found no reason to refute these judgments.

THE NEW ENGLAND BACKGROUND

THE city of Providence, Rhode Island, was the physical and emotional as well as the intellectual center of Charles V. Chapin's life. It was the place of his birth and of his death. It constituted the environment in which his work took on substance and meaning.

Like many New Englanders, Chapin kept careful record of his ancestral origins in England, Scotland, and France. In 1623, in the Devonshire town of Paignton, Samuel Chapin, son of a baker, married Cicely Penny. Samuel and his family were soon caught up in the current of religious controversy which was dividing England, and about 1635 they came to America with many of their Puritan neighbors. During the next century and a half, Samuel Chapin's descendants spread out over Massachusetts and into other parts of New England. Nearly everywhere they settled the Chapins filled responsible community roles as justices of the peace, selectmen, farmer-citizens, or preachers. One of them, Deacon Seth Chapin, in 1775 left his farm in Mendon, Massachusetts to participate in the defense of Providence during the American Revolution. After the war, Deacon Seth went back to his farm but devoted more time than before to religion. Eventually he was minister to a succession of churches in southern Massachusetts and Rhode Island. Seth Jr. also became a Congregational minister. During his studies at

Brown University and Andover Seminary, he was a friend of Adoniram Judson. Judson went to Burma as the first foreign missionary sent out from America, while Seth Jr. went first to a pastorate at Hillsboro, New Hampshire.

Joshua, the father of Charles V. Chapin, was born at Hillsboro in 1812 and grew up in the small New England towns where Seth Jr. was pastor. He got the best that New England could offer of religious and educational training. This included the stern discipline of a succession of educators in Day's Academy at Wrentham, Massachusetts, Williams College, and Brown University. Unlike his father, however, Joshua decided to minister to the physical rather than the spiritual needs of his neighbors and elected to become a doctor. After studying for a time with a preceptor, he enrolled at the Harvard Medical School but later transferred to the Berkshire Medical College in Pittsfield.

At Berkshire during that time the Professor of Pathological Anatomy and Materia Medica was Elisha Bartlett. Bartlett had not yet written his work on *The History, Diagnosis and Treatment of Typhoid and Typhus Fever* or his *Essay on the Philosophy of Medical Science*.[1] His lectures, however, mirrored the doctrines which he and other American medical students had learned in the famous Parisian clinical "school" of medicine. Joshua Chapin received his M.D. degree from the Berkshire institution in 1838 and, like hundreds of others whom Bartlett taught in the United States, he took with him into medical practice the clinical philosophy of members of the Paris school, Laennec and Andral but especially of Pierre C. A. Louis. Louis advocated extended clinical investigations of disease. His technique was the close observation of cases and their analysis through the "numerical method" of diligently amassing observed facts from significantly large numbers of cases. Closely allied to this method was the spirit of skepticism which Louis preached regarding drug-dosing, blood-letting, and other empirical measures which constituted so much of the medicine of the day.

Joshua Chapin established himself as a physician in Providence in 1838, but after five years increasing deafness forced him to give up active medical practice. He then went into partnership with George Thurber to establish what was reputed to be the "first scientific apothecary store in Providence." After ten years of trying the partners could still hardly make "more than half a living" and the firm dissolved.[2] Joshua's next venture, with the Manchester brothers in the new but flourishing business of photography, proved more successful.

On May 16, 1842, after a three-year engagement, Joshua married Jane Catherine Louise Value of Providence. Louise Value had a romantic family history. Her mother was the daughter of a Scottish soldier in Burgoyne's army who had been captured by revolutionary troops at Saratoga and after the war had remained in America. Her father, Jean Pierre Victor Value, was a French refugee who had had to flee successively from the terrors of the French Revolution and from those of one of the great slave uprisings in Haiti.

By the time of her marriage Louise Value had become a talented artist and successful teacher of drawing and painting in Providence, and she continued this work most of her life. She was skilled in oils, water colors, and crayon drawings, as well as in miniatures, and did portraits of such eminent men as Chief Justice John Marshall. She often painted hunting scenes on velvet, and around 1850 she worked out a technique, said to be original, of copying photographs and tinting them in oil or water color. This proved to be a popular line which was helpful to the family at the time when the drug business was not very remunerative. Louise Chapin's personality was pleasant as her work, and her Providence home became a center of help and encouragement to younger artists of the town.[3] She provided in her family a warmth and tenderness which balanced the austere traits of her husband. Where Joshua, "a strict Congregationalist," inspired respect and discipline, Louise was relaxed with her children, and they knew her as "a real sport." [4]

Joshua and Louise Chapin raised a family that was small for their day, even though sixteen years separated their first and last babies. Charles, the only son, was born on January 17, 1856. His sister Marie Louise was thirteen years older, while Virginia was two years younger than Charles.

Charles Value Chapin's early childhood was spent in Providence amidst the bustle which accompanied his father's photography and his mother's art work. But in 1859 the family outlook and routine changed considerably. Joshua Chapin was appointed State Commissioner of Public Schools, an office which he held for eight of the next ten years. He made no great contributions to the public educational system that Henry Barnard had started in 1842, but conscientiously attempted to improve its functioning. An able public speaker, he traveled over the state arguing for longer school years, for full-time school superintendents, and for wider use of women teachers.[5]

Providence people knew Joshua Chapin as a man who was dignified, gentlemanly, erect, and "faultlessly neat." [6] He had a strong character and expressed his convictions positively and often abruptly. From him his son inherited a habit of plain speaking along with a rarely concealed contempt for all forms of cant and hypocrisy. Joshua, an early riser, was devoted to doing regular exercises for his health. He read widely, particularly in science. He experimented considerably with horticulture and, like many of his fellow members in the Providence Franklin Society, he was interested in ornithology and other aspects of natural history. His loss of hearing and abandonment of medical practice was a real loss to New England medicine, for he had shown a considerable talent for scientific investigation. In 1842 and 1843 two of his papers won him the Fiske Fund prize of the Rhode Island Medical Society.[7] He always retained his interest in medical affairs. Under the influence of his friend Dr. Edwin M. Snow, long-time Superintendent of Health of Providence, this interest extended in the 1850's and 1860's to the registration of vital statistics and to the sanitary affairs of the city. In 1872 the City Water Commissioners engaged him to inspect the banks of the Pawtuxet River for possible evidence of pollution.

Charles Chapin thus had a father who was part of the long tradition of ingenious and inquisitive Yankees. The boy became engrossed in science very early in life. Even as a child, Charles found merit in the critical philosophy his father had gained from Louis and Bartlett, for, when spring came every year, he was spared the sulphur and molasses meted out to his playmates.[8] Likewise, the traits of skepticism, close observation, and reliance upon numerical analysis which Joshua Chapin combined in his practice and in his later occupations were eventually transferred to the son. These traits, together with the common sense and inventiveness which Joshua acquired from his Yankee environment, all helped form the earliest image of the physician which the young Charles formed for himself.

When he was sixteen Charles showed some signs of following in the footsteps of Benjamin Franklin, who was his first great scientific hero. Using the pseudonym "H.M.A.," he sent a first Franklinesque communication to a local newspaper.

I have been considerably interested in lightening [sic] rods recently, and I was induced by the article on the subject in this morning's *Journal,* to examine some of the buildings that were struck in the late thunder storm. In company with a friend I visited twelve houses: of these only *four* were protected with rods and these were insulated with common glass insulators.

The editor of the *Evening Bulletin* took approving note of this initiative and hoped that the young man would continue to be a careful observer.[9]

Charles Chapin was far from robust as a boy and had more

than his share of illness, including a serious attack of typhoid fever from which he almost died. When cholera threatened the city, he and the other children heard the terrifying admonition: "We ought to be as good as we can for, before the summer is over, we will die by the thousand." [10] Fortunately the cholera was not severe in 1866. Despite the periods of sickness, however, Charles' boyhood was happy and exciting, both during the periods when the family lived on their nearby farm at Barrington and when they were in the city.

Providence was a good place to live in, even if the millionaires were choosing Newport down the Bay. It was small enough for its residents to know almost everyone in their own social classes, and large enough to escape being provincial. Daily whistles called the workers to jobs in the textile factories along the rivers, or at Brown & Sharpe's and the Corliss Steam Engine Works. Trains puffed in and out of Union Station on their way to Boston and New York. At the foot of the hill near the old Market House the farmers gathered from outlying places and sold their produce or went shopping. New and bigger buildings were going up alongside the old ones, and in 1864 horse cars began to run on tracks through the streets.[11] On College Hill students hustled to and from classes and got in fights with the "townies." Across town from the old East Side section, houses were going up on farm land, and in certain parts of the city one could see strangers, poor people from Canada, Ireland, or Germany, who were packed together in dirty houses.

The most exciting part of the city was still the waterfront, with its bustle of cargo being unloaded, its sometimes exotic though often overpowering odors, and its old salts who had been everywhere and done everything. Narragansett Bay was alive with ships of all kinds, sailing vessels and steamers, ferries and scows, dories and sloops. At an early stage of his boyhood Charles briefly entertained the idea of becoming a newsboy and selling papers and candy on a train, but this ambition disappeared before the lure of the sea. Then he dreamed of being the captain of a schooner, sailing to the West Indies and getting his fill of oranges.[12] Although this project never materialized, he continued to love the water, and Narragansett Bay was his favorite playground all his life. Autumn was a sad time of year, when cold weather put an end to the lazy summer days of swimming, sailing, digging clams, or looking for Indian arrowheads on one of the islands or points which projected out into the Bay.

In the year when Lee surrendered at Appomattox, the Rhode Island Commissioner of Public Schools brought his family back to Providence from Barrington and entered his son in Mowry and Goff's newly organized English and Classical High School for Boys. Charles, only nine, first went into the Preparatory Department, and then moved on into the regular Classical course. There he took the customarily large amount of Latin and Greek, plus ancient mythology and geography, and lesser amounts of algebra, arithmetic, and English grammar. For the weekly exercises in English composition, he wrote on such standard subjects as "Pompeii" and "Proserpina" as well as on nonclassical topics of current interest like "The Great Gale of 1869." [13] School was pleasant for him and he finished the course without difficult in June 1872. At Commencement he won the second prize in Declamation for his oration about "Misrepresentation of Indian Character." [14]

Graduation from such a Classical course was, for Providence boys like Charles, one of the first steps toward becoming a community leader. Subsequently they were expected to profess their faith in one of the right (Protestant) churches, go to Brown University for four years, join a respected profession or one of the old firms, and then marry into another local family of the old stock.

The religious step was not a problem for Charles. With his

sisters he went to Sunday School regularly, and at the age of eighteen he became a member of the Central Congregational Church. Religion remained important to Chapin all of his life, although it became progressively less formal. More often he expressed his religious feelings through his concepts of "community responsibility—the antithesis of selfishness." [15]

If proper religious training was an essential ingredient for well-born Providence boys, higher education was equally so. Attendance at Brown University had become a family tradition with the Chapins by the time Charles started there in September 1872. Although one of America's older colleges, in 1872 Brown was as yet uninfluenced by the modern concept of the university; it was still little more than a classical academy. It had five buildings: two residence dormitories, a recitation hall, a combined chapel and library, and a new chemical laboratory. As they had for years, college exercises still began every day with attendance at prayers led by the President, and on Sundays all students had to attend public worship twice. The college was still run largely by clergymen on the boards of Trustees and Fellows, although few faculty members were preachers any more. The new President was the Reverend Ezekiel G. Robinson. Students paid $75 per year for tuition and $20 for their rooms. Library and laboratory fees were extra.

Since Chapin lived at home and was not an athlete, he was less distracted than other students by the plethora of college activities and clubs. Nevertheless, during his four years at Brown he became a member of Alpha Delta Phi fraternity, competed regularly and successfully in the Declamations, and participated in dramatics and the chess club. As a Senior he helped with the yearbook, went as most students did to the meetings of the Society of Missionary Inquiry, and was a member of the Ciderial Club—even though he was known as one of three members who didn't like cider. Most engrossing of his extracurricular activities, probably, were the meetings of the

Lavoisier Association "for the advancement of chemical science," which he formed with a few friends.[16]

Studies at Brown meant following the time-honored classical course, with few electives. A quarter of Chapin's college work was Latin and Greek, along with Rhetoric, some French and German, History, and an indigestible course called Moral and Intellectual Philosophy. He also took all the Mathematics courses that were offered.

The central part of Chapin's college experience was the opportunity, limited as it was, for the study of science. He took as many science courses as he could fit within the framework of a classical A.B. program. He studied Physics under Professor Eli Blake and Astronomy under Samuel S. Greene. His introduction to Physiology came from Dr. Charles W. Parsons, one of Rhode Island's most eminent physicians. The best-equipped science department at Brown was Chemistry, its laboratory run by Professor John Appleton. Chapin took the required course in Chemistry and, looking ahead to Medical School, he also managed to fit in as one of his few electives, Appleton's intensive practical course in analytical chemistry.

Another science attraction at Brown was the new museum of natural history in Rhode Island Hall which had been set up by J. W. P. Jenks, a disciple of Agassiz's concept of separate biological creation. Jenks taught a course in agricultural zoology, but Chapin had already covered this field with his father and was excused from taking it. He did squeeze in, however, a practical course in civil engineering. The total amount of science taught was small; most of it came to the student through lectures and occasional demonstrations, rarely if ever through the chance to do experiments.

Commencement climaxed a week filled with Class Day exercises, concerts and picnics, the horseplay of the class supper, Baccalaureate and other religious meetings, alumni gatherings, and lower-class prize competitions. Chapin did not win any prizes, although he was elected to Phi Beta Kappa and appeared on the program to deliver an oration upon "Samuel Adams and American Independence." [17] Among those who received honorary degrees in 1876 was Dr. Stephen Smith, the celebrated New York sanitary reformer. This award was of more than passing interest to the young men who were planning to go on after graduation into the study of medicine.

IN PURSUIT OF
MEDICAL KNOWLEDGE

Soon after graduating, Chapin, along with his boyhood chum
and Brown classmate Harry Whitmarsh, started his medical
training in the office of Dr. George D. Wilcox in Providence.
Dr. Wilcox was a member of an old New England family, a
Republican, and one of the leading physicians of the city, although he belonged to the homeopathic sect. His medical
training, superior to that of most Providence physicians of the
day, included a New York medical degree, two years of study
in Vienna, Prague, and Leipzig before the Civil War, and experience as medical interne at the London Homeopathic Hospital. Chapin and Whitmarsh went almost every day to Wilcox's office to use his medical books or watch while the doctor
received patients. When he made calls they went along. Usually
Chapin sat in the carriage and read anatomy while the doctor
was in the house, but sometimes he was invited to go in and
give an opinion of the case.

At the end of a year Whitmarsh elected to stay in homeop-
athy. Chapin, however, had come to the conclusion that the
results of homeopathic practice did not justify a separate sect
or school, so he rejected it. During his subsequent medical
career he did his best to hasten its gradual decline in his com-

munity. But he always treated the Providence homeopaths as neighbors and colleagues, and did not participate in the frequent hostility between homeopaths and the rest of the profession.

In September 1877 Chapin matriculated at the College of Physicians and Surgeons in New York City. Physicians and Surgeons then was governed by few of the standards we now expect in medical schools. Compared with other schools of the day, however, it stood out as one of the best. Chapin enrolled for the full course, paying a fee of $140, or $20 to cover the didactic lectures in each regular branch of medicine as then divided: The Practice of Medicine, Chemistry, Surgery, Obstetrics, Materia Medica, Physiology, and Anatomy. Like most medical schools of that time, Physicians and Surgeons had no entrance requirements to meet or examinations except finals to pass. The principal demand upon the student was that he furnish the name of a reputable physician as his preceptor. Chapin listed his father.

The College of Physicians and Surgeons had a capable faculty, whose members offered attractive clinics and special courses along with the regular didactic lectures. Among its leading professors were Alonzo Clark and Francis Delafield in Pathology and Practical Medicine, Edward C. Seguin in Diseases of the Mind and Nervous System, and Abraham Jacobi in the new specialty of Diseases of Children. Four hundred and thirteen students enrolled in 1877 from all over the United States to get instruction from these men.

At the end of a year Chapin transferred from Physicians and Surgeons to the Bellevue Hospital Medical College. The regular lectures at Bellevue were much the same as those at Physicians and Surgeons, but the professors were different: Austin Flint lectured on the Principles and Practice of Medicine; Austin Flint, Jr., on Physiology; and Edward G. Janeway on Pathology and Clinical Medicine. Bellevue also offered certain physical advantages, especially the availability for clinical purposes of a large number of patients at both Bellevue Hospital and the nearby Charity Hospital on Blackwell's Island.

Chapin absorbed what knowledge these two medical schools had to offer. A few of his professors taught that the physician should rely upon the full range of the Materia Medica. They suggested that its drugs constituted the ultimate in remedies, especially if used in conjunction with blood-letting and purging. Other teachers, however, including Clark, the Flints, Delafield, and Janeway, were followers of the tradition of Louis and Bartlett, and they passed on to the students an active skepticism of such remedies, a preoccupation with the enumeration of cases, and a passion for observation.

Perhaps the most electrifying teaching during Chapin's year at Bellevue was that of the young Dr. William H. Welch. Welch had come to the Bellevue College in the spring of 1878 as an assistant to Austin Flint, Sr., and had set up the first laboratory in America for the teaching of microscopic pathology. (T. Mitchell Prudden did the same at the College of Physicians and Surgeons soon afterward.) He had just returned from studies in Germany under Carl Ludwig, Julius Cohnheim, and F. D. von Recklinghausen, laboratory men of the first rank whose work and tradition contributed strongly to the breakthrough of the 1870's and 1880's in the biological sciences. Although the new science of bacteriology had made no special impression upon him at that time, Welch had thoroughly absorbed the creative tradition of medical science in the German laboratories. Out of this tradition he introduced at Bellevue a method of teaching pathology which relied neither on lectures nor texts but on laboratory demonstration. It was a method of learning by seeing and doing. The technique, revolutionary to America, was one which required something more productive than the sterile memorizing of questions and answers. The students at Bellevue, as well as those of the other medical schools in New York, were not long in finding out about the advantages which Welch's laboratory offered, and they flocked to get his instruction.[1] One of Chapin's fellow students was an athletic, soft-spoken man from Alabama named William Crawford Gorgas. Welch was evidently impressed by both of them, and many years later he wrote Chapin that he had "always kept your name linked with that of Gorgas." [2]

To qualify for the M.D. degree, Chapin, Gorgas, and their classmates put in their three years under preceptors (medical school counting as two of these years), completed the usual two full courses of lectures in the seven branches of medicine, and prepared theses. Chapin wrote on "Cirrhosis of the Liver." Then, if they had attended a competent "quiz" (a form of cramming in which tutors drilled the students on the questions to be expected), they usually survived the final examinations in the various branches. Chapin had no trouble in surviving.

Commencement exercises were on February 27, 1879 at the New York Academy of Music, and that night the class dined sumptuously at Delmonico's. The next day the new doctors scattered to their respective communities. As they went, leaders of the medical profession were asking themselves how many of the students being graduated every year had any business being doctors and how long it would take them to become a help rather than a menace to their patients.[3] The lack of standards in medical education was a long-standing disgrace to the profession, and many were looking anxiously for a solution.

Only a month after graduation Chapin began his interneship at Bellevue Hospital, one of eight to receive such an appointment. Gorgas began his Bellevue residency at the same time. Chapin spent six months as junior assistant (these lowly functionaries had to arrange for their own board outside the hospital) and then twelve months as House Physician, during which he received board, lodging, and laundry at the hospital. He was one of the few young doctors ever to serve as House

Physician (or House Surgeon) at Bellevue for two six-month periods.[4]

Bellevue Hospital was a most desirable place for an interneship. During a year there young doctors saw nearly every disease or condition. The great typhus fever outbreak of 1863–1864 formed part of the hospital's tradition of treating epidemic diseases. One of Chapin's deepest impressions of Bellevue was the memorial tablet in the lobby for the fourteen young internes who had been attacked by the disease during that epidemic, six of whom had died.[5] Bellevue was noted for its innovations. The first hospital ambulance corps in the world had been formed there in 1869. Now the staff members alternated in going out around the city to give first aid. The Training School for Nurses, which had opened in 1873, was the first of its kind in America, and by 1879 several wards employed trained nurses exclusively. Making his first rounds, Chapin noted that the trained nurses had "worked wonders" in their wards, while the untrained nurses provided a horrible contrast with their slovenliness and general lack of method.[6]

Above all, Bellevue provided a stimulating atmosphere of powerful and inquiring minds at a crossroads of old and new theories. The visiting staff of the hospital included the best men in the city. During his interneship, Chapin had particularly fruitful contact with three commanding physicians—the elder Austin Flint, Abraham Jacobi, and Edward G. Janeway. Flint, the leader of the New York medical profession, had done more than anyone in America to bring the stethoscope into general use.[7] Long ago he had demonstrated a gift for epidemiological inquiry, and he used Louis' statistical method of studying disease. He was a believer in contagion during a time when far more people considered that communicable diseases arose in the mysterious miasmas of decaying filth. His *Principles and Practice of Medicine* had been a standard American text through several editions since 1866. Above all, Flint had an open mind and delighted in introducing new methods such as Welch's laboratory.

Jacobi had come to America from Germany shortly after the political upheavals of 1848. He soon became famous in New York as a perceptive clinician and was among the first doctors in America to devote themselves to Pediatrics as a specialty. The internes learned much from him in the children's wards at Bellevue. He pointed out, for instance, that diphtheria was not always a severe illness but often came in a mild form that was sometimes difficult to diagnose.[8]

The influence of Edward G. Janeway on Chapin went beyond that of either Flint or Jacobi. Janeway was a stern and hard-bitten man whose tired eyes and grizzled beard suggested Pasteur. He was reserved, and had few interests except his professional activities. He had already gained great distinction in New York for his systematic and revealing autopsies and shared with Francis Delafield the American leadership in pathology. In his skepticism of unproved theory he was a worthy descendent of Louis.

Janeway was known above all for his uncanny powers of diagnosis and observation. The stories about this gift were legion around Bellevue. One day Chapin saw a man brought into the hospital from off the street. He was unconscious and dying of a strange disease. There was no clue as to who he was or from where he came, and none of the visiting staff could tell what the malady was. When Janeway arrived he immediately identified it as yellow fever, although it had been years since this disease had appeared in northern United States.[9] And Chapin long remembered that for some time in one of the wards there was "a patient whom Dr. Janeway would exhibit to the classes as cancer and Dr. Loomis as aneurism, and both believed it typical." Time proved that Janeway was right.[10]

While Chapin was interne Janeway was serving as Health Commissioner of New York City. He often brought the problems he encountered in this position into his hospital clinics or into his conversations with the internes as he made his rounds. During the 1870's, Janeway was concerned about the great ambiguity in the available knowledge of the causation of communicable diseases. There seemed to be little doubt that cholera and typhoid fever came *de novo* out of filth, while diphtheria, too, often seemed to be caused that way. Enthusiastic filth theorists traced almost every disease to such emanations. Janeway went along with these theories to some extent, but with such diseases as scarlet fever the statistical data made him skeptical. The discovery of the anthrax bacillus in 1876 by Koch and Pasteur increased his skepticism. In the Bellevue wards Chapin frequently heard Janeway speculate on the significance of microbes and on how the community might hope to control them if they proved to be the causes of other diseases.[11]

The fundamental problem was the necessity of determining just which communicable diseases, if any, did in fact have origins in filth and which might be due solely to contagion and germs. When such knowledge about disease should become greater and sanitary works sufficiently extended, Janeway looked forward with the great English sanitarian Benjamin Richardson to "Hygeia," the ideal healthy community. There seemed to be no reason, Janeway felt, why the city described by Richardson, however Utopian it might seem in the 1870's, should not "be approached in the future." [12]

Janeway hoped to interest physicians all over America in helping to gather the facts needed for inquiry into disease causation. He tried to convince successive groups of Bellevue internes of the importance of the problem.[13] Probably no teacher of medicine in the nineteenth century could have provided his students with a more challenging task than that suggested to Chapin, Gorgas, and the others. Janeway wanted them to place the knowledge of communicable disease on a rational or factual basis and to use this knowledge in an equally rational manner to guard the public health. Likewise, no teacher before this time could have hoped to suggest such a potentially rewarding combination of means for tackling the challenge: the blending of data furnished by rigorously honest field observation with those provided by equally thorough laboratory experiment.

Not long before he completed his interneship, Chapin participated in the first antiseptic operation at Bellevue. Listerism had taken several years to get to America after its introduction in England in 1867. In fact it was not until after 1876, when Lister himself came to address the International Medical Congress in Philadelphia, that the antiseptic technique of purifying the air of operating rooms by germ-killing sprays got a start here. Asepsis (scrupulous precautionary cleanliness directed primarily against the possibility of contact infection rather than against the air infection for which antisepsis was designed) evolved later as a modification and extension of antisepsis.

Many of the older New York surgeons scoffed at antiseptic surgery and subsequently at the idea of aseptic surgery. In the summer of 1880, nevertheless, one of the leading surgeons of the city decided to try Lister's techniques, and he asked Chapin as interne to be his assistant. In later years Chapin frequently recalled the event. In anticipation, the most elaborate preparations were made. "What was considered perhaps the chief antiseptic service was to be performed by the interne [Chapin], who arose at an early hour of the summer morning to start the carbolic spray which was to disinfect the atmosphere; the spray was kept going until the end of the operation." [14] At the appointed time a group of interested doctors gathered to observe the innovation. The operation went off smoothly. Chapin's handling of the carbolic spray left nothing to be desired, and only one minor incident occurred which was not in the script: during the operation the surgeon dropped his knife. Unperturbed, he picked it up, wiped it off on his gown, and returned to work with it. The physicians who were watching hardly noticed the incident, and nobody thought enough about it to comment.[15]

Chapin's interneship had passed quickly. He had come to know New York well, even though he returned to Providence when there was time—particularly during the sailing season. To a limited extent he had found his way to the New York theaters and points of interest. He had made some good friends outside the hospital and, as often as he could, went down to Rockaway to see them and enjoy the ocean. But, during the summer of 1880 he was concerned with the details of furnishing his future office in Providence. His sister Louise was taking care of things on the spot, although there were some problems to settle by mail—the kind of handles for his desk drawers, for instance.[16]

On October 1, Chapin finished his term at Bellevue, and the staff presented the retiring House Physician with a case of surgical instruments. The big city had given him all it could of medical knowledge. But Chapin belonged to Providence, not to New York, and it was the smaller place that gained the first fruits of that knowledge.

BEGINNING A CAREER:
PHYSICIAN, TEACHER,
AND HEALTH OFFICER

CHARLES V. CHAPIN returned to Providence full of enthusiasm for his chosen profession and eager to take an active part in the medical and civic life of the city. He had already become a member of the Rhode Island Medical Society and, in June 1880, had received its Fiske Fund prize of $200 for his paper on The Sympathetic Nerve, a thorough and useful review of existing literature.[1] During the next decade Chapin enjoyed a virtual monopoly of the Fiske Fund prizes, an accomplishment which reflected both his ability as a creative medical author and the generally low condition of the medical profession at that time.[2]

For generations the medical profession in the United States had been nourished largely upon theories; it was starved for facts. It had a few alert leaders who knew about recent advances in medical science, but it had far more who were ignorant even of past knowledge. Outside the profession there were many out-and-out frauds. Patent-medicine purveyors who called themselves "Doctor" often made a better living than the respectable practitioner, and many physicians were disturbed by the renewed popularity of mind healers. The profession had been seriously set back by the breaking off of many of its members into the

Homeopathic and Botanic sects. Despite years of talk, the profession lacked discernible standards as well as the rudimentary controls which existed for many lesser occupations or activities of life.[3]

Providence physicians around 1880 had the benefit, if it could be called that, of two local professional societies. The Providence Medical Association appeared to be in its senility. In the "dismal room" where the Association held its meetings, there were only a few "medical books of ancient vintage" lying around.[4] Attendance had dwindled to the point where, of the approximately 85 members, only 14 or 15 went to meetings. Occasionally it was impossible to muster a quorum of 7. Barely a third of the medical practitioners in the city even bothered to join the Association.[5] Papers read before it were long-winded, uncritical, and often filled with the most archaic of medical notions. Case reports were equally doddering, just as dull, and even more unscientific in the eyes of new young members. One of the old-timers summarized the state of Providence medicine by reporting that, during fifty years of practice he had "gone through the bleeding, depressive and stimulating systems of treatment," and he firmly believed that "a larger proportion of patients with pneumonia recovered half a century ago than today, and then bleeding was the established practice." [6]

The Rhode Island Medical Society was not quite as degenerate as the city association, chiefly, perhaps, because it only met quarterly instead of monthly. Yet the members were no more enlightened, the reports of cases were as deadly, formal papers were few, and there was a decided "lack of literary and scientific spirit." [7] In some years the Fiske Fund prizes were not even awarded because of a lack of papers submitted.

Despite the general lethargy, up-to-date ideas and worthy projects occasionally stirred the local profession. Sporadic movements were started to try to obtain legislation for the regulation of medical practice. In 1876 both societies endorsed the estab-

lishment of a State Board of Health and were surprised when
the Rhode Island legislature soon passed a bill to set one up.
Steps to organize a Medical Library had been started. Although
most local physicians believed in the spontaneous generation
of disease, a few such as Robert F. Noyes advocated the germ
theory on the basis of the latest experiments. As early as 1878,
Dr. Edward T. Caswell began using "all the precautions of
Listerism" in his operations at Rhode Island Hospital and
reported great success.[8] Few Providence physicians, however,
shared Noyes' or Caswell's breadth of view or scientific spirit,
and it remained for the new generation which Chapin represented to bring a progressive attitude into the local profession.

Upon his return from New York, Chapin moved in with
his mother and father. His office was a few blocks away in an
old building that looked like a Gothic temple. Chapin announced that he would have office hours three times a day in
this place, and he settled back to wait for patients. Like many
young physicians starting out in practice, he had a good deal
of extra time when there were no patients. He utilized this
time to make a number of investigations and to report upon
them to the local medical societies. In May 1881 Chapin delivered his first paper to the members of the Providence Medical Association, on "The Pathology of Phthisis." He cited the
increase of information on phthisis from Laennec and Louis
to Virchow, and described the microscopic structure of tuber-
cles. The year before Koch announced the discovery of the
tubercle bacillus as the cause of the disease, Chapin commented that "the idea that phthisis was a simple neoplasm had
been nearly abandoned, and it is now generally regarded as a
secondary result of cheesy degeneration, the cheesy material
acting as a ferment." [9] Chapin participated frequently in the
discussions at the Association during that year and presented
one more paper in 1882, but he became so disgusted with the

backward nature of the meetings that he stopped going altogether for many months.

In the fall of 1885 a number of young medical practitioners who had become similarly impatient with the Association agreed upon the "need of a live club where thoughts of advanced medicine could be exchanged and where one would not chafe because forsooth he might not freely speak his mind." [10] The outcome was the formation of the Providence Clinical Club, with Chapin one of the earliest members. This and other medical discussion clubs which were soon founded did a great deal by their example to bring about the renovation of the Providence Medical Association and, similarly, to improve the state society. For Chapin, the Clinical Club provided for many years a place where he could exchange ideas. It was a nucleus of support in his public career, a group of colleagues who could tell him how far he could go with the rest of the profession. But, more than anything else, the Club was a body of associates with the common ideal of the scientific attitude. This ideal of the scientific spirit had become Chapin's great passion in life, and he made it the goal for the entire medical profession.

Another activity which Chapin took on during the early lean period of his private practice was some poorly compensated medical charity work for the Providence Dispensary. He was appointed Attending Physician for the second district of the city. During the course of hundreds of house visits per year for two or three years, he became well acquainted with the poor of Providence, the conditions in which they lived, and the diseases they suffered.

In 1882 Chapin began a brief service on the staff of the Rhode Island Hospital of Providence. This institution, which had opened in 1868, was the only regular general hospital in Providence, although a Homeopathic Hospital had started recently, and in Butler Hospital the city boasted one of the finest mental institutions in the country. Rhode Island Hospital was a true community hospital which reflected the recently developed concern of New Englanders for the condition of their neighbors' bodies after generations of being more concerned with their souls. Chapin actually received three appointments in 1882. In December, the Hospital announced the opening of its new Training School for Nurses, and Chapin was selected as one of the two lecturers. In that first year of the school he gave the course on Anatomy and Physiology. He also became part-time Pathologist and part-time Librarian. The Library work was simple, while as Pathologist he was only called upon for an occasional autopsy or for special diagnostic work. After only one year, he resigned as lecturer in the Nurses' School—at the time he joined the City Health Department— but he kept the other two appointments until 1886.

During these same years after his return to Providence, Chapin began giving popular talks on medicine, physiology, and related subjects. Appearing at such places as the Y.M.C.A., the State Normal School, high schools, and churches, or before the ladies of the Irrepressible Society, he quickly gained something of his father's reputation as an effective, forceful, and appealing public speaker. He also contributed occasional articles to the leading local newspaper, the *Providence Journal*. There Chapin wrote entertainingly on such subjects as boating, education, going to church, or his occasional trips outside Providence. His cordial relation with the editors and reporters of this newspaper was of great value to him in his subsequent career as Health Officer.

In the summer of 1883 Chapin paused to take stock. By now he was making something of a mark with his peripheral activities, while his range of medical knowledge was already giving him stature among his professional colleagues. Yet, his private practice as a physician was still far from flourishing. The fact was that Chapin lacked the right temperament to make a success as a general practitioner. He was factual and abrupt, and often neglected the amenities of consolation and sympathy. Like Louis and Bartlett, Joshua Chapin and Janeway, he rebelled at giving medicine when he felt that plain advice was more to the point.[11] When patients demanded remedies for fancied ills, he refused them, and his practice suffered. But Chapin had to make a living, and in his day general practice was practically the only way in which the physician could pursue medicine as a career. There were still no research positions to speak of, and full-time salaried professorships at medical schools were some thirty years away.

In August Chapin traveled to Asheville, North Carolina, to look into the possibility of setting up in practice there. On his trip into the post-Reconstruction South, he found the water poor, the food "execrable, even at the best hotels," and train connections impossible. He found, however, that "Northern ways and Northern life are looked up to as nearly perfection," and that "everyone seems anxious to forget the past and only to look forward." [12] Asheville itself, which was surrounded by mountains that reminded Chapin of New Hampshire, was just coming into prominence as a health resort; it seemed to offer good prospects for medical practice. On his first day there, however, Chapin suffered a broken thigh in a buggy accident. The fracture was painful and slow-mending, so, as soon as he was able, he returned (in a baggage car) to Providence to convalesce.

This fortuitous accident which kept Chapin in Providence brought him the opportunity to continue his medical career in a new and challenging form. It put him in line for a position which, although it never made him rich, proved to be far more satisfying to him than private practice. In the fall of 1883, while he was still convalescing, Chapin was, without his knowledge, nominated and elected to the position of Superintendent of Health of the City of Providence. His acceptance of this position allowed him to give up private practice immediately. He also gave up the work for the Providence Dispensary and his appointments at Rhode Island Hospital. He did not, however, sever a satisfying academic connection he had made in 1882 at Brown University as part-time Instructor of Physiology, but stayed on for a dozen more years to take part in one of the University's most exciting eras.

When Chapin joined the Brown University faculty in 1882, a few buildings had been added, and the grounds no longer looked like an unused cow pasture, but essentially the college was little different from what it had been when he had attended it as an undergraduate. By the time he left in 1895 invigorating forces had sharply shaken the college's old liberal arts system and established the pattern for a new system. Chapin during that period epitomized the forward-looking spirit of the leaders of change at Brown.

Chapin went to Brown to give lectures on personal hygiene to Freshmen and a second-semester course in elementary physiology to Juniors. He quickly earned the reputation of being one of the most vigorous and stimulating members of the faculty. He used the standard texts of the day, but presented the material imaginatively and vividly. Such effective teaching earned him a promotion in 1886 to the rank of Professor of Physiology, even though he continued to devote only a relatively small part of his time to the University.

As a new teacher Chapin had no trouble in finding a working theory of education. In part, it must have come from Joshua Chapin's practical ideas, but in the main, it rose out of the exciting ferment of scientific ideas and discussion of the late nineteenth century. Like the great German Rudolf Virchow and many of his fellow investigators, for whom science had "become religion," Chapin also had come to regard science as much more than a means to a living.[13] It was an ideal by which to live, work, and think. From the writings of

Thomas H. Huxley, as well as Welch at Bellevue, Chapin had acquired the principle of learning and teaching science by doing rather than by reading books or listening to lectures. Huxley taught by experimenting on a live lobster. Chapin followed him by examining the stray cats that his students brought in from the Providence East Side.[14] Herbert Spencer, on the other hand, stressed that the proper method and order for imparting knowledge is that in which the human race first acquired that knowledge—that is, by placing the simplest first, and fact before theory. Chapin knew but failed to practice this method until he made the mistake at Brown of trying to present the theory of evolution first in his physiology course.[15]

Chapin was also deeply influenced by the former chemist, Charles W. Eliot. One of the campaigns which Eliot was waging in Cambridge, Massachusetts and which Chapin helped to carry on in Providence was the battle of the classics. Fifteen years after Eliot became President of Harvard, Chapin had to report that "medieval Latin and Greek is still the guiding spirit of our colleges, and it flows out from them into the preparatory schools and permeates the whole educational system." [16] He complained that nowhere in the American educational system, despite this classical orientation, could one gain the full cultural depth which the classics had as their potential. The tedious years of cramming and memorizing grammar, he argued, dulled the true beauty of the classics and made these studies into pointless exercises.

While at Brown, Chapin sought to change this situation by talks and articles. He asked that the classics be eliminated as requisites for admission to colleges, and at the same time he worked to get a larger place in the curriculum for the sciences, both in colleges and in secondary schools. He had in mind science courses which broke from the normal pattern of the day. In the service of the creative ideal such courses could go far toward eliminating the stifling educational evils of the day, oversystematization, cramming, and memorization. Science teaching, he felt, should be started with the smallest of children, but it could come into its own only when it really became a discipline, in the form of scientific method.[17]

If careful scientific study offered a promising creative basis for general education, it was a "must" for medical and pre-medical education. Chapin assumed that the only valid aim of medical education should be the production of the "scientific physician." "A different scheme would be needed for the would-be-successful physician." [18] But the realities of the mid-1880's could not be overlooked; thus, he asserted:

> I believe that the great reason for the problem of quackery without the profession and delusions within is the fact that the vast body of medical practitioners are not scientific men. I do not mean that they have not a good medical education, or that they have not a college education. Neither of them as at present conducted teach a man how to observe and to reason scientifically. Until the majority of the medical profession learn how to study disease and its treatment in the impartial and accurate manner in which Koch, or Tyndall or Darwin have studied the problems they have solved, until then the practice of medicine will be as it chiefly is now, little but a trade. Medical men must have a liberal education, not liberal in the ordinary sense as founded on the classics, but one which has a thorough and honest scientific culture as its basis.[19]

To bring about such a change in his profession became a major aim for Chapin for the rest of his career.

The method of instruction which Chapin used was at first the usual routine of daily lectures accompanied by dictated synopses of each lecture which the students took down word for word and then memorized. Chapin illustrated his lectures with diagrams and models, and gave experimental demonstrations on actual specimens. He also employed a class microscope so that each student could examine for himself the minute structure of many of the organs.[20]

In 1885 he began the experiment, novel to Brown University,

of lecturing without giving any dictation. Each student now supplemented his class notes by such outside reading as he desired. Chapin's precedent for this innovation must have come from Welch. It aimed to discourage study by rote and to promote the development of intellectual curiosity. The new technique was not an immediate success at Brown, since few of the students were prepared for such a change and none of the other professors were yet calling forth such initiative. Nevertheless Chapin retained it and in the time saved he presented more demonstrations and live experiments.[21]

In 1889, Chapin was able to have high school physiology made a requirement for admission to Brown. This done, he recast his course from an elementary survey "for every educated man" to a scientific course which was designed for students planning to study medicine after graduation.[22] Within a short time most of the students in the course were those working toward medical careers.

This turn which Chapin gave to the study of Physiology at Brown received a boost with the arrival of Hermon C. Bumpus as Assistant Professor of Zoology in 1890, one of several new faculty members trained in the exacting German ideal of higher education. Bumpus helped to make a reality of Brown's recently begun graduate program. He also became a kindred spirit for the inquisitive Professor of Physiology. Bumpus had been an undergraduate at Brown and had stayed on for some graduate work. He was in Chapin's class during that period and never forgot the impression he received. Chapin's presentation of physiology, he recalled later, was "the first departure from the old didactic doldrums that I had experienced. It was a revelation to me." [23]

Following the lead of his former teacher of Physiology, Bumpus proceeded to transform the teaching of biology from didactic lectures to experiment, from the mere transmission of learning to an active search for knowledge. Jenks' museum was gradually ousted from Rhode Island Hall to make room for laboratories, and students turned enthusiastically to the new type of course. To get money and support in developing his new program, Bumpus established the Brown Biological Club, an informal organization of friends and local doctors who acted as a sort of visiting committee. Chapin frequently attended the monthly meetings and occasionally spoke to the members.

In 1893, Chapin, Bumpus, and Professor Appleton were the leaders in establishing a coordinated program of premedical studies at Brown, under the general direction of Bumpus.[24] In order to assure the success of the plan, Brown alumni who were physicians were invited to join a cosponsoring organization to be known as the Brown University Medical Association. The precise plan for which this organization was formed, the integrated undergraduate premedical program, had probably never before been put into effect in the United States.[25] William T. Sedgwick, however, had a substantially similar aim in his four-year Biology course at the Massachusetts Institute of Technology as early as 1883, while Yale also attempted this at about the same time.[26]

Integrated premedical training was a sound contribution toward raising the level of medical practice in the United States. As such the ideal of the program at Brown was akin to the one behind the new Johns Hopkins Medical School, which opened that same year (1893). Yet neither of these steps could have its full effect on medical practice until reform could come to the whole system of medical education.

The activity surrounding the establishment of the Brown University Medical Association naturally stirred the interest of Providence physicians and called to mind the medical school which had been a part of Brown University early in the century. The plan for a premedical program, however, was initiated without any reference to a larger plan for the eventual founding of a medical school. If some had hopes for such a school, they were dashed by the inability of the University to find its Johns Hopkins or Ezra Cornell willing to provide the necessary funds. With no such backing in sight, Chapin, Bumpus, and the other promoters saw that the establishment of a medical school was a goal which stood no practical chance of realization at that time.[27]

The collaboration which Bumpus and Chapin stimulated between the University and the local medical profession continued to the profit of both institutions. The University provided space for the state medical society's anatomical collection. For several years both state and city medical organizations held their meetings at the University, and in 1896 Bumpus demonstrated a Holtz X-Ray machine to the physicians.[28]

As a part-time member of the faculty, Chapin did not have the supervision of graduate students, but the biology graduate students usually took his course. Among those who, like Bumpus, were deeply influenced, were Albert D. Mead and Frederic P. Gorham. Both became eminent biologists in their own right and eventually became Bumpus' successors at the head of the Brown Biology Department. Mead credited Bumpus and Chapin as "the two honored teachers" who made his graduate work at Brown "a lifelong inspiration." [29] Gorham was to spend the rest of his life being of service to Chapin.

By 1895, however, Chapin felt that his Physiology course had become unsatisfactory, and he recommended that the University drop it. It was inadequate because information about the human body had become vastly more intricate and voluminous than it had been a few years previous. College students now could best approach the study of physiology, he saw, by taking good courses in the biological sciences. Those who were going on to study medicine would get the specialized courses which they needed in anatomy and physiology at medical school. Chapin thus talked himself out of a job. But he had already decided to leave Brown, and it was an appropriate time for the college to adjust this part of the curriculum to fit with growing scientific knowledge.[30]

It was not as easy for Chapin to give up teaching as it had been to give up private medical practice. The ideal of improving mankind through education was important to him, and Brown had been a place in his own community where he could help further the ideal in many ways. To try to close the gap between townspeople and the college, in 1888 he had helped establish an annual community lecture series at the University.[31] In the early nineties he taught a Physiology course at Newport for the new Brown University Extension. Long critical of the neglect of physical education in American colleges, Chapin in the 1880's worked to obtain a gymnasium at Brown, in 1891 drew up a plan for scientific physical training for all Brown students, and then accepted a post as the first Director of Physical Culture just long enough to put the plan into effect. In subsequent years he continued to serve the University in many small ways, while in a large way he built up a cooperative work relation between his city Health Department and the University Department of Biology.

Chapin resigned from Brown University in 1895, in order to devote himself more fully to the main line of his career—to his work as Superintendent of Health of Providence. Brown's loss was a gain to the city of Providence and, more broadly, to the public health movement in America, which thus obtained his undivided services for the first time. Science, which was playing such a large role in strengthening the University and the medical profession, also seemed likely to invigorate this great movement.

Chapin had begun work as Superintendent of Health of Providence in January 1884 at a salary of $2,000 per year. In his work, he had the confidence of the Republican social, intellectual, and business leaders of the community, and in future years he could always fall back on their support. His appointment also had the endorsement of the Providence press, though there was a certain amount of grumbling over the unceremonious way in which his predecessor had been dropped.[32]

In 1884 there were no special requirements for the job of health officer, but Chapin brought far better qualifications to the post than most. Providence officials had wanted a "live man" for the job, and Chapin's activities at Brown University, his work at Rhode Island Hospital, and his service at the Providence Dispensary had proved him both live and capable. He had already demonstrated abilities as a public health investigator in 1880, when he surveyed an outbreak of malaria.[33] Like Benjamin Richardson and Henry I. Bowditch, he had also shown his awareness of the health aspects of the alcohol problem.[34]

Health officers of this era usually got their training largely from painful experience. There was no such thing in the United States as a school where public health principles or techniques were taught. William T. Sedgwick, however, joined the faculty of the Massachusetts Institute of Technology the same year Chapin was elected Health Officer and within a few years began to offer instruction along that line. Moreover, by 1884 a considerable body of sanitary reports, periodicals, texts, and other published information existed. Most important were the reports of the English sanitarians John Simon and William Farr, those from the Massachusetts State Board of Health, and those from such cities as New York, London, Munich, Berlin, and Paris.

Chapin had one considerable advantage over most other American health officers starting work in the 1880's: the city of Providence already had a well-established and distinguished sanitary tradition. Edwin M. Snow, who had had a thirty-year career as Health Officer of Providence, had been its principal architect. Beginning in 1855, when Providence established its permanent public health machinery (a decade before New York City's sanitary reform), Snow had become perhaps America's first professional medical health officer. As such, he played a leading role in bringing the dynamic British public health movement of the 1840's to America.[35]

Along with Snow in this pioneering had been the Boston statistician Lemuel Shattuck, the Massachusetts physician Henry I. Bowditch, and the New York doctors, John H. Griscom, Stephen Smith, and Elisha Harris. By 1884 the work of such men had given the sanitary movement in the United States a start. Nevertheless, it was still insecure. Theories existed in profusion, but there was as yet little firm knowledge as to the causes of man's communicable diseases. Thirty years after Shattuck's great 1850 *Report of the Sanitary Commission of Massachusetts*, boards of health were finally being organized in many states and cities; but as yet they had done little work.[36] Snow and a few others had organized the American Public Health Association in 1872, but its members were still largely amateur health officials, not professionals. Some heroic work had been done toward the gathering of vital statistics, but few communities yet had any registration of such data that was worthy of the name. George E. Waring, Jr., of Newport and New York, and other sanitary engineers were energetically promoting public sanitary works and private plumbing, but most cities had hardly started on these works.

As Chapin took office, the early revelations of the new science of bacteriology were causing increasing excitement. Eight years had passed since Pasteur and Koch had first, in their researches on anthrax, met Jacob Henle's exacting postulates (that before microscopic forms could be regarded as causes of disease in man they would have to be found invariably in the allegedly contagious material, they would have to be isolated from such material, and their potency put to actual test). In 1882, while Chapin had been trying to build up his private practice, Koch announced that he had isolated the tubercle bacillus. In the months just before Chapin became Health Officer, Koch discovered the "comma bacillus" of cholera. Pasteur by 1882 had developed protective inoculation against such animal diseases as fowl cholera, anthrax, and swine erysipelas, and in 1885 he successfully inoculated a boy against rabies. These were stirring times for medical scientists, and the emergence of simpler investigative techniques such as Koch's plate method for isolating pure cultures of bacteria, gave a great impetus to further discoveries in many European laboratories for years to come.[37]

In the United States, the science of bacteriology had scarcely made a start in 1884. The Army doctor George Sternberg was the chief American investigator. He had discovered the pneumococcus about the same time as Pasteur, had searched for the organisms of malaria and yellow fever, and had undertaken an extensive investigation of the effect of disinfectants upon bacteria. Daniel E. Salmon at the United States Bureau of Animal Industry and Thomas J. Burrill at the University of Illinois were among the scant half-dozen other bacteriological investigators in America. Nevertheless, a good many chemists, pathologists, and other scientists were making themselves familiar with the laboratory techniques of bacteriology through study of the published literature. Following Koch's 1882 announcement of the tubercle bacillus, men like Welch and Prudden in New York and Dr. Henry Formad of the University of Pennsylvania demonstrated the discovery to their classes and taught the techniques of cultivating and staining bacteria.[38]

Chapin himself had followed the literature on bacteriology ever since Bellevue. He was familiar with the methods of cultivating and staining bacteria by the time in 1882 when he started his work as pathologist at Rhode Island Hospital. There he viewed for himself the tubercle bacillus and such other bacteria as were announced and even undertook some original investigation. Possibly the first bacteriological experimentation done in Rhode Island was Chapin's unsuccessful effort between 1883 and 1885 to isolate the causative organism of gonorrhea, in confirmation of earlier reported researches of Neisser and others.[39]

Chapin brought this background in bacteriology with him into his work as health officer. Such a background made him a new kind of health officer. He had at his disposal the old methods of attacking disease by cleansing the environment. But he also had the new knowledge of disease germs. Practically speaking, before 1884 no city or state health department in the United States had been ready to take advantage of the breakthrough in medical knowledge. Chapin was ready from the beginning.

As he started his career as health officer, Chapin was formulating his ideas as to the extent of the sanitary program of Providence. In the beginning he had doubts as to just how far a municipal government should interfere with private rights in carrying out the sanitary work demanded by the preventive ideal. Reports of the experience in English cities, however, where death rates had been reduced some 30 per cent within a few decades, soon convinced him that a comprehensive program was essential, regardless of the cry of socialism which was sure to be raised in conservative Rhode Island.[40] The demands of a rapidly growing industrial city could not be ignored, and they were beyond the capacity of private initiative.[41] Hence, in addition to supplying public water and providing a good sewerage system, Chapin felt that the city should engage in eight broad areas of sanitary activity: control of communicable diseases; abatement of nuisances; removal of garbage and refuse; supervision of conditions in schools and public institutions; supervision of factories and trades; inspection of water, ice, and milk (food should be a state concern); local scientific investigations into sanitary matters (including registration and analysis of vital statistics); and the dissemination of sanitary information.

In general, Chapin disapproved of unnecessary governmental compulsion in sanitary or other affairs; but he could see no place for the laissez-faire philosophy in modern cities such as Providence.

When a man lives by himself, he can do as he pleases and let others do the same, but when 125,000 people are gathered together on 10 square miles of land they must of necessity give up certain of their liberties. It is the sacrifice they make for the sake of the advantages of city life. The denser the population the more stringent and exacting must be sanitary regulations and indeed all other regulations. Americans, particularly those whose memories reach back to the time when our cities were villages, are prone to forget this.[42]

Maintaining that municipal sanitation was nothing more than a matter of practical community necessity, Chapin refused to put an ideological label upon it. In fact, he looked to the leadership of the local Republican Party for the implementation of his program, feeling that conservatism was no excuse for blindness to social conditions or evasion of community responsibility. To push his program he had to undertake the task of persuading people to face up to this responsibility. From the first, he did not hesitate to talk plainly to the people of Providence about their shortcomings. By so doing, he prodded the dozing public health movement in his city into motion again, although at times it seemed to go at a painfully slow pace.

Throughout his career, Chapin got things done without antagonizing people or ruffling tempers. He was modest and unpretentious, though soon after taking office he sought to overcome his youthful appearance by growing a beard. People were pleased by his courteous and affable manner and by his willingness to hear every legitimate complaint. They were impressed even more when he acted upon these complaints. Chapin was not merely a desk man; every day he went out poking into the corners of Providence. Thin to the point of frailty, he frequently drove himself until he was forced to spend a few days in bed to recover his strength.

Chapin dressed carefully and conservatively and never gave up his stiff, wing-tip collars and high black shoes. As a person he was anything but stiff. His enthusiasm and sense of humor made him easy to talk to. Best of all, Chapin used simple language that everybody could understand. He continually amazed people by the vigor with which he stated his convictions. These things, together with his impressive fund of factual knowledge and plain common sense, gave him an air of authority which was disarming in one so unimposing in stature.

After Chapin had been Health Officer for almost two years, he became engaged to be married to a Providence girl, Anna Augusta Balch. He always remembered Christmas day of 1885, the day of the announcement, as the happiest Christmas of his life. "Gussie" Balch was smart and practical and came from the old New England stock. Her father had been before his death a prominent wholesale druggist, her mother a Comstock, member of a well-known family of seafarers, merchants, and bankers. The Balchs had considerable social position, and some felt that Anna was marrying beneath her. It is certain that Chapin augmented his standing with the elite of the community by this alliance.

The wedding took place on the afternoon of May 6, 1886 at Grace Episcopal Church in what the Providence newspapers described as a "fashionable" event. Following the reception and wedding supper the couple set out for a honeymoon trip to Washington, D.C. On their return to Providence, Chapin and

and his bride did what was expected of them by making their residence on the East Side. Their only child, Howard, was born a year later. Other than his work, his family became the central thing in Chapin's life, and practically all of his leisure time was spent with his wife and child. Later, they all went to conventions of health officers, from which Chapin took time off to visit the local sights with them. In this way they saw Niagara Falls, attended the St. Louis World's Fair, and practiced their French in Quebec. Anna never became a creative partner in Chapin's intellectual work, but she contributed incalculably to his success by her belief in him, by her solicitude for his health, and by her submergence of her own life in his career.

As he began that career Chapin set out to combat disease in his community by every way that he knew. In the first years, this meant largely continuing and elaborating upon the general sanitary program which Snow had begun. The campaign against dirt was, for the public at least, the essence of sanitary work.

ENVIRONMENTAL SANITATION

Few reforms in history have had as great a civilizing influence upon mankind as the systematic cleansing of cities. When the British sanitarian Edwin Chadwick maintained, in his famous "sanitary idea," that such cleansing would substantially cut down communicable diseases in cities, and when early experience in England proved him correct, an immense boost was given to this reform in Europe and in the United States. One of Chapin's early tasks was to further this important work in Providence. For him, as for the the sanitarians of forty years before, one of the great purposes of hygiene was "to secure pure air, a pure water, and a pure soil." [1]

In the decades before 1884, to be sure, Snow had outlined the environmental sanitation needs of Providence, and he had organized the routine machinery for coping with many of them. But much remained for Chapin to do. The city had obtained a good public water supply, its streets were relatively clean, it was fairly free from offensive trades, and the condition of its houses was comparatively good. On the other hand, fewer than a third of the houses were yet connected with the public sewerage system, many still relied upon wells for water, a majority had badly defective plumbing, backyards often reeked with piles of decaying garbage, and swill carts and night-soil wagons left trails of filth along the streets. Probably the most conspicuous aspect of the sanitary environment of Providence (as of other cities) in 1884 was the stench. It had odors from its hundreds of stables, its polluted streams, its dead dogs or horses, and its thousands of foul privy vaults and cesspools. When the odors became so intense that even the people who lived among them were nauseated, it is no wonder that many persons associated diseases with bad smells. And when disease did come out of certain kinds of foul smelling dirt, it was only logical for people to fear and wish to eliminate filth. In the decade or so after 1876, laymen and sanitarians alike visualized either disease germs or miasmata "swarming from every dung hill and garbage pail, pouring from drains and soil pipes." [2]

Chapin did not fear odors as such. He was one of a few in America before 1885 who followed the English sanitarian John Simon in pointing out that the danger from filth was not in the stench but in specific disease germs. Yet he knew that some diseases "are aided and increased by filth." [3] Moreover, throughout the 1880's, no one was able to prove conclusively that disease never arose *de novo* from dirt but *only* from germs. For many good reasons the cleansing of the city had to go on.

Thus, Chapin recommended that wells be abandoned, that yards be kept clean, and that plumbing be repaired. He prodded the city government to stop the pollution of public waters and to speed up sewer construction. He urged householders to connect to sewer lines or to clean their privy vaults and cesspools regularly.

When it came to specific action on these recommendations, Chapin was impeded by the confusion of existing laws. A new sanitary code which he prepared for Providence improved things somewhat. A general revision of laws, however, proved impossible to obtain, and he had to settle for whatever legislation he could get to cover specific conditions as they came up. Chapin never received the executive authority which some health officers and boards had—the New York City Board of Health, for one. Consequently, he often had great difficulty in taking effective action. General nuisance abatement, in particular, was bound up in a tangle of legal red tape which required the utmost patience, perseverance, and energy to overcome. This unsatisfactory condition continued throughout much of his career as Health Officer.

One of Chapin's earliest acts was to organize, in response to a threat of cholera in 1884, the first systematic sanitary canvass which Providence had had. His entire regular force then consisted of himself, a former policeman who was the sanitary inspector, and one temporary inspector during the summer months. During the year these three visited every house in the city and made a concentrated attack upon the many minor nuisances. They paid special attention to yards and the outside facilities for the disposal of wastes, while in the poor areas they also examined the interiors. Within ten months time, more had been accomplished along this line than in the previous ten years.[4]

Cholera threatened North America again in 1885, 1886, and several subsequent years; fortunately it failed to materialize, although the disease was prevalent both in Central Europe and in South America. Each year, however, Chapin saw to it that the city of Providence prepared for the disease as if a general onslaught were certain. In 1887, during a scare caused by contaminated immigrant ships which landed in New York City, Chapin obtained tighter quarantine regulations, put special inspectors at the railroad station and the New York boat landing, fumigated those immigrants who came to the city at the time, and conducted emergency cleanups. Although cholera did not spread to Providence during this era, the disease had much the same effect it had had back in the 1850's—that of creating a receptive climate of opinion for sanitary work. People were roused to realize the dangers in certain kinds of filth and to do something about conditions in their own homes.

In comparison to New York, Boston, and Philadelphia, the general sanitary condition of Providence houses was fairly good. The city, nevertheless, had its share of dwellings, frequently owned by absentee landlords and occupied by immigrants, "where people live and die in utter defiance of all sanitary laws." [5] Occasionally Chapin conducted members of the Board of Aldermen (which was ex officio the City Board of Health) and also of the press around to see such places. From time to time he condemned the worst tenements and got the Board of Health to order them vacated until they were cleaned up. Both landlords and tenants, he felt, needed "instruction and moral suasion and often something more in order to keep their tenements in proper condition." [6] Chapin believed that the city should compel landlords to provide healthful buildings and conditions of living for tenants. "I am not one of those," he said, "who believe that the lowest classes of society can be raised to a high level by any one agency, be it sewers, sunday [sic] schools or prohibition, but I know that clean and healthy homes will help to do it." [7]

Much of Chapin's time in these early days was claimed by the disgusting problems of vaults and cesspools. There had to be constant inspection and follow-up of complaints and occasional court action to get landlords to correct offensive conditions. The Health Department also was responsible for regulating and licensing the workmen who cleaned the vaults and cesspools. This involved inspection of leaky wagons and chasing after the farmers who did the work. Chapin tried without success for years to get the city to do the work itself, but finally in 1892 he obtained new regulations which greatly improved this service. [8]

One of the big problems connected with the building of the city's sewer system was that of getting the people to use the system. Thousands of persons who lived on sewered streets stubbornly continued to use the old privies and cesspools. The landlord offered the biggest obstacle to changing over, for, as sanitarians found, "to ask him to make sewer connections for a six family tenement, to supply a hopper closet in place of his noisome privy-vault is to him as preposterous as it is to ask for a rebate of rent." [9] Chapin felt, however, that this was a matter as basic as the building of the sewer system itself. After several years of agitation and court actions, in 1892 he finally obtained sufficient authority from the state to compel the removal of vaults and cesspools where sewers existed and to replace them with water closets connected with the sewers. For the next several years he conducted an energetic campaign to enforce this ruling, and by 1900 practically no vaults remained along sewered streets.[10]

In some of the older tenements, of course, the installation of water closets was just not feasible. To meet this situation, in 1887 Chapin devised, on the basis of a suggestion from the Medical Officer of Health of Birmingham, England, an ingenious self-flushing scoop to be adapted to the old privies. This was a swiveled cast-iron tank set in the ground under the privy which emptied itself when full and which was kept clean by water draining from the sink and roof. The water and feces in turn drained off into the sewer connection. Chapin tested the device successfully and made it available to all without patent rights. As used in a number of factory tenements and public buildings in New England, it served temporarily as a satisfactory and sanitary replacement of the old vault.[11]

With the gradual elimination of vaults and cesspools in the cities, good plumbing in houses became increasingly necessary. At first, plumbing fixtures were of poor quality and plumbers generally incompetent. At the same time, however, under the persuasive influence of engineers and sanitation propagandists like George E. Waring, fixtures became increasingly complicated. A few American cities enacted simple plumbing regulations in the late 1870's, but the first complete municipal plumbing codes did not come until after 1880.[12] Chapin was not able to obtain a code for Providence until 1893, but it was a good one. By not requiring the usual elaborate ventilation devices, the code ultimately saved Providence house-owners millions of dollars. Moreover, at Chapin's request, the Office of Inspector of Plumbing was established quite apart from the Health Department. Few other American cities provided for such a separation.[13]

Among the common nuisances in the city were the many heaps of trash, leaking garbage pails, and dead animals. Through a judicious mixture of education and compulsion, Chapin's department did what it could to keep these under control. But there were more dangerous nuisances and other more urgent work, so Chapin never stressed these activities, although his department could have spent endless amounts of time on them, as most other health departments did.

Supervision of the collection and disposal of garbage was a sanitary activity with which Chapin was charged by law and which took a great deal of his time. In Providence, contractors collected the garbage two or three times a week and hauled it to a central dump. There they loaded it on railroad cars and carried it several miles out of town to a farm where it was used as food for swine. This arrangement was reasonably satisfactory to the city, although it took constant inspection to guard against nuisances.

In the late 1880's, the contractors were losing considerable amounts of money, largely because of hog cholera among their swine. Trying to solve this disease problem for the contractors, Chapin conducted some experiments along the lines taken by Daniel E. Salmon. Salmon had successfully immunized pigeons against hog cholera by feeding them with sterilized cultures of what he thought was the causative bacillus, but he had had no success with hogs themselves. Chapin succeeded in finding the bacillus described by Salmon and also tried to produce immunity against the disease. Thinking that Salmon may have given too small a dose, he fed much larger quantities of sterilized bacilli to a group of hogs at the contractor's pens. This dose also failed to immunize them, however, and all died when the disease struck the herd.

In collaboration with Dr. Gardner T. Swarts, Chapin also experimented upon swine, cattle, chickens, pigeons, and monkeys to determine whether animals might be a source of typhoid fever in man. Typhoid bacilli which they fed to these animals failed to produce the disease. Likewise, a review of literature on the subject failed to show that other animals were susceptible. The account of these experiments and their negative conclusions won for the authors the Boylston Medical Prize in 1889.[14]

Chapin's effort to immunize hogs was part of a broader concern during the late 1880's with the problems of immunization. Among other aspects of immunization, he was interested in the recent researches upon toxins, some of which until that time were called ptomaines. The work done before 1889, chiefly by Brieger, Selmi, Gautier, and Vaughan, indicated to him that these so-called ptomaines had a definite effect in rendering tissues "refractory to the action of microbes." Chapin was one of those who quite early saw that there was a hopeful field for research in trying to produce immunity through doses of these substances. Inoculation then was difficult to handle and dangerous to use. "But," Chapin wrote, "if immunity can be secured by the use of chemical substances, the action of which can be measured and regulated, and which can be prepared outside of the body, we shall obtain an invaluable means of controlling the infectious diseases." This hope was fulfilled within a few years with the successful introduction, by Roux and Behring, of antitoxin for use against diphtheria.[15]

After Chapin's failure to immunize swine, the Providence garbage contractor promptly got out of the business, and it appeared that the city might be forced to do the job. Chapin began to consider other methods of disposal. The result was a pioneer experiment in the disposal of garbage by reduction. Chapin had been considering the possibility of separating the grease from garbage by means of naphtha, when he heard that this process was already in operation in Buffalo. He inspected the Buffalo works, which were the first large-scale plant for the reduction of garbage, and then induced the operators of the plant to bid for the Providence garbage contract. Their bid was too high, but he was determined to use the method. Together with the successful bidder, Chapin and four other local men formed a company, The Riverside Chemical Works, to build and operate a reduction works. The resulting pioneer plant used the Simonin reduction process rather than the Merz, which the Buffalo works used. In this process the garbage first had to be drained. Then it was dried and the grease removed in the same operation by treating it in a closed receptacle to the action of hot naphtha and naphtha vapor. The dried garbage was then ground and packaged for fertilizer. The grease which drained off was sold commercially and provided the chief income from the process.

Chapin took the leading part not only in organizing the local works but in actually putting the process into operation. He also developed a number of mechanical refinements which modified and were added to the original process, although he did not take out patents upon them. After several months of experiment the Providence works started operating in the spring of 1890. The Company ran the plant for about eight months. As far as sanitary results were concerned the works were a success, for there was no odor or nuisance except in the unloading of garbage. Economically, however, the plant ran at a loss, so the Company leased it to the inventor of the process, I. M. Simonin, who ran it for the next three years. In his effort to make a profit, Simonin cut corners sharply, with the result that the plant soon became a great nuisance. The plant was sold in 1894, and Providence went back to feeding its garbage to swine. Garbage reduction processes needed further refinement before they were practicable.[16]

Feeding garbage to swine, however, was generally considered risky from a health viewpoint because of the danger of diseased pork and because of the belief that it produced meat of poor quality. Chapin originally shared this view. After 1894, however, he gradually changed his views and came to consider this as a thoroughly desirable method of garbage disposal. As the years went by he did not trace any sickness at all to hogs fed with garbage, while experiments showed that neither tuberculosis nor trichinosis were present any oftener in pork from garbage-fed hogs than in other pork.

The chief argument in favor of feeding garbage to hogs was its economy. Chapin pointed out in 1902 that, because of this, garbage disposal (though not the collection) in Providence had not cost the city anything for over fifty years.[17] Some other New England cities also defrayed part of the costs of collection by selling their garbage; and Worcester reduced these costs almost to nothing by maintaining its own municipal hog farm and selling the garbage-fed swine. Providence never authorized this step, but under Chapin its garbage collection and disposal was systematic and thorough. Some asserted that during the 1890's and afterward it was unexcelled by any other American city.[18]

One final aspect of environmental sanitation engaged much of Chapin's attention: water purification. In the decade after 1871 a sizable proportion of people in Providence turned to the city's new municipal water supply. Partly as a result of this there was a drop of nearly 15 per cent in annual typhoid fever deaths. Unfortunately, the water furnished by the municipal system was also liable to pollution. During his first ten years in office, Chapin devoted himself to the improvement of this supply. The pioneer investigations on water purification which he and his associates conducted were of major significance. They rank in importance close to the great work which was being done about the same time at the Lawrence Experiment Station of the Massachusetts State Board of Health.

The Providence public water supply came from the Pawtuxet River, a stream which flowed through a thickly populated manufacturing region to the south and west of the city. Chapin and other city officials tried for several years to get the co-operation of mill owners along the river in preventing gross contamination from the privies of the many mill tenements. When these efforts failed, Chapin in 1887 recommended that the city, for protection, look into the various methods of water purification. As it was, a single case of typhoid fever in the Pawtuxet valley could cause an epidemic in Providence.

In the fall of 1888 this fear was confirmed when a short but severe typhoid fever outbreak occurred in the city, the first explosive epidemic which Chapin had had to handle. Over a two-week period he and his associates tracked down some 223 cases and 47 deaths from the disease. Their efforts to control it resulted in an important epidemiological investigation in the tradition of William Budd and Austin Flint, but one which gained distinction for being among the first to take into account the new discoveries of the bacteriological age.[19]

In a search for the cause of the epidemic, Chapin had to cope with the various contradictory factors which a filth disease like typhoid fever presented, even though proof of its germ causation had been demonstrated. He considered but quickly rejected special meteorological conditions as causative factors. The likelihood of local unsanitary conditions playing a part, on the other hand, seemed strong for some time. According to this theory, recent heavy rains, having saturated the ground in areas honeycombed with leaching vaults and cesspools, had the effect of bringing typhoid germs to the surface. This theory was ruled out, however, by the wide distribution of cases, many of which occurred even in well-sewered areas. Under the circumstances, water pollution was the more plausible explanation, so Chapin looked into this possibility.

He wrote to all the doctors in the Pawtuxet River valley and personally examined the banks of the river on both sides. He learned that only the factory town of Natick had had any unusual excess of typhoid fever recently. In Natick, one group of the village's mill tenements which clustered along the bank of the river was occupied by workers of French-Canadian origin, whom Chapin described as "ignorant" and "careless and filthy in their habits." [20] There had been twenty cases of the disease among these workers. When he examined the premises, Chapin discovered that those persons who had cared for the patients had not bothered to deposit the feces in privy vaults but instead had been throwing them on the ground to the side or in back of the vaults, from which places they had easily washed down into the river. Rainfalls known to have fallen during the period accomplished this. The rest was a matter of computation. Chapin figured the elapsed time from the cases at Natick until the outbreak in Providence, allowing for incubation of the germs, distribution time in the water mains, and the time that the polluted water remained in the reservoir. When it turned out that the one section of Providence which escaped the epidemic was supplied by a different reservoir from the rest of the city and that this reservoir had received little or none of the Pawtuxet water, Chapin was able to establish the polluted river water as beyond a doubt the cause of the epidemic. [21]

Having traced the course of the outbreak by traditional epidemiological methods, Chapin went on to test his conclusions by a new method, the use of the bacteriological laboratory. Such a laboratory had become possible in Providence only after the appointment of Dr. Gardner T. Swarts as part-time Medical

Inspector for the Health Department in 1885. This position was itself something new, for up to then most American health departments merely had lay nuisance inspectors who made no attempt to investigate diseases or to correlate them with the filth they found. Chapin regarded the obtaining of a competent Medical Inspector as one of his most important early steps. Swarts was one of the most active and scientific minded of the younger generation of Providence doctors. He brought to the Health Department a busy energy and an openness to new things which made him invaluable as Chapin's first trained assistant. He lacked Chapin's intellectual depth but had initiative, ambition, and administrative ability.

About a year after Swarts entered the department, he had taken, with Chapin's encouragement, special instruction in the latest bacteriological techniques under Professor Harold Ernst at the Harvard Medical School, one of the first places in the United States where it was available. In the Harvard laboratory he began a series of tests of the various popular household water filters then on the market. He continued these tests through 1887 and 1888, partly at Harvard and partly in Providence. He reached the conclusion that almost all varieties sold in the United States were not only useless but actually dangerous because of their tendency in heated rooms to act as incubators for germs.

The Providence Health Department's Bacteriological Laboratory, first of its kind in the United States, was an outgrowth of this work. It was established in the City Hall early in 1888 under Chapin's general supervision but under the immediate direction of Swarts. Swarts, who had independent means, purchased the equipment for the laboratory and ran it largely at his own expense for several years.

At the time of the epidemic of 1888, the houses of many of the people in Providence who had been attacked by typhoid fever were found to be equipped with household filters. Chapin collected some of these filters and had them examined for the presence of typhoid bacilli. Swarts examined some, while others were sent to Prudden in New York and Ernst at Harvard. Bacilli were found in several of the filters, in some cases accompanied by actual fecal material. These investigations thus reaffirmed clearly the dangerous character of the household filters. More important, they proved the utility of the first municipal bacteriological laboratory, even though it did not, in this instance, provide conclusive proof of the role of the public water supply in the epidemic.[22]

The principal work done in the Providence laboratory for several years was routine bacteriological testing of the water supply and further testing of household filters. There were also extensive tests of commercial spring water and ice. Both Swarts and Chapin did the laboratory work, Chapin to a lesser extent. Diagnostic procedures to determine actual cases of disease were experimented with, but they did not become a routine part of the Providence laboratory work until after the New York City Health Department Laboratory introduced them in 1892 and 1893.

After the 1888 epidemic Chapin devoted a great deal of time to a new inquiry—an investigation of one of the two principal methods of large-scale water filtration. Reports showed that the slow-sand type of filter, such as those in use in the London and Berlin municipal water systems or the experimental filter at Lawrence, Massachusetts, with proper care could remove well over 99 per cent of the bacteria. Chapin found, however, that to install this type at Providence would be an expensive proposition.

The other possible method was that of mechanical filtration, in which the water was filtered under pressure and with the addition of a chemical coagulant. Several types of these filters came into use for municipal water supplies in the United States during the middle 1880's, although they had been used earlier for industrial purposes. Chapin could find, however, no published reports or analyses of this type of filter, so he began his own inquiry. He wrote to all cities he knew of that used mechanical filters. He learned that nearly all were satisfied with their filters and that there had been no harmful effects due to the coagulant, which was usually aluminum sulphate. He also learned that mechanical filters were a great deal cheaper to install and operate than sand filters. There had been, however, no known bacteriological tests to determine if mechanical filters effectively purified water as well as clarified it. To remedy this situation, in 1889 Chapin made a trip to inspect a Hyatt filter which had been recently installed at Long Branch, New Jersey. On the basis of three culture tests of the water before and after filtration, he found that the filter removed an average of 98.8 per cent of the bacteria. He also tested a National filter in use at a bleachery at Canton, Massachusetts. It was evident, however, that before he could recommend any type of filtration to his city, there would have to be far more exhaustive testing of the mechanical filters.

Largely upon Chapin's urging, the Providence City Council in 1892 agreed to conduct such an investigation. It established an expert commission of Chapin, the City Engineer, and the Commissioner of Public Works.[23] The principal part of the investigation was an extensive experimental use of a typical mechanical filter in the city water works. This experiment extended through most of 1893 and part of 1894, under Chapin's immediate supervision. Swarts did most of the voluminous bacteriological analysis, while the rest of the detailed testing was performed by Edmund B. Weston, then Assistant Engineer in Charge of the Providence Water Department. In order to take advantage of experience elsewhere, Chapin again canvassed cities using mechanical filtration. In June 1893 he visited a number of these places. At Atlanta and Chattanooga he obtained first-hand assurance for Providence mill-owners that filtered water would not produce scale or corrosion on their boilers. The Commission likewise got valuable help from such outside experts as Ernst and Prudden, George W. Fuller of the Lawrence Experiment Station, and Thomas M. Drown and Ellen H. Richards of the Massachusetts Institute of Technology.

This Providence experimentation provided the first careful tests anywhere of the mechanical type of water filtration. Chapin and his Commission concluded from the experiments that mechanical filters were easily managed and that they were "more efficient than any other practical method with which we were acquainted." [24] Together with even more elaborate later tests under Charles Herman and George Fuller at Louisville, these tests did for this type of filter what the Lawrence tests did for the slow sand filters in establishing their reliability and utility. Local conditions determined which method was best in any given case. Perversely, having authorized this experiment and actually having appropriated money for a mechanical filter, the Providence lawmakers finally reversed themselves, ignored the recommendations of their own Commission, and chose to erect the excellent but much more expensive slow sand type of filter. When the city adopted a new water supply in 1926, however, Chapin was happy that the cheaper mechanical filtration was installed.[25]

The results of water purification in reducing communicable diseases, particularly typhoid fever, were closely observed by sanitarians. During these early decades of its use, many claims were made which subsequent experience proved ill-founded or excessive. Chapin himself eventually scaled down his own estimate of the value of filtration in reducing typhoid fever when it became apparent that other causes were more important than water. Some eminent sanitarians, however, fell into something of a trap in this matter. Allen Hazen, a well-known sanitary engineer and early student of Sedgwick, was one. After a study of the records left by Hiram Mills on the working of the Lawrence filters and by Reincke on the Hamburg filters, Hazen worked out an ingenious, highly plausible, and enthusiastically received formula since known as Hazen's Theorem or the Mills-Reincke Phenomenon. This formula specified in substance that "where one death from typhoid fever has been avoided by the use of better water, a certain number of deaths, probably two or three, from other causes have been avoided." [26] Sedgwick himself and another of his pupils, J. S. MacNutt, later substantially accepted and elaborated upon this theorem.[27] Chapin, however, strongly criticized such a formula as far too general. He pointed out that there were too many external factors (contact infection by healthy carriers, for example) which had not been considered.[28] Water purification by itself was not the panacea that some suggested.

Nevertheless, by the early 1890's, the Providence Health Department, largely as a result of its water purification experiments, had come to be known widely as being "exceptional not only in vigilance but also in unprejudiced and progressive inquiry." [29] Chapin's trip to investigate the Hyatt filter was regarded as setting an unusual example of initiative to other health officers. At the Denver 1895 meeting of the American Public Health Association Peter Bryce of Toronto thanked the Providence investigators for their work, and Rudolph Hering of New York publicly expressed the indebtedness of the nation's sanitarians.[30] Not only Chapin but Swarts and Weston acquired national reputations from this work on water filtration.[31]

Chapin's efforts to improve the sanitary environment of his city were valuable to sanitarians across the country. But he was impatient with much of this work. He had early realized that cleansing of the physical environment was, by itself, insufficient for improving the public health. Minimizing the broad dogmas of the filth theory from the first, and concentrating on the truly dangerous forms of filth, Chapin progressively deemphasized nuisances that had no direct or demonstrable connection with disease and avoided much of the tedious routine of nuisance abatement. Employing only one permanent inspector of nuisances where other cities the size of Providence usually had ten or a dozen, Chapin put his faith instead in the medical inspector.[32] Attuning himself to the age of bacteriology, he turned from general measures against disease to specific measures against particular diseases.

THE OPTIMISTIC VIEW:
"STAMPING OUT"
INFECTIOUS DISEASES

In his first report as Health Officer, Chapin made clear his view that "more attention might well be given to the prevention of the more common infectious diseases, and more time devoted to their scientific investigation." [1] Despite the demands of environmental cleansing, he made it his business to devote increasing amounts of time to these other concerns, to diseases like scarlet fever and diphtheria which increasingly appeared to be caused by bacteria and spread by contact. Such a change of emphasis over the next decade by Chapin and other progressive health officers represented an important break with the dominant tradition of general sanitation through engineering and nuisance abatement. It was a break arising from an optimistic faith in the ability of such measures as isolation of patients and fumigation of the environment to prevent the spread of disease germs. This conviction partially replaced the earlier faith in environmental sanitation as the cure-all for the health of society. In place of the hopeful prospect of Chadwick and Richardson, there was now the promise of Pasteur, that "it is within the power of man to rid himself of every parasitic disease." [2]

Providence was among the first American cities to undertake a vigorous and well-coordinated program of specific measures against the ordinary communicable diseases. Chapin's development in Providence of this modern program of separate attack on each disease provided leadership for the development of similar programs in cities all over the United States. In the beginning Chapin shared the optimistic belief that such a program would provide "perfect control" or "stamp out" the communicable diseases within the "near future." [3] In keeping with this aim, during the next fifteen years or so he made the enforcement of his program progressively stricter. His continued examination of the various measures, however, together with the hard results of practical experience, forced him to scale down sharply the ideal of absolute prevention soon after 1900.

The case for stringent control of the ordinary communicable diseases rested largely upon the success which health officers had already had in holding smallpox in check, presumably by this means. In 1884 popular opinion demanded the absolute seclusion of all smallpox patients in pesthouses, the thorough fumigation of effects, and widespread vaccination. Snow had kept Providence remarkably free from smallpox by these measures. Chapin also went to great lengths to keep it out of the city. In 1885 he conducted an effective general vaccination to ward off a severe outbreak that was spreading from Canada into southern New England. A few years later, when smallpox broke out in a nearby city, he took the precaution of boarding all incoming trains and examining the passengers for signs of the disease. Sometimes he called upon the police to round up alarmed immigrants for vaccination after they had been exposed to the disease. In one way or another Providence was spared any great outbreaks of smallpox during Chapin's career. Chapin attributed this partly to luck and partly to the fact that Providence was better covered by vaccination than most cities. Yet the Health Department officials continually had to persuade people to protect themselves.

During the early 1890's the anti-vaccination movement, led by an elderly crank named Samuel Darling and by an agent of the British Anti-Vaccination Association, became particularly annoying and even alarming in Rhode Island. On a wave of propaganda and with support from a few physicians, a series of bills went to the General Assembly to try to repeal the state law on compulsory vaccination for public schoolchildren. Public hearings upon these bills were lively sessions. With Chapin taking a prominent part in the discussions, the state medical society made a strong stand against the repeal and the bills were defeated. Actually, Chapin would have liked compulsory vaccination for everyone. It was entirely irrational, he maintained, for people to neglect prevention and then expect the state or city to step in when smallpox did strike.[4]

Chapin's own confidence in vaccination was complete. During the summer of 1887, when there was a smallpox case in the pesthouse, he used to drive out every afternoon with his wife and three-months-old baby to see how the patient was doing. Anna wrote letters for the patient. Such confidence upon the part of the Health Officer made a vivid impression upon the many persons in the city for whom the very sight of the pesthouse stirred up all sorts of fears.[5] But it took a long time for Chapin to put across the idea that smallpox germs "do not go flying through the air like butterflies." [6]

One of the few controversies which Chapin ever carried on in public was his argument with Dr. S. C. Martin of Roxbury, Massachusetts, over the merits of "humanized" virus as against bovine virus in vaccination. The controversy began in 1885 when Martin, a commercial producer of the bovine virus, asserted that there was no longer any humanized virus and that if there were it would be inferior in protective power to the bovine variety. Chapin rushed to the defense of humanized virus in a series of letters in the *Boston Medical and Surgical Journal*. The Providence Health Department, he pointed out, had used humanized virus ever since 1856. He was convinced, moreover, and Snow backed him up, that the vaccine used in Providence in 1885 was of direct arm-to-arm descent from virus sent to Benjamin Waterhouse in 1801 by Edward Jenner, virus which in turn was part of the original supply Jenner had taken from a heifer in 1796.[7] Due to careful handling and guarding against secondary infection, protection was still as complete as it had been in the beginning.

Actually, Chapin had nothing against the bovine virus and granted that it had certain advantages when properly prepared. The difficulty was that it had become an article of commerce, prepared with few standards of quality. Under those circumstances it seemed wise for municipal and state health departments to prepare their own virus or at least to supervise its production. He continued to use humanized virus almost exclusively in the public vaccinations in Providence until early in 1901, when he adopted the recently developed glycerinized bovine virus prepared by the New York City Health Department. Since 1902, with federal standardization, the problem of standards and safety has been solved.[8]

Through the 1880's and 1890's, the strict measures used against smallpox constituted the ideal which health officers began to apply to other diseases which now increasingly appeared to be mainly contagious, particularly scarlet fever and diphtheria.[9] Chapin himself made it one of his first acts as Health Officer to propose and put into effect a whole range of measures which English sanitarians (especially since 1878) had begun to use against the common communicable diseases. He got the city, the school authorities, and the medical profession to agree on rules regulating children's attendance at school when they or members of their family had communicable diseases. He made arrangements with the public library to refuse books to families having scarlet fever or diphtheria. He obtained a city ordinance requiring the funerals of persons who had died of communicable diseases to be private. As a means of teaching people to avoid contagion he tried placarding houses on a voluntary basis and then made it compulsory when there was little objection. Most important of all, he made it a matter of policy to isolate every infected person from those who were well and to see that their living quarters were disinfected after the disease.

To impose such measures on a community involved much legwork, a great deal of education, and a judicious amount of compulsion. Chapin's chief assistant in this work was the medical inspector, Swarts. To educate the public, Chapin and Swarts distributed large numbers of circulars on such subjects as how to care for communicable disease, how to isolate patients, and how to disinfect premises properly. Occasionally householders would resist having placards put on their houses, or undertakers would "forget" the requirement of having private funerals. A few prosecutions and fines for such violations obtained reasonably good cooperation.

The key figures in informing the public about the new disease controls were the physicians of the city. Before they could do this successfully, however, the physicians themselves needed educating in recent scientific developments. The general apathy and ignorance of the profession about public health work were among the chief reasons why Chapin placed so much importance upon improved medical education, and why, until he retired, he had to play a continuing role as pedagogue to the local medical profession.[10] As a part of this, in the late 1880's he conducted an aggressive campaign to get medical practitioners to report all cases of scarlet fever and diphtheria promptly to his office. The fines he handed out to delinquent doctors gained him national attention.[11]

Occasionally Chapin tested some new measure for which great things were claimed.[12] But, by far his greatest attention centered upon the various forms of disinfection and isolation. These were the measures which really sustained hope of stamping out communicable disease.

Disinfection had been used for centuries against various plagues. The chief form it took in 1885 was the terminal disinfection of premises after infectious disease, although the disinfecting or deodorizing of privies, stables, and other such places was also often done. As used after smallpox and other diseases, disinfection was essentially a process of fumigation by the burning of sulfur in the infected rooms or houses. Chapin adopted fumigation enthusiastically in 1885 and was convinced of its value in preventing the spread of contagion. Yet, although he accepted it as being effective in disinfecting rooms, he felt that the objects in the rooms such as bedding and clothing were not thoroughly disinfected by sulfur. Here, steam seemed to be the answer.

In 1889 Chapin obtain a small amount of money and constructed the first municipal steam disinfection facility in the United States.[13] (The United States Quarantine Stations in Boston and New Orleans, however, had used this means of disinfection previously.) The Health Department now sent a wagon around to houses after cases of communicable disease and removed all movable contaminated articles to the steam house to be disinfected. The Department's second-hand wagon and bony old horse were objects of some amusement to the townspeople. Occasionally a wag would ask, "Why don't you fumigate the horse?" [14]

Chapin also experimented with steam disinfection of rooms themselves by a portable boiler. It disinfected thoroughly, but it also had the disastrous effect of causing paint to blister, wall paper to peel off, and furniture to fall apart. Steam was obviously practicable chiefly for fabrics.

In his steam disinfection chamber (the original wooden structure was soon replaced by a large metal boiler) Chapin conducted a series of bacteriological tests to determine the effectiveness of steam disinfection. With the articles being disinfected he put clothes impregnated with germs and cotton-plugged test tubes filled with various kinds of bacterial cultures. Some of them were packed deep in piles of mattresses but in every case the germs were effectively killed. Chapin was convinced that steam was an effective disinfectant.

While steam disinfection was being proved, Chapin became dissatisfied with sulfur fumigation. He observed statistically that diphtheria spread as often when fumigation was done as it did when it was omitted. The same appeared likely with scarlet fever. He also repeated some of the bacteriological tests which George Sternberg had recently made. Like Sternberg, Chapin was almost never able, even under favorable conditions, to kill typhoid, anthrax, or pus-forming microbes which he placed in rooms being fumigated. In 1890 he was also impressed by research which showed that the Klebs-Loeffler bacillus was not affected by sulfur dioxide. With such results Chapin decided from this time on to discontinue compulsory fumigation, although he continued to perform it when requested.

Before 1890 Chapin had thus partly abandoned faith in the measure which was one of the chief reliances of most health officers against the spread of communicable disease. It seemed to him that thorough scrubbing and washing of apartments was a far better preventive than sulfur fumigation. The delegates to the American Public Health Association convention at Brooklyn in 1889 discussed this heresy with some dismay. Sternberg agreed that as ordinarily practiced, fumigation was "a good deal of a farce," but he adhered to his view that if properly used it was an "efficient agent" in preventing disease.[15] Most cities swore by the measure, farce or no.

In 1895 Chapin surveyed the disinfection practices of the fifty-seven principal cities of the United States and Canada and reported on his findings at the American Public Health Association meeting in Denver that year. Disinfection after small-pox, scarlet fever, and diphtheria was now almost always done, he reported, while only a few cities disinfected after tuber-culosis or measles. Sulfur fumigation was the universal method, and only a dozen cities had as yet installed steam disinfection facilities. Chapin was disappointed that none of the cities had any exact data on the effects of disinfection, and he asked the other health officers to join him in evaluating this practice.[16]

At the same Denver meeting Chapin heard Dr. J. J. Kinyoun first suggest the use of formaldehyde gas as a fumigant. Within an amazingly short time, formaldehyde fumigation had com-pletely replaced sulfur. It was inexpensive (although one could buy costly, dial-covered machines), penetrating, easy to use, and did not injure household objects as sulfur or steam did. Above all, it was shown to be much more effective than sulfur in killing germs. It also had a bad odor, which was one of the popular criteria for a perfect fumigant.[17]

As soon as Chapin returned to Providence from Denver in 1895 he, too, began to experiment with formaldehyde and test the various methods of using it. By 1899 the Providence Health Department used mainly a formalin spray along with the so-called "Chicago" method. This was simply the soaking of sheets in formaldehyde and allowing them to evaporate in the room. Chapin also distributed formalin and corrosive sublimate for cleaning purposes to nearly every house where there was a communicable disease. With the advent of for-maldehyde disinfection, he completely stopped the use of sulfur. Steam disinfection, too, began to decline in use every-where and after 1900 was seldom used in Providence, for fabrics could now be sprayed with formalin.

Still, Chapin was never particularly satisfied with any of the methods of using formaldehyde, and he never made it a compulsory preventive measure. In fact, he had increasingly strong reservations about the whole process just as earlier he had had about sulfur. The greatest danger, it was increasingly apparent, was not from inanimate articles or rooms but from the patient himself. By 1900 Chapin had thus ceased to hope that terminal disinfection would effectively prevent diseases from spreading. The rest of his profession continued to look for great things from this measure for years to come.

Although terminal disinfection had promised much in the way of controlling infectious disease, isolation promised more. Isolation was, indeed, the measure upon which the whole hoped-for success of disinfection depended. If the sick could not be separated from the well there was no use in fumigating houses or steaming bedding. Chapin made strenuous efforts to accomplish this separation.

Among the upper economic classes effective isolation in the home was not much of a problem. Poor families crowded into tenements were another matter. Usually these people had no conception of the need for isolation. Moreover, there was no extra room where patients could be separated. Disease spread readily under these circumstances. The solution which seemed most likely to cope with this danger was for cities to provide isolation hospitals.

England began to build special hospitals in the 1860's; by the 1880's they had become important in the preventive work of many English towns. American cities were slow to build such hospitals. Except for the pesthouses for smallpox, there were few before 1900. Chapin, like Snow before him, made strong efforts to obtain an isolation hospital in Providence. Two tiny isolation wards became available in 1889, but really satisfactory facilities were not obtained until 1896 when Rhode Island Hospital built a large building for this purpose. By that time the traditional fear of hospitals had begun to abate, and hospital isolation became an increasingly useful preventive measure.

In his campaign against communicable disease, Chapin was aware from the outset that he had little information either about the etiology or about the behavior of the various diseases. To know better how to go about his work he began to collect careful data on scarlet fever and diphtheria as he and Swarts observed patients on their rounds. He began to study statistically the spread of diseases within tenement families and to adjoining families in order to discover just how communicable they were. He observed the distribution of cases and amount of susceptibility by age. He gathered data on the contagiousness of diseases at the various stages in their progress and decline. He noted the effectiveness of disinfection, inunction, and isolation in preventing the spread of diseases. He observed the frequency of occurrence of disease in well children who had been staying with relatives but returned to their homes while other family members were still infectious. He noted the recurrence of particular diseases in epidemic form at fairly regular intervals and found that energetic measures interfered with this rhythm. He obtained data on the immunity produced by previous attack and compared this immunity with that naturally acquired with age.

After 1887 Chapin's Annual Reports are increasingly filled with these kinds of data, much of them presented in cumulative statistical tables with careful interpretations. Chapin was among the earliest, perhaps the first, of that small number of American health officers who undertook this painstaking work for the ordinary infectious diseases. His data had great value for health departments across the country, and his reports were important sources of fundamental epidemiological information. To the present day, they provide a fund of information not duplicated elsewhere in the United States. As late as

1928 public health leaders were asking the question, "How contagious is diphtheria, scarlet fever, measles?" And the answer they got was: "Except for the city of Providence, Rhode Island, nobody knows." [18]

In his continued use of the statistical method, Chapin remained a faithful disciple of Louis, Bartlett, and Janeway. In the emerging age of bacteriology, he often used it to support the findings of laboratory research. Yet he also relied upon it as a fruitful method of investigation in itself. He used its laborious techniques to search for and find epidemiological information which the laboratory itself had not discovered or for which it was not adapted. In the age of bacteriology the field epidemiologist and his statistical methods became almost forgotten. Chapin was among those few (Sedgwick of Massachusetts and Victor Vaughan of Michigan were others) who kept the tradition alive. Meanwhile, in most circles, the methods and findings of the laboratory were receiving far more attention than those of field investigation.

By 1890 the infectious agent of diphtheria was finally confirmed. Shortly thereafter research contributed two dramatic new measures to use against this disease.[19] With these developments, diphtheria became the prime exhibit of scientists and health officials in the common hope of eradicating the ordinary infectious diseases through scientific knowledge and techniques. Successful control of all, it was thought, could not be far off.

In 1894 diphtheria antitoxin first became available. Following its successful use in Germany and France, it was introduced into the United States by Dr. Hermann Biggs and the New York City Health Department. New York began to manufacture its own antitoxin in the fall of 1894 and several other large cities followed suit quickly.

Chapin's Department began in 1895 to distribute free antitoxin to Providence patients who could not afford to pay for it. Most of the serum was purchased in New York, although some was imported directly from the laboratories of Roux and Behring.[20] In Providence as in most places antitoxin was used mainly as a cure and only slightly for its temporary immunizing effect. Nevertheless, Chapin observed a definite, although not spectacular, reduction in the diphtheria death rate in the city due to the use of antitoxin.[21]

An even more significant and hopeful discovery was the development of a scientific means of diagnosing diphtheria. Community control had been greatly handicapped because diagnosis was so uncertain and difficult. In 1893, however, William H. Park introduced his successful method of making bacteriological examinations to determine the presence of the diphtheria bacillus. In that year Park became an employee of the new laboratory of the New York City Health Department, and that city immediately began to make diagnostic tests. In the summer of 1893, the department began to require negative cultures for the release of patients from isolation for diphtheria. During the next year several other cities adopted this measure.[22]

Chapin had already, in 1890, begun to consider a bacteriological method for diagnosis of diphtheria. In 1891 he sent Swarts to New York City for two months to study the subject with Prudden. On his return the two men examined the problem critically. They were unable, however, at this time to find a technique simple enough for routine work. Park's practical method soon filled this need.[23]

When Chapin adopted the bacteriological method of diphtheria diagnosis, he made negative cultures compulsory for release of home patients. If the patient was at the hospital he had to have two successive negative cultures before release. In 1896 Chapin took the additional step of requiring negative cultures from *every member* of families where there was a case of diphtheria before the placard could be removed. With this requirement the campaign to bring about perfect isolation went into its final and most stringent phase. Laboratory techniques, it was hoped, would now make sure that patients were not released too soon and would indicate if other members of the family had been infected without outward sign.

One of the important results of the diphtheria research of Park and others was to identify large numbers of mild and often unrecognized infections. Moreover, ostensibly well persons could carry diphtheria bacilli in their throats. Chapin realized the full significance of these missed cases and "carriers." He did not believe their revelation by the bacteriologists was the novelty many people thought. Since his studies under Jacobi at Bellevue he had recognized the importance of mild and hidden cases. Bacteriology confirmed this knowledge, at the same time revealing these sources of infection as far more prevalent than anyone had suspected.

For almost seven years Chapin hopefully applied the new bacteriological methods of diagnosis to determine the need for isolation. Using them along with disinfection and antitoxin, he conducted an unprecedented campaign to try to stamp out diphtheria in Providence. He tried hard to obtain perfect isolation in every private case in the city. He made strenuous efforts to control outbreaks in asylums, hospitals, and other public institutions.[24] By 1899 The Providence Health Department was having thousands of cultures examined every year for diphtheria bacilli. Chapin felt that Providence was making "a far greater effort than has probably been made in any other city to search out and isolate those infected with this organism." [25]

The use of the method as a control measure had a stormy history in Providence. It was bitterly resented by many laymen, and, although most doctors readily agreed with Chapin, a small group strongly opposed it. Some claimed the Klebs-Loeffler bacillus had no causative relation to diphtheria and refused to take cultures; some claimed this method of diagnosis was unreliable; and some regarded as an outrage the detention of people who had diphtheria bacilli in their throats but otherwise were not sick.[26] By 1902, the use of culture diagnosis for healthy people was causing so much friction and hostility to the Health Department from all sides that it was becoming impossible to enforce. Therefore, early in that year Chapin gave up the culture method entirely as a control for diphtheria isolation in the home. He stopped trying to control healthy carriers other than schoolchildren. For release of the sick from home isolation he now set a time limit of ten days from the end of the clinical symptoms instead of a time determined by negative cultures. With this he abandoned the effort to obtain perfect isolation for diphtheria.

Although it was partly public opinion which forced Chapin to relax his use of bacteriological control measures, other factors led him to the same conclusion. For instance, the most drastic efforts often had failed miserably to rid public institutions of diphtheria. Sometimes cultures showed at any given time from 25 per cent to over 50 per cent of healthy staff and inmates with bacilli in their throats.[27] Obviously, all of these persons could not be isolated. Moreover, researchers were showing that a single negative culture did not assure freedom from bacilli in a throat. It was manifestly impossible to impose two or more cultures upon well persons, especially in the face of the existing antagonism. The laboratory had thus provided a measure theoretically allowing perfect control of diphtheria but so exacting that its use and effectiveness were limited.

Chapin was by no means alone in trying to obtain perfect control over diphtheria through isolation determined scientifically by bacteriological diagnosis. Alert health officials in Boston, New York, Detroit, and other cities had applied similar formulas, only slightly less rigorous than that of Chapin. Yet all eventually had to face the limitations he had found.

The most authoritative demonstration of these limitations came from an inquiry by a committee of the Massachusetts Association of Boards of Health.[28] This committee emerged principally because of Chapin's continuing skepticism about the measures he was using, and, on the basis of this skepticism, he was made committee chairman.

Chapin's Committee on Diphtheria Bacilli in Well Persons conducted a cooperative investigation which lasted almost two years and went far beyond the confines of the Association before it reached a conclusion. Among the prominent members of the Committee was Theobald Smith, whose momentous discovery of the transmission of Texas Cattle Fever by ticks had made him one of America's leading medical investigators. Smith was then Director of the Massachusetts State Board of Health Antitoxin Laboratory and Professor of Comparative Pathology at Harvard. The Committee also included Samuel Abbott, Secretary of the Massachusetts State Board of Health; Hibbert W. Hill, bacteriologist of the Boston Health Department, who advocated even stricter isolation than Chapin; Frederic P. Gorham, Brown University bacteriologist, and five others. Chapin in addition enlisted the services of F. F. Wesbrook, the Minnesota bacteriologist who had made important researches into the morphology of the diphtheria bacillus and whose culture types had become accepted as standard for classification and diagnostic purposes. William H. Park and Anna H. Williams of the New York City Health Department cooperated closely in some phases.

To obtain reliable information on the extent of the danger which healthy carriers presented, the Committee secured the results of culture tests on over four thousand people in various parts of the United States. Twenty public and private laboratories around the country were asked to send data, while questionnaires went to the larger health departments. Most of the tedious job of analyzing the data was by Chapin and Gorham in Providence, by Wesbrook in Minnesota, and by Hill in Boston.

The problem was elusive and baffling. Wesbrook referred to his own frustration when he wrote to Chapin in 1902: "I have come many times almost to the point of adopting your motto and the very forcible translation of it which Hill tells me is yours, to wit: 'To hell with bacteria.'" [29] Frequently it seemed as if each member of the Committee would come to different conclusions.

When completed in 1902, however, the investigation provided impressive data on the frequency and virulence of the various Wesbrook types of the diphtheria bacillus in healthy persons. In so doing, it made Chapin more aware than any other person in America of the extent of such infection. In the end the Committee members unanimously recommended against isolating well persons as a general rule. This strongly vindicated Chapin's original skepticism.[30]

Medical journals generally praised the Report of Chapin's Committee. Doctors everywhere were relieved that friction resulting from imposition of arbitrarily severe controls in cities could now be eased.[31] Chapin made it clear, however, that although stringent isolation had been impossible to enforce in urban communities, it might be highly effective in outbreaks in small or rural areas.[32] Experience in the smaller communities of Michigan was already proving this to be a fact, while within a few years the staff of the Minnesota Board of Health confirmed the finding.[33]

With the demonstration that even rigidly applied scientific controls could not eliminate diphtheria, mainly because there were just too many people who had diphtheria bacilli in their throats, the campaign for perfect isolation in cities failed. Almost simultaneously, research showed that mild cases and healthy carriers were important factors in the spread of many other communicable diseases. The optimistic hope that such diseases could be stamped out by isolation and disinfection thus came to nothing. Chapin observed ruefully that the period of the strictest control in Providence—the use of steam and formaldehyde disinfection, culture diagnosis, extensive home isolation, and the opening of the isolation hospital—was accompanied by the greatest prevalence of contagious disease in ten years. The same was true in other cities which had similarly strict controls.[34] Chapin and other health officers were frankly disappointed. Yet it was a useful lesson. Partly as a result of this experience, Chapin began a reassessment of public health measures that was not only salutary but revolutionary in its ultimate effect.[35]

Isolation certainly had considerable value, but Chapin now realized that moderate isolation could accomplish as much in cities as does strict isolation and with less effort. From this time on he sought to reverse the current practice. "Instead of constantly endeavoring to render isolation more complete," he now argued, "the effort should be made to reduce the restrictions to the lowest limit compatible with the object sought. This object is not the extermination of these diseases, for such an end is impossible of attainment." [36] He began to release patients as soon as they were no more of a danger than well people, and ended the practice of keeping wage earners needlessly from their jobs. Effective public health work thus came to mean not necessarily the strictest, the most complex, or even the most "scientific" methods. It often meant having a health officer who knew when to change his mind and start out in another direction.

TOWARD THE MAKING
OF AN AUTHORITY

IF public health work slowly began to acquire greater precision in these decades than previously, it is because it was part of a larger shift of medicine itself, in an age of discovery, from empiricism toward exactness. Having looked for long years chiefly to the sanitary engineer for his best results, the health officer now started to look somewhat more to the doctor and to the laboratory researcher. Such a shift in focus did not come easily. It took a long series of forceful arguments and demonstrations to jolt the old sanitarians out of their set ways. There was also required a long, productive interplay of ideas in the medical and public health forums between the leaders of change.

Chapin's participation in this interplay at both the local and national levels was of such a caliber that he quickly earned the stature of a sanitary authority. As a local authority he showed local doctors what a truly scientific physician was. As a national authority he did as much as anyone to persuade public health workers that change was desirable and that the new elements of science, like bacteriology, could be useful to the public health.

In American communities during the 1880's and 1890's, the

medical profession struggled painfully with the implications and requirements of the scientific method. Under the goad, however, of the younger generation of physicians and of the new discussion groups such as the Providence Clinical Club, some progress was made. The Providence Medical Association began to supplement the tedious case reports of its members with up-to-date reports on recent progress in the various fields of medicine. Chapin presented several reports on aspects of bacteriology, hygiene, and physiology. In the state society, the movement to build up a good medical library gathered strength. Chapin, who served on the society's Library Committee for several years, did perhaps more than anyone except George D. Hersey to promote and develop this library. As one of the principal donors year after year, he supplied huge numbers of health reports, sanitary journals, and other medical and scientific publications.

The chief indication that the organized physicians were moving toward a scientific standard was the persistence of their long effort to obtain legislation to regulate the practice of medicine. In 1889 it was estimated that there were over 200 untrained men and women in Rhode Island who were practicing as physicians, while in Providence there was at least one untrained practitioner for every four who had gone to medical schools. "Ignorant, impudent and unqualified," the regular profession characterized these persons, "self-styled professors in so-called medical institutes or the veriest charlatans of low degree." [1] Regulatory bills to eliminate such persons were introduced in the Rhode Island legislature almost yearly starting in 1887, with Chapin as one of the most active supporters. Rhode Island was one of three states which as late as 1895 still had no such regulations, but in that year a weak licensing law finally was passed. It was 1901, however, before the state required practitioners to take examinations and prohibited some kinds of pseudo-medicine.

Chapin frequently talked to his colleagues about medical quackery and superstition. As President of the Providence Medical Association in 1894, he made a special effort to encourage "a more earnest scientific spirit" among the members. He wanted to see every doctor "do his mite" toward the advancement of science by being accurate and careful in his daily work, keeping careful records, and making systematic reports to his colleagues. Doctors might also undertake modest researches, although Chapin felt that the collective investigation ordinarily offered the individual greater opportunity for worthwhile contributions.[2]

At the end of the nineteenth century Chapin knew that medicine was still lagging behind the other sciences. Yet the situation was improving. The demonstration of the germ theory had opened a new era. "The constant attention which has been directed to bacteriological work," Chapin pointed out, "both in the medical schools and in the professional journals, appears to the writer to be exerting an enormous influence in developing logical methods of thought in the medical profession." Yet, although the biologists had taught a great deal, "they are not infallible. Their work should be questioned by those who deal with the practical problems of medicine, but only those criticisms are of value which come from men who are thoroughly trained in scientific method."[3]

In his efforts to advance the scientific spirit, Chapin was motivated by a strongly humanitarian concept of the objects of medical science. The pursuit of science or truth for its own sake did not seem a worthy ideal.

As long as the world is filled with weakness and pain, and sickness and poverty and sorrow, the highest aim that any human being can have is to do something, be it ever so little, to make that suffering and sorrow less. The ultimate reason for the pursuit of science is to increase the sum of human happiness.[4]

Chapin remained a loyal member of the local medical profession, if often a critical one. He joined his colleagues in 1896 in protesting the antivivisection bill before Congress. He joined them in supporting bills to establish a Federal Bureau of Health. He did more than his share of going around to speak at local hospitals, where he pleaded with the nurses to get rid of their institutionalism and to remember that they were treating "not patients but sick human beings." [5] Chapin helped to raise contributions for the Pasteur Monument Fund in 1896 and for the Walter Reed fund in 1905. He joined in the state medical society's censure of San Francisco officials who tried to hush up their plague epidemic to the peril of the country. In 1905 he was elected Vice-President of the state society, and two years later he was President. Following this he served the society for many years on its important legislative committee as well as on its Committee on Medical Education. He represented Rhode Island in the medical education work of the American Medical Association at the time when concern over this subject reached its climax. There he helped to bring about the fundamental changes which followed the famous Flexner Report of 1910.[6]

In 1900 the Providence Medical Association began to publish its own journal for the first time. As an editorial collaborator for many years, Chapin channeled material into the journal, drew the attention of the profession to valuable public health literature or developments, and frequently wrote editorials or book reviews. Between 1904 and 1912 he contributed a column which gave statistical information upon current diseases and causes of death in Providence. In 1910 he was chairman of a special committee whose recommendations reshaped the journal from a city organ into one for the entire Rhode Island medical profession.[7]

Chapin enjoyed the intimate relation which was possible

between members of the medical profession in a city the size of Providence. Public health administration in Providence was also conducted on a personal and neighborly basis. The nuisance inspector and the driver of the disinfection wagon were fixtures upon the civic scene, while Chapin and Swarts were also well known all over town. Yet some things were changing.

At the very end of 1888 Snow died. Chapin wrote his predecessor's obituary for the Rhode Island Medical Society, conceding the strong conservatism of Snow's later years but emphasizing his great achievements as a man of science.[8] The city fathers promptly appointed Chapin to take Snow's place as City Registrar. For the rest of his career he held this position as well as that of Superintendent of Health.

In 1893 Chapin's right-hand man, Dr. Swarts, resigned to become Secretary of the State Board of Health upon the death of Dr. Charles Fisher. This was a major loss to the Department, as few other doctors in Providence had had bacteriological training. To replace Swarts in the routine duties of the Medical Inspector, Chapin obtained his scholarly and self-effacing college classmate, Dr. Eugene P. King. To handle the bacteriological work, he brought in one of his most promising students at Brown University, Frederic P. Gorham. In 1894 Bumpus and Chapin persuaded Gorham to do additional graduate study at Harvard, including intensive study in bacteriology under Professor Harold Ernst. Gorham came back to develop bacteriology courses at Brown and to become one of the University's great teachers and research men.

When Gorham returned to the University laboratories early in 1895 Chapin began to send some of the Health Department's diphtheria cultures to him for analysis. From this informal beginning Gorham eventually became the official Health Department Bacteriologist. He made himself increasingly useful to Chapin over the years by taking on several difficult Health Department jobs. He also made available to Chapin the services of large numbers of graduate students. The students received good training under this arrangement, while the Health Department was able to have routine work done well at low cost. Gorham was the key person in a close and mutually profitable relation between the Department and the University.

Swarts, too, continued to help Chapin with a great deal of his bacteriological work and in other ways. He also carried bacteriological techniques over into the work of the State Board of Health for the first time. The diagnostic laboratory which he established in 1894 for the Rhode Island Board was one of the first established by any State Board of Health. In the same year he began to distribute free antitoxin and to make free laboratory examinations for tuberculosis. An active state health officer, Swarts did much to spread Chapin's ideas, not only in Rhode Island but in other parts of the United States.

In the meantime, in the course of his vigorous sanitary action in Providence, Chapin was becoming well known in public health circles in other parts of the United States. He carried on a large correspondence and exchanged his reports with other health officers. He also traveled a good deal to see for himself how various kinds of garbage disposal worked, how effective the latest water purification systems were, how disinfection was handled and hospital isolation carried out. In New York he inspected model tenements, visited the splendid Health Department laboratory, and discussed current problems with his friends at the medical colleges. Before 1900 he had a reputation as the "leading health officer of New England" and, many would have added, of the country.[9]

Chapin became a member of the American Public Health Association soon after his election as Health Officer. By around 1890 many of the founders and early leaders in this national professional body—men like Snow, Elisha Harris, James L. Cabell of Virginia, and John H. Rauch of Chicago—had died.

John Shaw Billings and George E. Waring, however, remained, as did George Sternberg. And there were rising new men such as the epidemiologist and teacher Victor Vaughan; the statistician Cressy Wilbur; the sanitary engineer Rudolph Hering; and the bacteriologist Theobald Smith. Chapin gave his first paper to the Association in 1892. Before long he was taking an active part on such important committees as those on Demography and Vital Statistics, on the Disposal of Refuse Materials, and on Disinfection.

Between 1897 and 1899 Chapin served as Chairman of a special Committee on Municipal Public Health Administration. This committee made a modest early effort to determine the sanitary practices of 129 cities, to give its ideas of preferred urban practices and organization, and to point out the functions more properly belonging to the states. Chapin's views dominated the committee's report, which remained for twenty years the American Public Health Association's principal standard for city health organization.

By 1899, when the Report was issued, Chapin was already, due to the notoriously high casualty rate of health officers, one of the elder Association members in terms of service. Because of this, as well as by reason of his various contributions, he played an increasingly prominent part in the organization. He did not aspire to office but was chiefly interested in the scientific work of the various sections or committees. Swarts, on the other hand, was active in the administrative and political councils of the Association and early held a succession of offices including the Presidency in 1908.

Important as the American Public Health Association was to Chapin as a forum for the discussion and interchange of public health ideas and measures, for many years he found the Massachusetts Association of Boards of Health more valuable. In fact, over a period of some two decades the Massachusetts association probably exerted more influence than any other body upon the development of American municipal and local public health practice.

During the quarter-century 1890 to 1915 this organization was the meeting place for a brilliant group of top-level public health leaders. Henry P. Walcott, President of the Massachusetts State Board of Health, was President also of the association from its organization in 1890 until 1912. Samuel Durgin, Chairman of the Boston Board of Health, was first Vice-President during that same time. Samuel Abbott, Secretary of the State Board, was Second-Vice-President until his death in 1904. Another of the early members was William T. Sedgwick of the Massachusetts Institute of Technology. Inspiring, dedicated, and immensely friendly, Sedgwick in 1890 had already turned out the first of an impressive group of scientifically trained sanitary engineers and public health workers. He and his colleagues had also performed some of their important laboratory and field investigations on water, ice, and sewage in connection with the Lawrence Experiment Station. Other M.I.T. personnel who participated in the Association discussions included the chemist and nutrition pioneer Ellen H. Richards, the sanitary engineers George W. Fuller and Robert Spurr Weston, and the food bacteriologist Samuel C. Prescott. During the middle 1890's Theobald Smith and Hibbert W. Hill became active members. In subsequent years the association gained such men as C.-E. A. Winslow, one of Sedgwick's students, who was just beginning a great career as bacteriologist, administrator, and public health educator, and Milton J. Rosenau, who came from the United States Hygienic Laboratory to Harvard to take the first chair of Preventive Medicine and Hygiene in an American medical school.

Chapin had already made friends with many of the Massachusetts sanitarians by 1890, so he received a special invitation to join the association. The fact that he continued to go regularly to the quarterly meetings for at least twenty-five years is an indication of the value of the Association to him.

Like the other leading members, Chapin from time to time presented papers. In addition, he brought to the discussions a critical faculty which was matched, perhaps, only by that of Theobald Smith. His combination of sound scientific knowledge and practical administrative experience made him unique in the organization. Consequently, he was the principal link between those who were chiefly laboratory men, Smith and Hill, for example, and those such as Abbott and Durgin who were mainly concerned with public health administration. Even when Chapin had nothing particular to volunteer at the meetings, Walcott almost invariably called upon him for comment. Chapin also was always chosen to the special committees, such as its Committee on Diphtheria in Well Persons, which the Association from time to time created to investigate particular problems.

The Association's transactions were publicized throughout the United States by its *Journal*. This periodical gradually expanded its scope until, in 1910, it became the official organ of the national public health organization. Between 1904 and 1911, Chapin contributed a department of news and commentary on "Municipal Sanitation." Here he reported significant work at home and abroad, and summarized important researches. In 1914 Chapin was elected to the Board of Advisory Editors of the *American Journal of Public Health*, which grew out of the Massachusetts *Journal*, and he remained on it until the Board was abolished in 1922. He contributed a number of hard-hitting editorials to the *Journal* from this time up to the end of his career.

In 1905 the Massachusetts sanitarians paid Chapin the compliment of electing him to succeed Abbott as a Vice-President of the Association, although technically he was an outsider.

He felt close to the Boston sanitarians because they were engaged in common objectives and spoke in the same New England terms. Sedgwick was especially close. The two men had a similar community spirit, a similar liking for the views of Marcus Aurelius, and, of course, a similar devotion to the scientific ideal. To help pursue this ideal Sedgwick brought Chapin into the more informal fellowship of the Boston "Bug Club," a group of men who met to discuss bacteriology over their glasses of beer. Chapin was not a drinker, but his pungent humor made him welcome among those who were.[10]

About 1910 the outstanding leadership of the Massachusetts Association of Boards of Health began to break up. First, some of the younger public health leaders were lured away to other parts of the country: Hill to Minnesota, Winslow to New York and New Haven. Then, in quick succession, Durgin and Walcott retired. Chapin wrote a splendid appreciation of Durgin's career for the *American Journal of Public Health* in 1912.[11] When Walcott retired the following year, Chapin and Theobald Smith were asked to deliver papers for one final and extra-special program in honor of that elder public health statesman.[12] In 1915 Smith himself moved on to Princeton, while in that same year Chapin retired from the Vice-Presidency after ten years in the office. The association from then on declined considerably in importance both for Chapin and for the public health movement. National activities claimed increasing amounts of whatever time he could spare from his local work.[13]

Chapin led, throughout these years, the quietest sort of private life. In a career that was busy in the extreme, he looked to an Epicurean ideal of simple pleasures and calm repose. His home filled the largest part of his private life. His father had died in 1881 and his mother in 1890, but by the latter date he had a wife and child to take their place. Chapin took pride in keeping his house and yard in good repair. He was handy with tools and enjoyed fitting his study with bookshelves or setting up mosquito traps in the yard. After work he was often seen walking around the East Side of Providence with his dog. And in the evening he relaxed, when he could, not with books filled with the problems of the world but with pleasant volumes such as the *Essays of Elia,* the contemplations of Izaak Walton and Thoreau, or the writings of Irving, Cooper, and Scott.

In the early 1890's Chapin built a shingle cottage at Oakland Beach, not far from Providence, where the family could spend its summers. There was a big resort hotel nearby, but for years there were no other cottages in the vicinity. Anna grew petunias all around the cottage, while Chapin built and looked after a succession of rowboats and skiffs. He loved being out on Narragansett Bay, sailing his boat in a stiff breeze or fishing in the peaceful evenings. Early in life Chapin concluded that "the excitement of money getting, of politics, of philanthropy, of social reform, are disappointing." In their place he combined his Epicurean philosophy with his humanitarian scientific ideal to achieve a character of simplicity yet richness that was unusual in an age of materialism.[14] Yet, as a hard-working pioneer health officer he found little enough of the repose he prized so much.

In 1901 Chapin solidified a growing national reputation by completing and publishing his massive book on *Municipal Sanitation in the United States,* a work designed as a "comprehensive study of public sanitary methods." [15] It was admittedly not a treatise on the principles of sanitation, although it inevitably reflected the principles upon which Chapin's own practice was based. Primarily it provided data about sanitary practice all over the country; and it made clear where the best work was being done—mostly in a few cities, such as Boston, New York, Brookline (Massachusetts), and Providence.

In his book Chapin tacitly acknowledged that the work of the first period of the public health movement—that is, the cleansing of the physical environment—was still grossly incomplete in the bulk of American cities. He devoted pages to detailed discussions of such matters as refuse disposal, water and sewerage systems, nuisance work, and plumbing regulation, as well as vital statistics. Chapin gave equally thorough consideration to what he felt should be of increasing concern to the health officer, once that first period was completed, the scientific control of the ordinary communicable diseases. Despite its definitive program for the two early stages of public health work, Chapin was busy making his own book out of date from the moment it appeared. He was becoming less and less concerned with the physical environment, and at the same time he was inclining away from the strict controls which characterized the second stage.

At the time, Chapin's book was a reliable and necessary guide for the many new and mostly untrained health officers of the United States. It was particularly welcome because of the frequent opinion that books on this subject were "deficient both in quantity and quality" in the United States.[16] The reviewer in *Municipal Engineering* considered it to be "the only American book which considers the question of garbage collection and disposal in a satisfactory manner." [17] Cressy Wilbur admired the discussion of vital statistics.[18] Other specialists praised the sections which pertained to their own work. Several journalists suggested that the book "does for the United States what Palmberg's *Public Health* did for England and the chief European countries; and it does it in a thorough and complete manner." [19] Only a few antivaccinationists and a few conservatives who thought that any governmental sanitary work was unjustified spoke up against parts of it.[20] But most people wanted more, not less public health work.

As a by-product of his work on municipal sanitation, Chapin

gained considerable knowledge of public health law, and in his book he included many details about sanitary legislation. Following its publication the New York State Education Department invited him to contribute to its annual *Review of Legislation* a summary of new public health laws passed in the United States. Chapin undertook this during the years 1901 through 1905 and furnished short noncritical compilations each year. In 1905 and 1906 he expanded these summaries considerably for the Rhode Island State Board of Health, which distributed them in book form. In later years he shared his authority in this area with such men as Henry B. Hemenway and James A. Tobey. He appreciated the need for law and for a respect for law, particularly with cities growing so fast and civilization becoming ever more complex.[21]

As a practical administrator, one of Chapin's continuing tasks was to work for desirable public health legislation in his own community. He was reasonably successful, although often he chafed at the compromises of the politicians. Chapin ran his department with economy, efficiency, and conscientiousness, although outsiders sometimes felt that he ran too much of a one-man show.[22] He handled the City Councilmen carefully in order to gain their long-range understanding and support. He enjoyed the continued favor of the Republican city leaders, while the people themselves had no doubt they were getting the best health protection available. The city was happy in the reflected prestige of one of its public officials "who stands at the head of his profession." [23]

Despite economy, reputation, and services rendered, Chapin could not avoid periodic cuts in his departmental budget which greatly harassed him between 1900 and 1903. In 1902, at the height of the greatest smallpox outbreak in twenty-five years, a severe slash in funds made it necessary to dismiss several key employees, to stop the free distribution of antitoxin, to stop sending cases of communicable disease except smallpox to the hospital, and to eliminate laboratory expenses by rising early in the morning and making examinations himself. By summer there was no money even to pay for garbage collection and enough to pay the remaining employees only because Chapin deferred his own salary for two months. Worst of all, there was no money left to pay for the hospitalization of smallpox patients just when it was most needed. Somehow Chapin got his department through the fiscal year, but only to find the situation virtually repeating itself in 1903. Literally worn out from trying to carry on under impossible financial conditions, he submitted his resignation in April.

Chapin's resignation was a shock to the civic and medical leaders of Providence. It produced action. For two weeks everybody protested that the city needed him. Finally, when the authorities promised to find more money in the future, he agreed to withdraw his resignation.

Chapin now badly needed a rest. The city granted an immediate four-month leave, so in May, he and his wife and son set out on their first European trip.[24] The Chapins did a good deal of energetic sight-seeing in Europe, trudging through art galleries, and shopping. In Rome they peered into the end of the Cloaca Maxima, reputedly the first sewer in the world. At Saint Peter's they looked to see how many pilgrims were sufficiently germ-conscious to wipe off the toe of the bronze saint before kissing it. Chapin got into the enchanting mood of Venice by having a friend read passages from Ruskin to him every morning at breakfast. Greece and Switzerland proved even more delightful than Italy.

More venturesome than his wife or son, Chapin was always ready to taste some exotic dish, look at ruins by moonlight, or climb hills to get good views for photographs. On the Fourth of July, Anna insisted they wear small American flags on their lapels. In Paris a few days later, Chapin's pronounciation of Hotel des Invalides gave great enjoyment to their driver, "who kept slapping his leg, repeating it out loud and laughing the rest of the drive." In Holland they made a special point of visiting Leyden and Delftshaven because of the associations those places had with the New England Pilgrims.[25]

Although this was not a business or professional trip, Chapin called upon health officials in Paris, Brussels, and England. Most important was his visit with Dr. Arthur Newsholme in Brighton at the end of July. Newsholme, who had been one of the earliest Fabians, was among the most creative and energetic of the local Medical Officers of Health in England, and had a standing comparable to that of Chapin in the United States. The day that Chapin spent with Newsholme was the beginning of a lifelong friendship, correspondence, and exchange of health views. It also marked the beginning of a more active relation between Chapin and the English public health profession, although he had been exchanging reports and views for some time with many English officials. Over the next two or three decades he did much to interpret English experience in America and to keep English health officers informed as to significant American work.

Chapin returned to America refreshed and glad to be back among his friends. He was also glad to get back to work, for, despite its frustrations, he found a real zest in the "pleasure of duty well done." He took great satisfaction, moreover, "in taking the best journals, in keeping in touch with the latest discoveries, and in learning what the scientific men of all lands are doing," all with a view toward advancing the profession. Few health officers were destined, Chapin conceded, to make truly momentous contributions to public health work. Nevertheless, he argued, "it should be the ambition, and the reasonable ambition, of every one to add some stone, however small, to the structure of our science." [26] He could have added that, besides building with new stones, it was sometimes possible for a health officer to advance his profession greatly by demolishing the old and no longer useful parts of the structure.

MUNICIPAL CLEANLINESS:
THE PUBLIC HEALTH AND THE
PUBLIC COMFORT

ALTHOUGH a few health officers like Biggs in New York, Durgin in Boston, and Chapin in Providence were using advanced techniques during the 1880's and 1890's, most members of their profession clung to the traditional municipal sanitary work and to the vague filth theories upon which it was based. Before the younger generation could go far in spreading the new methods and knowledge across the United States, the old sanitary ideas and traditional measures had to be exposed, rooted out, and replaced by something more adequate. Chapin saw the need for such a program, launched it, and was instrumental in carrying it through. His campaign, which started out against the filth theory of disease, eventually extended to the whole body of surmise and conjecture about communicable disease.

During the 1890's Chapin was satisfied that he had a conclusive answer to Janeway's question as to the real causes of communicable diseases. So far as he was concerned, none of the diseases which occurred in Providence originated through spontaneous generation out of dirt. All had their original sources in microbes, although not all of the microbes had been identified.

A large part of Chapin's answer came from his use of statistical method applied to carefully kept Providence data. In 1890 he analyzed the findings of six years of sanitary inspections of houses. He compared the data for diphtheria and typhoid fever, diseases which were widely believed to be caused by the ordinary "unsanitary conditions" in homes, with those for scarlet fever, a disease which was almost universally attributed to direct contagion. If defective plumbing, for instance, were truly a significant factor in the causation of typhoid fever and diphtheria, then it should be found consistently where these diseases occurred and rarely where scarlet fever occurred. Chapin's figures showed that defective plumbing existed in 50 per cent of the houses with scarlet fever, in 49 per cent of those with diphtheria, and in 51 per cent with typhoid fever. Likewise, there was hardly any difference in the percentages of the three diseases in relation to filthy vaults and cesspools or garbage-strewn yards. Such unsanitary conditions, moreover, were equally prevalent in houses where there were no cases of disease and in those where disease occurred. Chapin's conclusion was that there was "no causative relation between unsanitary conditions, as ordinarily understood, and scarlet fever, diphtheria and typhoid fever." [1] His findings were supported after 1890 by laboratory discoveries that germs were not easily given off from moist surfaces and that they rarely multiplied outside the body, as in drains or dirt.

Chapin was all but alone among sanitarians before 1900 in believing that general filthy conditions had no causative relation to disease. Feeling sure of his ground, he took upon himself the difficult task of trying to enlighten the rest of the profession. He wrote articles in popular journals; he argued in professional circles; and he wrote and argued on this subject for the rest of his career.

Chapin received important support soon after 1900. Numerous authorities who otherwise endorsed the germ theory still maintained that yellow fever must have its source in filth because no causative organism had been found. The epoch-making work of Walter Reed, William C. Gorgas, Carlos Finlay, and their associates in Havana showed the fallacy in this argument.[2]

Early in 1902 Chapin went to Cuba to see for himself. Finlay and Gorgas took him to Las Animas Hospital and showed him some clothing that had been worn by yellow fever patients. They took him to Camp Lazear to see where groups of volunteers had been subjected to the bites of the yellow fever mosquito. They showed him the small dirty building where other volunteers had slept for weeks in sheets and garments putrid with the vomit and excreta of yellow fever patients. Here was vivid demonstration that diseases were rarely spread by fomites (inanimate objects, clothes, furniture, and so on) or dirt per se. "I realized as never before," Chapin wrote about this, "how very much greater are the difficulties in observation than in experiment, and it seemed that the time had come when the prevailing views as to the importance of fomites infection in other diseases than yellow fever should be seriously reviewed." [3] Gorgas and Finlay also drove Chapin around the city of Havana. He saw at first hand the newly immaculate streets and the fine sanitary facilities planned by George E. Waring, facilities which by themselves had failed to eradicate yellow fever. But he also saw the anti-mosquito measures which were what really counted in the decline of yellow fever.

He left Cuba convinced that Reed and Gorgas had driven "the last nail in the coffin of the filth theory of disease." [4] However, large numbers of people in the United States at this time had the impression that it was Waring's cleanup which had reduced the yellow fever death rate in Havana. Seeking to put the record straight, Chapin came back to this country to argue that "Havana is healthy today because the health officials have studied the cause of certain diseases and have fought each on a special line. It is a triumph for the scientific physician, not for the engineer." [5]

There was no longer any place in a modern public health program for the filth theory of disease, Chapin felt. He conceded that the early sanitary reformers had accomplished a great deal of good, but he vigorously opposed "those who in the light of more accurate knowledge, still hold to the crude ideas of an earlier age." [6]

Chapin's realization that dirt per se had little or no connection with infectious diseases led him to the novel view that the preoccupation of health officials with measures against this harmless filth was irrational. Most such measures, he felt, should be performed by other municipal departments, not by the health department, for they could be justified only on grounds of the public comfort, not as contributions to the public health. Admitting the direct health value of pure water and of sewerage systems, Chapin began to stress that, as a *general* health concept, "municipal cleanliness is no panacea. There is no more a royal road to health than to learning. It will make no demonstrable difference in a city's mortality," he concluded, in a famous 1902 passage, "whether its streets are clean or not, whether the garbage is removed promptly or allowed to accumulate, or whether it has a plumbing law." [7] Such nuisance abatement, so far as he could see, had "no relation to the general health, nor any value in the prevention of specific diseases." He felt that the health officer, as a public servant, should be concerned not with the aesthetic improvement of the city but with the prevention of disease. He should be a man of science, not a cleanup man.[8]

Chapin had been trying for some time to rid his own department of routine cleansing work. He had never had the responsibility for plumbing inspection or street cleaning, and he hoped some day he could rid himself of garbage collection and disposal. As early as 1889 he proposed that the police take over the inspection and abatement of nuisances. Since this proved impossible, he simply pursued a policy of doing as little as possible.[9]

Chapin carried these convictions to the nation's sanitarians in two 1902 papers, one presented in Boston and the other in New Orleans.[10] As Sedgwick had warned Chapin ahead of time, these views shocked the traditional sanitarians.[11] At the meeting of the Massachusetts Association of Boards of Health, several persons deplored such revolutionary notions and lamented that this was such an "age of iconoclasm—that a good many of our cherished beliefs were being smashed." [12] Sedgwick, on the other hand, defended Chapin and asserted that the paper was "epoch-making." With this new viewpoint it seemed to him that "a better day was dawning" for sanitary science.[13]

The next day Sedgwick wrote Chapin that the paper was a great success and would do much good even if it had caused momentary flutterings. He had long wanted to do such a thing himself. "It gave me much pleasure," Sedgwick added, "to back you up and I think that you and I can well afford to stand together against the other speakers." [14]

Reaction in general public health circles to Chapin's proposal to eliminate routine nuisance abatement work from health departments was as mixed as it was at the Massachusetts meeting. Samuel Durgin of Boston strongly backed the idea in 1902, observing that "the trend for the last quarter of a century has been in this direction." [15] Milton J. Rosenau agreed that Chapin's logic was unassailable. He began to teach the concept in his classes when he joined the Harvard Medical School and spread it even further through his great hygiene text of 1913.[16] E. O. Jordan, the University of Chicago bacteriologist, likewise became an early exponent of those principles, along with Hill of Boston and Minnesota and M. N. Baker, editor of *Engineering News*.[17]

Opposition came from all parts of the country. In Baltimore, William H. Welch, who as early as 1889 had himself reminded physicians that "hygienic cleanliness and aesthetic cleanliness are not identical," had foreseen this opposition years ago and had felt that one should go slowly with the old sanitarians.[18] Even some of the progressive health officers could not accept Chapin's doctrine. William C. Woodward of Washington wrote that he was not prepared to relegate to such an insignificant position the sources of infection extraneous to the body. A few years later James Niven of Manchester, echoing the position of almost all English health officials, told Chapin the same thing.[19] Meanwhile, a group of progressive health officers from Southern states, whose spokesman was Ernest Levy of Richmond, began to criticize Chapin because it seemed to them that he was belittling the entire role of the environment in disease as well as all types of measures for environmental sanitation.[20]

Chapin, having jumped a long distance in his own thinking and looking to a third great stage of the public health movement, had indeed moved much too swiftly for the many health officers whose communities had hardly reached the first stage. But he was far from repudiating the enormous importance of those basic measures for municipal cleanliness. On the contrary, he recognized them as among the great civilizing influences which made life in cities "more comfortable, more decent and more wholesome." [21] As he pointed out, "where typhoid fever and dysentery and hookworm infestation abound, where 95 per cent of the schoolhouses have no privy, where cities are unsewered and surface wells furnish the water supply, the health officer may well give much time to environment," just as he himself had done for over fifteen years. On the other hand, he insisted, "when these communities have learned to dispose of their excreta, they, too, can turn over to the police what remains of nuisance control." [22] There was no justification for continuing this work at a sacrifice of the really significant new lines of public health work.

Despite the logic of Chapin's revolutionary argument, throughout his own career he continued to have a hand in many forms of environmental sanitation in Providence. Some of these he could justify as direct health measures. Others had his attention mainly for their contribution to the aesthetics or comfort of the city, under circumstances when the community could find no one else to do them as well.

Probably no one in the city cheered louder than Chapin when the Providence Chamber of Commerce, like those of other American communities of the time, in 1914 organized an annual spring Clean-Up Week. This was not a new thing, for nineteenth-century sanitarians used the annual cleanup religiously, but it had fallen into disuse in the twentieth century. Chapin aided Clean-Up Week by educational measures to get individuals to accept responsibility for municipal cleanliness. He put on extra temporary inspectors, put up large posters around the city, distributed thousands of pamphlets to school children.[23] He took the city Clean-Up Committee on tours of the filthiest spots. But he always argued for a cleaner city for reasons of comfort, aesthetic pleasure, and decency, never of health.

Chapin's enthusiasm for Clean-Up Week waned after a number of years. As an orgy of civic righteousness its energy was soon spent, its slogans forgotten, and its place taken by other equally fugitive, though well-meaning, outbursts of enthusiasm. Chapin could not understand how people could be satisfied with doing all of their cleaning once a year and then living in filth the rest of the time. He felt that every week should be Clean-Up Week, that this should be one of the continuing, automatic functions of the civilized community.[24] Yet, like Martin Arrowsmith, Chapin was even more disgusted because many health officers, who took Clean-Up Week seriously as an important health measure, took months in getting ready for it, spent large chunks of their annual budgets upon it, and justified it by arguing that it reduced disease.[25]

Housing was another matter to which most health officers gave attention because of its presumed connection with health. Chapin was a somewhat ambiguous exception. He stated his position as follows: "I have not as health officer taken much interest in improved housing. As a citizen I do, but not as health officer, because I fail to see how poor housing in itself produces much disease." [26] Actually, he did concern himself considerably with the housing of the poor, for the filthy privies and polluted water of many slum tenements could directly affect the health. And, he investigated and took over the inspection and licensing of abominably filthy transient lodging houses. Chapin's distinction was a hard one for most people to follow, and they did not much care which hat he wore when he looked after housing, that of citizen or that of health officer, just as long as he was willing to do the work.

In 1910, Chapin represented Providence at the organization meeting of the National Housing Association and became one of its first directors. Local interest in housing was roused in 1916 when the Association scheduled its annual convention in Providence. In anticipation of that meeting the Chamber of Commerce established a local Committee on Improved Housing. As its Vice-President, Chapin gave much time, particularly to its careful work of drafting a new housing code and to the carrying out of an extensive housing survey of the city.[27] Still, in carrying on these activities, he was only concerned with the need for housing per se and was careful to avoid connecting it with health.

Chapin also became officially involved in much work against insects and rodents as a phase of environmental sanitation.

As Health Officer he extended the studies of malaria in New England which he had started in 1880, and before 1900 he published several papers upon this disease.[28] Thorough as he was, he added little to information dating as far back as Holmes.

In 1900 and 1901, following the demonstrations by Ross, Grassi, and others that malaria is transmitted by mosquitoes, Chapin and Gorham devoted much time to the mosquitoes of Providence. Their first aim was to confirm the relation of mosquitoes to malaria. This done, they surveyed breeding spots in the city and experimented with various measures against malaria and against the general mosquito nuisance. In this investigation Chapin and Gorham made the original observation that the principal breeding place for the chief common house mosquito in cities was in catch-basins at every street corner.[29] Chapin did not advocate a control program against mosquitoes since malaria was rapidly disappearing from Providence in 1900. As the years went by, however, there was an increasingly insistent demand for measures against the ordinary mosquito, a nuisance which made summer nights a time of torture to those who could not escape to the seashore.

In 1913 the City Council voted funds for a mosquito extermination program and put Chapin in charge. He in turn persuaded Gorham to take over the immediate direction. Over the next dozen years the two conducted the most energetic sort of campaign, draining swamps, checking back-yard breeding places, and organizing a "mosquito fleet" of wagons manned by college athletes for oiling work. Chapin even brought in as advisers outside experts such as Joseph A. LePrince, who had been Gorgas' chief assistant in mosquito-control work in Panama. However, mosquitoes continued to plague Providence. Only after 1923, when state appropriations made extermination measures possible in the surrounding towns, was any great improvement achieved.

Flies were a further nuisance in most cities early in the

century. The belief was widespread in popular and in scientific circles in the United States and in Europe that the fly was a major factor in the spread of disease. Some felt that tuberculosis and cholera were transmitted in this way, and probably the majority of health officials believed that typhoid fever and diarrheal diseases were transmitted mainly in this way. Health departments and anti-tuberculosis leagues used their bulletins to warn against the fly danger, some in the most lurid language.

Chapin was greatly interested in any possible relation of flies to the spread of disease, and conceded that as a possible danger they should be eliminated.[30] He was not, however, impressed by the evidence favoring this means of transmission. Between 1898 and 1910 he and Gorham conducted a number of bacteriological tests to determine the actual connection between flies and various infectious diseases.[31] The results showed no consistent relation. In 1908, Chapin was Chairman of a Committee on Flies of the Massachusetts Association of Boards of Health; this committee reached no conclusion except that local studies were badly needed. Again taking the lead, in 1909 and 1910 he engaged a Brown University graduate student to conduct a careful study of the distribution and breeding places of Providence flies and to correlate them with disease incidence. The results led Chapin to conclude that "there is nothing to show that flies are much of a factor in the spread of either typhoid fever or diarrhea" in cities with adequate sanitation. Military camps or cities without sewerage were exceptions.[32]

By 1910 Chapin spoke out frequently against the virtual wave of hysteria over the fly danger.[33] His conclusions had a mixed reception from other health authorities. During the next few years the matter became increasingly academic. With the advent of the automobile and the disappearance of the stable with its piles of manure, the fly lost many breeding places, with the result that numbers declined rapidly in the cities.[34]

Several times during his career, acting upon suggestions of the United States Public Health Service, Chapin conducted investigations of rats because of the danger of bubonic plague. In 1912 he offered the public five cents for each live rat, and fifteen cents for one with fleas; yet only a few hundred specimens were obtained. Gorham assigned one of his graduate students to perform the laboratory work. In a later survey, with several especially trained men, the catch was considerably greater. There was, however, no evidence of plague in either year.

From 1906 on, the Providence Health Department had to contend with rabies in its dog population. The first persons bitten by rabid dogs were sent for treatment to New York, some by popular subscription and the rest by public funds. As the epidemic continued into the fall of 1906, Rhode Island Hospital made arrangements to receive daily shipments of the spinal cords of rabbits so that inoculations could be done in Providence. The Brown University laboratory made the diagnostic examinations of suspected animals. Chapin tried, during this time, to overcome popular ignorance about rabies and to show why the scientific diagnosis of the disease required the killing of such dogs. He made some headway in this, but there was less that he could do with the stubbornly individualistic frame of mind which frustrated the muzzling law and maintained, as he said, "the inalienable right of every American citizen to keep a dog to bite his neighbor." [35] As a result, rabies continued to appear almost every year.

Although for the most part Chapin kept acquiring new responsibilities, circumstances did permit him to give up one activity. This was maritime quarantine. When he was appointed Health Officer in 1884, he became ex-officio the Quarantine Officer of Providence, ordinarily not a burdensome duty, since there were rarely more than fifteen or twenty ves-

sels requiring inspection during any one year. Chapin's philosophy of maritime quarantine was like his later view of home
isolation. He supported, in short, the modern concept that
"quarantine is a sieve, not a dam." This was a position which
allowed the fullest normal operation of commerce until specific
information of specific diseases in given countries called for
particular restrictions.[36]

In 1911, when regular steamship service began bringing large
numbers of immigrants from southern Europe to Providence,
the Health Department had to make special arrangements to
process them expeditiously. During the same summer the presence of cholera in Marseilles and Naples brought an order
from the Surgeon-General of the Public Health Service that
all immigrants from these ports must have bacteriological
examinations. Again, Brown University graduate students assisted the Health Department in the emergency by perform-
ing the examinations, while extra doctors and nurses were also
hired. But these were makeshift arrangements. There had to
be a properly equipped quarantine station. Since the city was
not financially able to build one, Chapin recommended that
quarantine functions in the city and state be turned over to
the United States Public Health Service. When this transfer
was completed in June 1912, Rhode Island was one of the last
states to give up its quarantine authority to the federal government. Although the United States provided floating quarantine
facilities at Providence for a few years, these were soon discontinued. No permanent facilities were built despite Chapin's
repeated request to the Surgeon-General during the 1920's
and the latter's repeated endorsement of the request.[37]

Whatever leisure Chapin gained by ridding himself of maritime quarantine was offset by ever-increasing work connected
with the inspection and protection of food and drink. Early
in his career Chapin stirred up great excitement by his unan-

nounced investigations of markets and his seizures, with police help, of large quantities of inedible produce and rotten meat. With the subsequent help of his Inspectors of Provisions, he achieved considerable improvement of the quality of foods in Providence. In 1886 and 1887, aware of the agitation in various other states, Chapin made a thorough investigation of local adulteration in food, spices, and drugs. His report to the City Council noted that, of the foods he could test, coffee, spices, cream of tartar, baking powder, syrup, mustard, honey, and probably butter, lard, and oils, were badly adulterated. Drugs were also frequently involved in this practice.[38] Unlike many reformers of his day, Chapin saw that adulteration was a matter which affected primarily the pocketbook, and health, little, if at all. Nevertheless, for years he pressed for state pure-food legislation, repeatedly, if without much success.

In 1906 the publication of Upton Sinclair's novel, *The Jungle*, with its revelation of conditions in the Chicago packing houses, shocked public opinion. Chapin regarded the health scare stirred up at this time as unwarranted, for little sickness was caused by meats from diseased animals. Labor conditions in the packing houses, he pointed out, certainly improved as a result of Sinclair's exposé. Nevertheless, the resulting legislation for federal meat inspection which Congress passed as a health measure did not even cover the most serious of the animal diseases, trichinosis. Critically viewed, this incident in the pure-food campaign left much to be desired from the point of view of at least this one public health scientist. Chapin wished that the money put into meat inspection could have gone into productive sanitary research.[39]

Chapin also took the unpopular side of the argument when the matter of prohibiting oleomargarine was discussed in Rhode Island. In an 1891 legislative hearing he deplored the prejudice against oleo merely because it was an artificial product, and described its manufacturers as being "among the greatest benefactors of the age." They had developed a product which was not only as healthful and wholesome as butter but inexpensive enough to be within the reach of the poor.[40]

Early in the twentieth century, Atlantic coast shellfish, notably the oyster, needed the same sort of defense Chapin gave to oleo. At the time that flies were being blamed for so much typhoid fever, it was learned that raw oysters also could transmit that disease. When it was realized that large quantities of American oysters were raised in waters polluted by sewage of big Eastern cities, a great hue and cry arose in the popular and medical press and among health officers. The result was federal action to ban contaminated oysters from the market. The Rhode Island oyster industry, one of the largest in the state, was hard hit because Narragansett Bay was grossly polluted.

Chapin was interested in the situation and gathered careful epidemiological data. To put the record straight, he noted that Providence, where unusually large amounts of oysters from polluted waters were consumed, actually had a typhoid fever rate less than half that of the average American city, while he could trace no cases at all to this source. His conclusion that the danger of infection from shellfish had been considerably exaggerated drew the fire of many of his professional friends as well as those having a built-in phobia about filth. Yet Chapin did not press his point. Instead he agreed that aesthetically no one wanted to eat oysters grown in sewage. Moreover, he felt that "while the amount of typhoid fever due to the use of raw shellfish is not very great, this danger ought to be eliminated entirely, and state boards of health should have the authority to forbid the sale of shellfish from polluted waters." [41]

Due to local circumstances Chapin for many years had no administrative responsibility for the inspection of the milk supply. In his concern for infant mortality, however, he constantly interested himself in it. He was much concerned with outbreaks of communicable disease, chiefly typhoid fever, from milk supplies. As early as 1893, he reported upon a possible outbreak of typhoid fever in Providence from milk, and during the next two decades or so he had to investigate and handle a good many such outbreaks, sometimes two or three in the same year.

His concern over the handling of this problem led him during 1908 and 1909 to conduct a personal survey to determine ideas current among leading health officials of the United States and England. The replies to Chapin's questionnaire indicated much uncertainty as to what health departments should do about carriers who might be found in connection with milk outbreaks of disease and as to how far health departments should go in shutting down dairies. George Goler, Health Officer of Rochester, replied that Chapin's questions were "posers." All of the officials hoped that he would work out something useful to the profession.

In 1909 Chapin reported his findings and suggested a tentative control program. He advocated either the shutting off or the pasteurization of contaminated milk supplies, together with a thorough examination of all milk handlers. Milk handlers who were actually sick or were healthy carriers were to be removed from work until no longer dangerous to the public. Yet, Chapin pointed out, great care had to be taken not to injure a dealer's business unnecessarily or similarly an employee's personal livelihood by hasty or excessively severe measures. "The management of our common contagious diseases," he observed, and particularly in this case, "is and must be for the present frequently inconsistent and illogical from a scientific viewpoint. We must carefully estimate the difficulties in the way of proposed action, consider the opposition to be aroused, the burden to be imposed on the individual or the public, the cost to the community, and what is particularly important, the results likely to be obtained." [42]

This investigation of typhoid fever spread by milk led Chapin to further studies of carrier-borne typhoid fever. He was chairman of the committee of the Massachusetts Association of Boards of Health which in 1910 considered the disease and outlined for the profession a whole program of control measures, including isolation, placarding, supervision of carriers, and removal of privy vaults. This was a revelation to those who thought that environmental sanitation alone would take care of typhoid. It was a stiff program but, as an English reviewer remarked, "if we aim at the moon we may succeed in hitting the tops of the trees." [43]

In 1913 a scandal involving the Providence Milk Inspector and some of his staff resulted in Chapin being given responsibility for the work, at first temporarily and then permanently. Over the next dozen years, even with a poor milk law, he did much to improve the quality of the city's milk. Gorham was his most effective deputy. First off, Chapin prosecuted a good many dealers for selling low-grade milk or for adding formaldehyde. As another measure he began to publish a quarterly list of the bacterial counts of the milk supplied by each dealer, leaving it to public opinion to choose the best. He also had the power to withhold licenses from offending dealers.

Chapin received some local criticism because, by having his staff concentrate on the laboratory inspection of milk at the point where it was distributed, that is, at the dealers, he largely neglected routine inspection of the sanitary condition of the farms. Most health officers also opposed him here. But Chapin felt that in this matter they were attaching too much importance to the environment. Even on the cleanest farms, he pointed out, helpers who were carriers could infect the milk.[44] Sanitary inspection of farms was fine if there was plenty of money available, but where a choice had to be made he unhesitatingly chose the most effective measure. Chapin's viewpoint paid off over the years in steadily improving milk, as more and more dealers turned voluntarily to pasteurization in order to meet competition.

It was a slow process to educate the laity in distinguishing between measures for health and those for comfort or aesthetics. It was an equally slow process to educate health officers. Not all sanitarians, by any means, agreed with Chapin's distinction. The viewpoint became, however, an integral part of a total reassessment of public health measures which Chapin was working out in the first decade of the twentieth century. The final rationale of this reassessment was so convincing that this and other controversial parts eventually came into their own.

THE SOURCES
AND MODES OF INFECTION

By 1900 the age of bacteriology had produced an immense amount of scattered information. But no one as yet had attempted to draw it all together into a coherent pattern of logical public health principles and measures. Chapin, with his practical experience, scientific background, patience, and analytical mind, was perhaps uniquely qualified for such a task. Refreshed by his European trip, he first suggested, in his Annual Report of 1903, an outline of what had to be done. For the next several years he busied himself with filling in this outline. This meant fashioning the authoritative synthesis of the new bacteriological and epidemiological information as to how communicable diseases spread as well as the definitive statement as to their control. Moving boldly, a decade or so ahead of most other health workers, he challenged and came to grips with several additional old sanitary ideas and measures. The outcome was the launching of a revolutionary third stage of the modern public health movement.

Personal cleanliness, it became increasingly evident after 1900, was the central life-saving concept of this third stage which could replace both municipal cleanliness and strict isolation as a hopeful basis of preventive health action. Although by no means a new doctrine, it had become part of the modern public health campaign with the initiation of measures against spitting. The need for such measures was obvious when one contemplated the disgusting messes on most sidewalks, in railway smoking cars, and in many public rooms. Chapin and Biggs issued circulars against spitting before any other cities did. That was in 1889.[1] By 1895, Paris, Belfast, Philadelphia, and many other communities had begun campaigns against spitting in public places, and many of them passed laws.[2] After Providence passed an anti-spitting rule and placed warning signs along the streets, the spitting habit decreased by 90 per cent, to the vast benefit of ladies with their long skirts.[3]

The concepts of personal cleanliness became still more important factors in public health programs when sanitarians began to realize the full extent of the role of human contact in the spread of communicable diseases. Chapin himself had become convinced—largely as a result of his epidemiological observations since 1887 of the spread of disease in multiple-family tenements—that scarlet fever and diphtheria rarely spread from family to family through the air or by fomites any more than they did by general filthy conditions. The principal means, he noted, was fairly direct contact between members of the families. Sedgwick came to a similar conclusion in 1892 as to the importance of contact infection in the spread of typhoid fever.[4] Other investigators began to make similar observations about other diseases.

During the middle and late 1890's Chapin's conviction of the important role of contact infection was tremendously reinforced by laboratory demonstrations of the wide prevalence of missed cases and healthy carriers. Koch showed these phenomena were involved in the spread of cholera. Park and Beebe established this condition even more convincingly for diphtheria. The Reed, Vaughan, and Shakespeare Commission pointed it out for typhoid fever. Proof for other diseases, including insect-borne diseases, followed. The evidence became so convincing that soon after 1900 Chapin had no hesitancy in asserting that carriers and missed cases were "by all odds the chief factor in the spread of the communicable diseases." [5] In the 1900's, few health officers knew enough to support this belief. Chapin was surprised, however, that most bacteriologists likewise largely ignored the full significance of carriers. Even Park and Beebe "minimized the danger to be apprehended from these carriers." [6] Chapin felt otherwise about this danger, and drew forth its full implications for communicable disease control. He proceeded to make the unsettling reality of healthy carriers and missed cases a central feature of his reappraisal. Building upon this reality, Chapin became the foremost teacher of the paramount role of contact infection in its various forms.

While pointing out the danger from healthy carriers, Chapin questioned whether a community was morally or legally right in confining an occasional carrier who might be discovered, leaving hundreds or thousands of others free. He was particularly critical of the heavy-handed methods of the New York City Health Department in confining the notorious "Typhoid Mary," feeling that surveillance by health officials would have accomplished as much and would have been fairer.[7]

A major impetus to the doctrine of personal cleanliness came in 1901 out of Chapin's Committee on Diphtheria Bacilli in Well Persons. At that time the members of the Committee were discouraged over the implications of healthy carriers. During one of the exchanges of views Theobald Smith, that remarkable man who had so many fruitful ideas, observed that perhaps something might be done to offset this new-found menace if only schoolchildren could be taught the essentials of personal cleanliness. The idea appealed to Chapin, and he set the whole Committee to studying the matter. The result was a report issued in 1901. The report advocated better hygienic practices in schools, such as eliminating the common drinking cup and arranging for students to have their own textbooks, slates, or modeling clay. It proposed health instruction for teachers so that they could guide the children. Above all, Chapin's Committee suggested a set of fundamental health rules to be taught to children:

Do not spit if you can help it. Never spit on a slate, floor or side-walk.

Do not put the fingers into the mouth.

Do not pick the nose or wipe the nose on the hand or sleeve.

Do not wet the finger in the mouth when turning the leaves of books.

Do not put pencils into the mouth or wet them with the lips.

Do not put money into the mouth.

Do not put pins into the mouth.

Do not put anything into the mouth except food and drink.

Do not swap apple cores, candy, chewing gum, half-eaten food, whistles or bean blowers, or anything that is put into the mouth.

Never cough or sneeze in a person's face. Turn your face to one side.

Keep your face and hands clean; wash the hands with soap and water before each meal.[8]

This set of health rules became the virtual catechism of twentieth-century hygiene. Chapin issued copies to Providence schoolchildren, and distributed teaching instructions to all public and parochial schoolteachers. Chicago, Boston, and other cities were almost as quick to use the Committee's material. Within a few years the teaching of personal hygiene had become widespread in American city schools.

The "don'ts" of personal cleanliness also spread among adults, while various public measures promoting individual cleanliness came into effect. Cities began to build public baths and to make arrangements for up-to-date comfort stations. Some states eliminated the requirement of kissing the Bible at swearing-in ceremonies or court cases.[9] Churches introduced individual communion cups. Above all, cities and states began to prohibit the public common drinking cup and the public roller towel. People were beginning to learn that "personal cleanliness is less expensive than municipal cleanliness, and is within the reach of all." [10]

For Chapin contact infection and personal cleanliness emerged as two fundamental and complementary concepts. "It is infected persons not infected things," he stressed increasingly, "that are to be feared." By strict attention to personal cleanliness and avoiding the secretions of others, it seemed as if "each one has it very largely in his own power to avoid the infectious diseases." [11] This encouraging prospect brought renewed optimism to modern health officers after the discouraging failure of scientifically strict isolation.

The implications of these ideas led Chapin, as a further part of his reassessment, to continue his examination of disinfection. By the 1900's virtually all health departments employed large staffs and elaborate apparatus for terminal disinfection, and made it a compulsory measure in order to combat the spread of disease through fomites (inanimate objects such as furniture).[12] For the general public, disinfection was one of the most understandable and popular of sanitary measures. At the very height of this popularity, however, Chapin reached the conclusion that terminal disinfection was not nearly as essential a measure as people supposed. For one thing, if germs could not live long outside the body, then the danger from fomites must be negligible. Likewise, he argued, "in diphtheria where after recovery the patient and other members of the family frequently continue to grow the germs in their throats for weeks, and in those cases of tuberculosis where no attempt to care for the sputum has been made during the sickness, any disinfection is a farce." Before 1900 Chapin was convinced that "the most effectual disinfection is the strictest cleanliness daily through the whole course of the illness." (This later became known as concurrent disinfection.) In 1903, epidemiological data for Providence indicated no greater chance of the spread of certain diseases when disinfection was omitted than when it was performed. Two years later he finally announced that he was abandoning terminal disinfection after diphtheria.[13]

Chapin presented his ideas on terminal disinfection nationally for the first time to the Section on Hygiene and Sanitary Science of the American Medical Association at its annual meeting in Boston, June 1906. Throwing off his cautious early approach, he now attacked disinfection as a "fetich." "The expiatory sacrifice of disinfection," he pointed out, "is believed to atone for every sanitary sin." Public faith in this measure was the greatest hindrance to the development of better methods of handling disease and guarding against infection. "Hygienic salvation," Chapin concluded, "can only be attained through the good works of personal cleanliness. As the surgeons have given up antisepsis for asepsis, so the health officer must substitute cleanliness for disinfection." [14]

This paper fell like a bombshell into the Boston meeting and the medical world in general. Not a single doctor at Boston supported Chapin in his views, and few even understood them. One confused and angry delegate asserted that such a doctrine threatened to overthrow the whole germ theory of disease. Another felt that Chapin's heresy was "close to Eddyism." [15] One editor of a sanitary journal regarded Chapin's paper as "the cheapest form of professional notoriety," while others deplored his iconoclasm as ruthless and dangerous.[16]

The number of health leaders who agreed with Chapin's position on fomites and disinfection at this time was small. The few included A. H. Doty, Health Officer of the Port of New York, and Milton J. Rosenau, then Director of the Marine Hospital Service's Hygienic Laboratory.[17] The editors of the *Journal of the American Medical Association* also felt that in general Chapin was correct. "Dr. Chapin's paper on disease," they commented, "is one of the kind that may do much good because it is likely to lead physicians to review critically their own ideas, convictions and practices anent disinfection." [18] The editors of *American Medicine* considered it a "brilliant and revolutionary paper" and felt that Chapin deserved "a far more respectful hearing" than he had had in Boston.[19]

A few days after the meeting C.-E. A. Winslow scribbled off a note to Chapin. "I was glad," he wrote, "to see that you gave the doctors some good sense about disinfectants. I should sympathize with you on the reception it received if I did not know your thorough enjoyment of it. They will all be with you in ten years." [20]

In Providence, Chapin's bold experiment succeeded, despite many local misgivings.[21] It was risky. He himself realized that if an unusual amount of diphtheria appeared after his abandonment of disinfection he would be finished professionally.[22] As it was, there was no more diphtheria without disinfection than there had been before. By 1910, Chapin noted with relish that the record of secondary cases occurring in Providence where there was no disinfection was no different from that of Baltimore where disinfection was unusually thorough.[23] On this evidence he ceased to urge disinfection after scarlet fever or any disease widely distributed by mild cases and carriers.[24]

Almost the sole justification for using terminal disinfection, Chapin now thought, would be as an extraordinary measure when a new or rare disease invaded a community. Once the disease was established, such a measure was judged to be useless, just as strict isolation was useless. He expressed his philosophy in an epigram which became the credo for the new generation of health officers: "A spark in the dry grass should be stamped out at any cost, but it is useless to waste time in extinguishing the smoldering flames left here and there as the line of fire is sweeping across the prairie." [25]

Other health departments did not rush to adopt these views. However, a second Chapin paper on the subject, in 1910, finally provoked a number of cities into following the lead of Providence.[26] George Goler, always alert in keeping Rochester progressive in its health work, abandoned routine disinfection in 1911.[27] Boston partly stopped the practice in 1912, while New York followed suit in 1913. Over the next decade, experiments in these and other American cities repeatedly confirmed the logic of Chapin's argument. The viewpoint steadily gained favor with health officers.

Conservative sanitarians continued to make dismal prophecies for the communities which stopped disinfection. At the same time, manufacturers of disinfectants redoubled efforts to keep alive fears that germs lived indefinitely on inanimate objects. Chapin's talk on disinfection at the Fourth International Congress on School Hygiene, held in Buffalo in the summer of 1913, sounded as radical to many delegates as his Boston paper.[28] Here he pointed out that routine disinfection in schools was absurd unless authorities first found and removed the children who were carriers of infection. Among those rushing to the defense of disinfection after this paper was Dr. J. T. Ainslie-Walker, a British scientist who had helped develop a well-known test for disinfectants and was now trying to sell Americans his own method of direct spray disinfection.[29] Walker, together with other promoters and the leaders of several well-meaning but misguided civic groups, helped keep up some considerable demand for terminal disinfection for years.[30]

The repudiation of terminal disinfection was Chapin's most dramatic break with tradition. It was a key step that had to be taken before the doctrine of personal cleanliness could achieve its full effectiveness.

Another break with the sanitary past was Chapin's introduction to America of a revolutionary form of hospital isolation for the infectious diseases. Up until around 1900 isolation hospitals were based upon another old and inadequate theory, the concept of indiscriminate infection through the air. People for centuries had lived in dread of miasmata flying from building to building, from ship to shore, or from one part of a city to another. Infectious disease hospitals were located as far from other buildings as possible. In addition, they were so constructed as to separate the various diseases as far from each other as possible, usually in separate buildings, in order to try to prevent cross-infection which supposedly was carried upon the air. The age of bacteriology brought a different concept.

Between 1903 and 1906 Chapin was trying to obtain additional hospital facilities for infectious diseases in Providence, and the city decided to erect its own isolation hospital. About this time Chapin learned of a new kind of hospital in Europe, one based upon the principle of medical asepsis, or aseptic nursing. Under this principle, the spread of disease through cross-infection was guarded against simply by minimizing the opportunities for infection by contact. The watchword was strict cleanliness. Although usually not done unless necessary, different diseases could now be cared for in adjacent beds and by the same nurse, with a red card on the bed or door as the only "barrier" or reminder that special caution was needed. As a rule patients with different diseases were put in separate wards or at least in separate rooms or cubicles in order to minimize contact, though with completely free circulation of air. Nurses and doctors who handled patients scrubbed themselves religiously and changed their outer gowns before leaving the area to care for a different disease or to mix with other staff members. No disinfection was necessary after each case, for concurrent disinfection or thorough washing was practiced throughout the course of the illness.

J. J. Grancher developed the cubicle or barrier system of

medical asepsis betwen 1890 and 1900 in the Hospital for Sick Children in Paris. The Pasteur Hospital from 1900 and then a number of other French and English isolation hospitals subsequently applied the technique. However, neither Grancher nor any other Europeans generalized from their experience.[31] It remained for Chapin to note the significance of the innovation and to draw from it justifiable conclusions and principles. The French and English experience proved anew, "that contact infection is by all odds the chief factor in the spread of the common contagious diseases." [32] Conversely, he saw that it effectively disproved the old belief in indiscriminate infection through the air as an important form of disease transmission.

In 1906 Chapin spent a summer vacation in Europe and took the opportunity to visit this new type of hospital. Shortly after his Boston address on disinfection, he and his family sailed for England. They arrived at Bath in mid-July just in time to attend the Jubilee banquet of the Incorporated Society of Medical Officers of Health of Great Britain. The previous year Chapin had been elected one of the few American Fellows of that society.[33] At Bath, he renewed his friendship with Newsholme, and made personal contact with other leading health officers with whom he had corresponded, such as James Niven of Manchester, E. W. Hope of Liverpool, Killick Millard of Leicester, D. S. Davies of Bristol, and James Kerr of the London school system. Few of the English officials yet agreed with Chapin on the minor danger presented by general filthy conditions, and none had considered abandoning terminal disinfection. They were, however, a decade ahead of their American colleagues in the refinement and scientific basis of their methods. Chapin was one of the few Americans who approached the English standards, although even he had not been able to bring Providence to accept all of the public health work that was commonly demanded in English cities. Their isolation-hospital techniques were among the advanced practices which especially interested Chapin at this time, and he spent considerable time observing them when he was in England.

In London on this trip, Chapin and his family were intrigued by their first ride on a motor bus. They stayed at the same friendly lodgings they had occupied in 1903 and usually ate at Ye Olde White Horse Cellars. They visited cathedrals, museums, and historical sites, and took the train out to the quiet East Anglia towns where many New Englanders had originated.[34]

The principal point of interest in Paris was the immaculate Pasteur Hospital. There Chapin examined the place where aseptic nursing had come into its own. He left it convinced that the new Providence hospital should use the same methods. After a week or so in Paris, the Chapins took the train to Spain. They enjoyed olive and orange groves, the coolness in quiet patios before the heat of the day, and the spectacular beauty of the palaces and mosques. Near the end of their vacation they took a short side trip across to the dirty and almost lawless African port of Tangiers.[35]

Back in Providence, Chapin had to work hard to persuade officials and citizens to accept an isolation hospital based upon the technique of medical asepsis. More than one proposed site had to be given up because the people living in the vicinity were sure that they would all come down with frightful diseases if such a hospital were erected in their midst. After long delays the plans were perfected and construction started in 1908. In 1910 the hospital opened its doors.

The new Providence City Hospital was the first in America to use aseptic nursing on a large scale, although two or three hospitals in New York had tried it.[36] Its performance was closely watched in American medical, hospital, and public health circles. The Superintendent of the Boston City Hospital expressed a common view when he said that Chapin had gone "too far" with his views on air infection and that the Providence hospital was a reckless experiment. On the other hand, a good many of the delegates to the 1911 meeting of the American Hospital Association praised the introduction of the aseptic nursing technique, and a Boston paper hailed it as the "latest and boldest of American practices" in caring for infectious diseases.[37]

The technique proved itself its first year, for the Providence City Hospital had an extremely low rate of cross-infection. Visitors came to observe the methods. The hospital quickly became a center for the training of nurses and doctors in modern techniques. By the end of a decade cities all over the country began to build or reconstruct their isolation hospitals in accordance with what became known variously as the "Chapin technique" or the "Chapin cubicle system." [38] At the same time, the citizenry of Providence discovered that there was no special hazard in living near a communicable disease hospital, even one conducted on such radical principles. The institution became socially accepted.

Chapin did not try to administer the new hospital himself, but he maintained close supervision over it from his position upon the newly created Board of Hospital Commissioners. The hospital's first Superintendent was Dennett L. Richardson, who handled the aseptic system with conspicuous efficiency and success. He became one of Chapin's closest personal disciples, at the same time building for himself a national reputation as initiator of the system and the foremost American expert in this type of hospital administration.[39]

Almost as soon as it was completed, the scope of the hospital began to expand. Early in 1910 the Commissioners authorized the treatment of advanced cases of tuberculosis, and in 1912 a tuberculosis wing was added. At about the same time the old pesthouse was closed, so smallpox was admitted. In 1913, Chapin obtained the new drug salvarsan for the treatment of syphilis at the hospital. By that year Richardson could affirm that the Providence City Hospital was the first one in the United States to accept all of the communicable diseases. Again, as early as 1912, Chapin and Richardson, realizing the greatly increasing importance of mental illness as a public health problem, began to agitate for the construction of a psychopathic ward, but it was over fifteen years before this was realized.[40]

Chapin never went as far as English health officers in the hospitalization of patients with communicable disease. This was partly because he felt that many cases were equally well cared for at home, and partly because English experience had shown that isolation hospitals were not the decisive forces in stamping out infectious disease that many British doctors had anticipated.[41] Only a few years after its completion, Chapin began to question whether special hospitals like the Providence City Hospital were needed. Aseptic nursing had fully demonstrated that infectious disease need not be a danger to other patients. He thus began to advocate that in the future facilities for such diseases be put back in the general hospitals. He did not press this suggestion, but in another decade or so after World War I it came to have considerable weight among hospital and public health administrators.[42]

The Providence City Hospital always meant a great deal to Chapin, and he visited it religiously at least once a week for the rest of his career. The scientific method in public health work had a great triumph when the aseptic technique was introduced into the isolation hospital. Yet Chapin never forgot that each case involved a human being. He felt that, since to some extent he was responsible for most of the patients being in the hospital, he should do what he could to make them comfortable, well-fed, and happy. Christmas was always a very special time, when Chapin and his wife toured the wards to visit and talk with every patient. He saw to it that each had gifts and each ward a decorated tree.

At the end of the first decade of the twentieth century Chapin elaborated his reappraisal of principles and measures for the control of communicable disease in a book which became the bible of the new era. *The Sources and Modes of Infection* provided the "definitive synthesis," which few other persons could have made, of the vast amount of laboratory and epidemiological findings collected during the previous forty years.[43] Here Chapin restated the points he had been preaching during the previous decade. The evidence completely refuted the filth theory and the fomites theory. It minimized air transmission of disease, including its spread by dust, as a practical hypothesis, although Chapin conceded that much more definite knowledge was required as to the actual role of air and dust. He pointed out that undue weight had been given to food and drink in the spread of disease. He was skeptical of the widely asserted importance of flies but stressed the imposing role of other insects, particularly in warm climates. Above all else, he emphasized the prime place of contact infection in its various forms—direct, indirect, droplets, healthy carriers, and missed cases—as by far the principal means of transmission, especially for the ordinary diseases in reasonably clean cities of temperate regions.

Rationalizing from facts about modes of transmission, Chapin went on to evaluate various public health measures. Measures for municipal cleanliness were directly valuable from a public health viewpoint only so far as they removed human excreta and the germs contained therein. He made clear the limitations of isolation and of traditional infectious disease hospitals. Pointing out again the absurdity of terminal disinfection, he proclaimed the virtues of concurrent disinfection and aseptic nursing. Finally, he stressed the new doctrine of personal cleanliness by which each individual could avoid contact infection and thus could become responsible for his own sanitary salvation.

In the light of the realities of contact infection, *The Sources and Modes of Infection* demolished theory in order to provide health officers with a rational and scientific basis for their work. Chapin ridiculed, for instance, such practices as the wearing of caps by doctors in isolation hospitals, particularly when they ignored the simplest rule of washing their hands after leaving a patient. He refuted the tradition that the buildings in the so-called "lung-blocks" of New York, London, and other cities were themselves repositories of tuberculosis or other diseases, and showed instead that excesses of disease in these areas were due to carriers in the densely packed population.[44] Observing that even physicians had a long way to go in learning personal cleanliness, he noted that at the Sixth International Tuberculosis Congress in Washington in 1908 the eminent speakers drank without protest from the same glass at the speakers' stand. Some of his friends, including Sedgwick, felt that Chapin tended to overemphasize the danger from contact infection. But he was not deterred. "If the most distinguished investigators and health officials of the world . . . show no appreciation whatever of the importance of contact infection," he observed, "it is certainly time for some one to be emphatic." [45]

Chapin insisted upon the quantitative evaluation of factors in the spread of communicable disease. "It is not so important to know," he pointed out, "that typhoid bacilli live in water for weeks, as it is to know that 99 per cent die in one week. It is not enough to discover that diphtheria bacilli can be recovered from articles in the sickroom; we must learn how often they are found and how often disease is traced to such a source. We have for years been much alarmed because tubercle bacilli are found in milk, but since a serious effort has been made to measure the actual danger, the alarm has greatly diminished." [46]

After seeing his book into print, Chapin took his family on a short trip to Bermuda in the summer of 1910. Even before he returned, comments on the book had begun to come in.

The Sources and Modes of Infection was a radical publication for the health officers who still looked for guidance to Parkes or Buck. It also went far beyond the works on hygiene of Harrington and Sedgwick. Yet, it fell on fertile ground in a profession ripe for an authoritative guide. The book had an excellent reception in the medical journals of America and Europe, *The Lancet* of London standing almost alone in finding fault. All over the world, health officers praised it and saw it leading to saner methods. Arthur Newsholme, now Medical Officer of the English Local Government Board, wrote to congratulate Chapin "on a very important contribution to public health literature, perhaps the most important general contribution of the last few years. One thing you have made me do, and will have made many others do—*sit up* and consider the foundation of my action as a Medical Officer of Health." "You have given us all a good shaking!" [47]

The Sources and Modes of Infection was a landmark at the beginning of the modern era of the public health movement. It expressed superbly the concepts which were coming to be known as the "New Public Health." Chapin's reassessment provided a rational guide to health officers everywhere for reshaping methods of control of the communicable diseases. At the same time, his viewpoint was an important factor in turning the public health movement into wider channels and a great new breadth of concern.

THE NEW PUBLIC HEALTH

IF one of the marks of the new era in the public health movement which emerged before World War I was the sloughing off of old theories of disease and methods of communicable disease control and the substitution of rational principles and techniques, another was the extension of public health activities into important but hitherto neglected areas. Prominent parts of this extension were the great campaign against tuberculosis, the growth of health services for schoolchildren, and the movement for infant hygiene, all fields in which Chapin could apply his new gospels of disease control. The opening of these fields around the beginning of the twentieth century was accompanied by a greatly increased concern for the individual and his education in health matters. New voluntary lay organizations helped in this work. Chapin, having contributed much of the theoretical groundwork for this "New Public Health," also participated in its practical development.

Before 1889 no health department in the United States and few in the world had done anything about tuberculosis, although it was the greatest killer of all the infectious diseases. Little was known about it; the very breadth of its distribution made it appear an insuperable problem. In 1889 the health departments of Providence and New York City took individually the first planned action toward a program of prevention and control. The action was modest but significant; the preparation and issuance of educational circulars to physicians and to the public. Chapin shares with Biggs, Prudden, and Loomis of New York the credit for a step which some health workers have marked as the beginning of the great work of education against tuberculosis.[1]

Chapin distributed thousands of circulars in Providence. He emphasized the communicable nature of tuberculosis at a time when physicians and health officers generally did not realize or accept it as such, despite Koch's discovery a few years earlier of the tubercle bacillus. He stressed the danger from sputum of consumptives and pointed out the value of a healthy constitution and good personal hygiene in warding off the disease. Chapin's circular was concise and effectively worded. It was reprinted in several medical and sanitary journals and had a more than local effect in drawing attention to this public health problem along with some of the means to combat it.

It was more than ten years before Chapin instituted a full program of action against the disease in Providence. Meanwhile, Biggs in New York City, with better support, had rammed through a path-breaking and comprehensive tuberculosis program that included compulsory reporting, medical supervision of isolation and home care, disinfection, bacteriological examination of sputum of patients, separation of cases in hospitals, and a continuing educational campaign. Other cities and some states, including Rhode Island, followed New York. Chapin retained his deep concern for the disease, but he rejected a comprehensive program for Providence before 1900 chiefly because of anticipated difficulties in getting physicians to report active cases. The main measure he supported during this time was a bill to give the State of Rhode Island the authority to examine and destroy tuberculous cattle. In 1890, hoping to gain the necessary knowledge to fight tuberculosis more effectively, Chapin considered going to Germany to study and observe the disease. This was at the time that Koch made his unfortunate and premature announcement of a proposed cure through tuberculin. Chapin's project never materialized due to lack of funds.

Chapin and other health workers watched with fascination as mortality from tuberculosis dropped steadily and substantially throughout the world. In the middle 1880's, many sanitarians attributed this to the environmental cleansing of cities. By about 1900, health officers were beginning to credit the new uses of hospitalization, disinfection, and an active concern about sputum. But Chapin did not believe any of these were as responsible for the lower observed death rates as was "the constantly improving social condition of the native born." [2] And in 1906 he wrote:

No very wonderful results can be hoped for from any or all of these methods. It is often claimed that they are eminently successful. The reduction of consumption in New York City is instanced as a brilliant example. But in Providence where very little has been done in the way of prevention, consumption has decreased nearly as rapidly and is less prevalent than in New York. Race, age and numberless other factors so complicate the problem that almost nothing is known of the cause of the world-wide decrease in this disease. It will, however, do no harm, and may do much good to teach personal cleanliness, and the responsibility for this teaching rests almost wholly with the practicing physician.[3]

Chapin differed also with the view advanced by Newsholme and widely held in England, that the extensive isolation of tuberculosis cases in hospitals had been the chief factor in the decline of the disease. Chapin pointed out that in Providence and other American cities the decline had set in long before isolation or other administrative measures were undertaken. Matthew Hay, the Medical Officer of Health of Aberdeen, Scotland, was one of the few who agreed with Chapin.[4]

Around 1900, tuberculosis work began to expand greatly,

due largely to the impetus provided by Biggs in New York, Lawrence Flick in Pennsylvania, and Edward L. Trudeau in his sanatorium at Saranac Lake. Sanatoriums multiplied, more health departments took on control programs, and private voluntary associations began to appear, modeled after Flick's Pennsylvania Society for the Prevention of Tuberculosis. In Providence, Chapin finally made tuberculosis reportable in 1903, began the careful registration of the disease, and expanded his distribution of educational circulars. He also began to collect epidemiological information. In 1909, however, he had to drop most of this program when a new state law made tuberculosis reportable to the state board instead of to local health departments. Accelerating Rhode Island interest in tuberculosis likewise brought the founding of voluntary city and state antituberculosis societies by 1907. Chapin was intimately associated with them throughout his career.

Between 1906 and 1908 Chapin served on a committee of doctors and businessmen attempting to arouse interest among factory owners of Providence and vicinity in measures to deal with tuberculosis among their employees. This committee developed out of a local experiment begun by Dr. Frank T. Fulton to detect and treat cases among workers before the disabling stage of the disease had been reached. Fulton had considerable initial success; some workers received home treatment, others went to institutions. Treatment was paid for by the employer. Few firms followed up the idea, and the medical profession in general was cool to it, so the experiment was shortly given up. Despite this, it was a significant early move to establish effective industrial hygiene arrangements for this disease.[5]

A principal part of the antituberculosis campaign was the promotion of fresh air, both as preventive and as therapy. Fresh air was, along with rest and proper diet, a central feature of the sanatoriums. The national tuberculosis organization spread its views through the *Journal of the Outdoor Life*. Health lectures and circulars increasingly emphasized for the ordinary citizen the importance of sleeping with windows open. Fresh Air clubs were organized in schools. Chapin and Swarts noted that immigrant children who heard these lectures and joined these clubs had a great influence in educating their whole families in keeping their windows open and in adopting other wholesome sanitary habits.[6]

In the summer of 1907 two women physicians of Providence established a small open-air day camp in the city for children with latent tuberculosis. The physicians were Ellen Stone, one of Chapin's inspectors, and Mary Packard. As a result of the success of this camp, the two organizers, together with Chapin and other leaders of the antituberculosis association, formulated a plan for the continuation of the work throughout the school year. The result was the first all-season Fresh Air School in the world, begun in 1908. This school was conducted within the public school system of Providence in conjunction with the Health Department. The idea caught hold immediately in other cities, and within a few years had become a standard measure against tuberculosis.[7]

In 1908 Chapin was one of the Rhode Island delegates to the Sixth International Congress on Tuberculosis, in Washington, D.C. He delivered a paper on the need for epidemiological studies of tuberculosis. Referring to the family histories he had been keeping on diphtheria and scarlet fever, he suggested that similar histories for tuberculosis would throw much light upon the modes of infection, the liability to the disease according to age or sex, the value of isolation or disinfection, and the incubation period. His own effort along this line had not yet borne much fruit due to inadequate diagnosis and reporting by the physicians, but this only served to point up the value of such work. English Health Officers, Chapin observed, were now giving some attention to the collection of accurate family

histories for various diseases, as he had been doing, but this
was true of few of his American colleagues.[8] The tuberculosis
experts at Washington in 1908, however, were so absorbed in
their controversy with Koch over the communicability to man
of bovine tuberculosis that the keeping of family statistical
records had small attraction. Such a suggestion had to wait
for a man of the discernment of Wade H. Frost before it became a reality in the United States.

The laboratory investigation of tuberculosis was another
thing. Yet, although many laboratory experiments upon the
disease had been conducted, Chapin complained that few if
any had been made under natural conditions. As a contribution
in this direction, he conceived and directed an experiment in
1908, with the help of Dr. Mary Packard. Susceptible guinea
pigs were placed in cages in a room occupied by a consumptive
laborer. The consumptive cared for half of the animals while
a well person fed the others, but the consumptive frequently
talked to all of them with his face close to the cages. As a result,
nearly all of the animals became infected with the disease.
Although such a limited experiment was inconclusive, Chapin
observed that in this case infection was probably entirely due
to mouth spray and not to dust as was then held by most observers. He hoped that there would be other well-conducted
experiments under natural conditions to test how important
dust really was.[9]

Perhaps Chapin's most valuable contribution to the anti-
tuberculosis movement was the critical viewpoint he brought
to it. The editor of *The Journal of the Outdoor Life* found
Chapin's reports unusually "refreshing" because "the primary
effort of the writer does not seem to be to show how rapidly
the death rate from tuberculosis is decreasing, but rather to
show all the facts about the disease." [10] Winslow noted the
same thing and said that Chapin's reports were the "most ag-

gressively honest" he had ever seen.[11] This was the more notice-
able because so many physicians and others were uncritical in
supporting measures that purported to cure tuberculosis.

In 1913 a German, Friedrich F. Friedmann, came to Rhode
Island with a widely publicized cure for tuberculosis, earlier
announced before the Berlin Medical Society: a serum drawn
from turtles. With much fanfare, the Governor of Rhode Island
invited him to demonstrate his cure in the state's public institutions. Friedmann also established an Institute to which patients flocked in large numbers. When Chapin and most other
medical leaders were skeptical, particularly in view of the
secrecy which surrounded the process, they were accused of
jealousy. The Medical Society, however, condemned the commercial exploitation of the treatment, and later censured those
who participated in Friedmann's Institute.[12] Exhaustive tests
eventually proved it worthless, but long before that Friedmann
had returned to Germany with sizable sums obtained from
hopeful and credulous Americans. Fake cures were serious obstacles to the progress of the antituberculosis campaign.[13]

School medical services constituted a second major field
of new public health activity. Chapin had long been concerned
both with disease among schoolchildren and with schoolhouses
themselves. He was probably the first municipal health officer
in the United States to make systematic examinations of the
sanitary condition of schools.[14] He carried on these investigations of schools in the same tradition that John Howard, two
centuries before, had performed his inspections of English
prisons, measuring tape in hand; but Chapin also used the
anemometer extensively. He looked into the plumbing or lack
of it, safety features, size of rooms, and play yards. He devoted
special attention to heating and ventilation, and devised intricate tests to track down odors and drafts.[15]

Medical inspection of schoolchildren themselves, in addition to the buildings, followed shortly as a municipal activity. Although France, Belgium, and other European countries had done this for years, school medical inspection did not develop to any significant extent in the United States until after 1900. Samuel Durgin showed the way in 1894 when he organized a system in Boston. Chapin began to urge regular medical inspection of schoolchildren as early as 1889, five years before Boston began the practice.[16] It was fifteen years, however, before he and other interested persons could persuade Providence to adopt it.

Although larger cities often had several hundred inspectors who made daily visits to schools, Providence provided only a small amount of money for Chapin's program. For some years he got along with two physicians as medical examiners. Two obviously could not inspect each school daily, so the Providence system relied for much of its effectiveness upon the teachers. Children with ailments were sent home or to the Health Department where they saw the inspector. Although this system had drawbacks, it proved helpful and had the merit of economy. It was subsequently adopted by many small or parsimonious communities.

The principal original purpose of the medical inspection of schoolchildren was to locate unrecognized cases of infectious disease. By the time Providence began medical inspection of schools in 1904, experience in other cities had shown that, although there may have been many such cases, relatively few were being discovered in this way. The principal attention of the inspectors, then, shifted to such conditions as body lice, defects of vision and hearing, adenoids, skin diseases, and mental defects.[17] School inspection in time became concerned with "everything connected with the child's physical well-being." [18] Once the movement got under way the services began to expand. In 1906, Providence became one of the first American cities to establish an eye clinic for schoolchildren.

In 1909 Chapin employed a school nurse to follow up the various conditions in the home and to show mothers how to apply simple remedies. During the same year, Providence became one of the first cities to extend public medical inspection to parochial schools.[19] Two years later Chapin induced the city to authorize a Dental Inspector and a Neurologist for the school medical program. By 1912, with a corps of five school nurses and eight physicians, he gave immediate supervision of the program to Dr. Ellen Stone.

Treatment of diseases in schoolchildren by school physicians followed closely on institution of diagnostic services. Almost from the beginning the Providence examiners had been treating minor skin diseases and supplying ointment so that children could get rid of head lice. As the program developed, arrangements were made with private agencies to supply eyeglasses free or at half price to poor children. It was also standard procedure for many of the students who needed operations— for tonsils or adenoids, for example—to get free treatment if their parents could not afford it.

The amount of free treatment provided in Providence before 1910 was fairly limited compared with some cities, particularly in Europe. Nevertheless, even this was vigorously opposed by the conservatives of the community, particularly those of the medical profession. The Providence Medical Association in 1910 adopted a report (not quite a censure) opposing general school treatment and pointedly sent a copy to Chapin.[20] The members were only partly placated when Chapin argued that free treatment did not cut into private practice but actually stimulated it, while it also relieved doctors of large amounts of charity work.

The main objection to the extension of school medical work was, of course, the fear of socialism, that bugaboo so often raised against sanitary measures. Chapin did not sidestep the charge. "This free treatment," he wrote, "as indeed medical inspection itself, is a form of medical socialism, but the writer sees nothing to fear in that word." [21] On the contrary, it was a benefit, not only to the physicians and to the children themselves, but to the future of the community. "Even those who plead most earnestly for the restriction of the functions of government would admit that it is certainly as wise to prevent children from becoming blind and deaf as it is to furnish them with free text-books." [22] There were many conditions which, if neglected, might eventually cause permanent dependence upon others and upon the city itself. Chapin left no doubt as to his position. "I believe in the paternalism that makes healthy men and women. Does the reader, or does he say let the devil take the hindmost?" [23]

Chapin's small force of school inspectors accomplished "a vast amount of good." [24] Lice became a rarity, and skin diseases decreased greatly. After only two years of dental inspection, one of Chapin's staff could report that "even among the foreigners tooth-brushing is now the rule rather than the exception." [25] Considerable improvement could often be seen in backward children as a result of special efforts. Children who were doing poor work because of poor eyesight often made remarkable progress after getting glasses. Other school services had correspondingly good results.

Although medical inspection of schoolchildren failed to detect many patients with communicable disease or healthy carriers, the belief remained that many serious outbreaks of these ordinary diseases were spread in the schools. The usual remedy was to close the school, send all the children home for varying periods, and fumigate the place from top to bottom. In 1891, Chapin shared this view with practically every other health officer, but in the next dozen years he changed his mind.[26] Sir Shirley Murphy and others in England maintained that the infectious diseases of childhood were much less frequent during the summer than at any other time because that was the time when the schools were closed for vacation. Chapin found, however, soon after 1900, that in Providence the summer decline in the ordinary diseases often began even before school let out, while the usual autumn increase often began before the end of the vacation period. Experience showed him that children ran much more chance of contracting infectious diseases from their play at home or in the streets than from their largely controlled contacts in school. Real school outbreaks were rare.[27]

Chapin was almost alone among health officers in teaching this view that there was no special connection between the schools and increases in scarlet fever or diphtheria. By 1913, however, his position was supported by the Chief Medical Officer of Schools in London and by observations in Liverpool.[28] Leading American health officials subsequently accepted the view, although many medical practitioners did not. Since it was particularly difficult for laymen to accept, most communities continued to close their schools whenever a severe outbreak of disease occurred.[29]

The third of the great new fields of individual care was infant and child care. Before 1900 a large proportion of yearly deaths was among children under one year of age. In 1888, Chapin put the average in Providence at about 19 per cent of the total, while in some cities it was as much as 30 per cent.[30] Many of the deaths were caused by acute diarrheal disease. Abraham Jacobi was teaching before 1880 that improper and nonsterile feeding of infants was responsible for much of the high mortality. A few other physicians occasionally spoke up against the condition, but organized health department action was almost totally lacking.[31] Chapin's action, therefore, as early as 1885, in preparing and distributing circulars on the feeding and care of infants marks a pioneering step.[32] With infant care, as with the control of tuberculosis, Chapin from the beginning hit upon popular education as one of the best measures the health officer could take.[33]

During the 1890's, Rhode Island began to require midwives and nurses to report infant eye diseases to health officers or physicians. With Massachusetts, Connecticut, and New York, it began at that time the licensing and inspection of infant boarding houses, in order to correct the evils connected with poorly run, so-called "baby farms." Chapin took energetic and efficient charge of this work in Providence.[34]

Early in 1897 Nathan Straus of New York, after his successful philanthropic experiment with infant milk stations in that city for four years, wrote to every Board of Health in the United States pointing out the value of sterilized milk in reducing infant mortality. In Rochester, Health Officer George Goler acted upon the New York City example to establish the first municipally run milk stations. Many other cities followed suit quickly. Chapin strongly endorsed the idea and felt that some sort of milk distribution scheme was desirable, but the city of Providence never established its own milk depots.[35] In the summer of 1906, however, Chapin induced a group of his friends among the Providence physicians to try the experiment as a project of the Providence Medical Association. With Chapin as Chairman of the project, a committee raised money to set up and staff five milk depots for the summer. The committee aimed, like Rochester, to obtain milk that was so clean that no pasteurization was needed, for there was then a feeling that the pasteurization process destroyed some of the nutritive value of the milk. The committee went to great lengths to supervise the dairy which produced the milk for the depots and to test the milk each day for bacteria. At the depots, nurses distributed the milk to poor mothers and taught them various principles of infant care. Chapin and his committee repeated the work in 1907. Although there were good results in both years, the committee decided that more education of poor mothers was needed before milk stations could be of full benefit. Consequently, in subsequent summers the money which was collected went to pay for additional baby nurses for the poor.[36]

Undoubtedly the best infant hygiene work done anywhere was by visiting nurses. Established in 1900, the Providence District Nursing Association was in many ways the most important of the voluntary health organizations which sprang up in the city. Chapin quickly established a close cooperative relation with it for his Department, and for many years he was on its advisory councils. From a single nurse in 1900, the Association grew to include over seventy-five nurses thirty years later. These included special tuberculosis nurses beginning in 1906 and infant welfare nurses from 1907. Although many such organizations were founded in the United States and in other countries before it, the Providence District Nursing Association became a model organization of its kind, particularly in its development of new nursing procedures and in its standardization of methods.[37] Its executive head during most of this time was Mary S. Gardner. Miss Gardner wrote a book on public health nursing which became a standard reference work in her profession, while she rose to share with Lillian Wald and Mary Beard the national leadership in that field.[38]

Chapin considered the establishment of this organization of major importance to his city, and through it he achieved many public health objectives which otherwise would have been impossible. He was particularly interested in the educational work which the visiting nurses did in teaching simple hygiene. "The nurse," he pointed out, "teaches real cleanliness; she shows how to avoid infection; she preaches the gospel of fresh air, by opening the window. The nurse prepares the milk for the baby, and the mother, watching her, remembers how it is done." [39] The effectiveness of the private nurses led health officers like

Chapin about this time to begin to employ public health nurses for communicable disease control and other work.

In 1911 Chapin helped start a class for "Little Mothers" at a school in the Italian section of town. In this project one of his nurses gave up-to-date instruction in child care to the young girls who tended babies when not in school. The class turned out to be a considerable factor in the acculturation of the girls and of their neighborhood. Once a week the girls brought in their little brothers or sisters "to see them bathed in American fashion and put to sleep in the American way in an American bed." [40] The girls also learned proper foods and proper ways of dressing the babies. After learning the various lessons, they would go back to the tenements. There they spread the new doctrines to their mothers and neighbors, often more effectively than the nurses themselves could because of language problems. Little Mothers' Leagues were not formed in Providence to the extent that other cities took them up, but nevertheless they served as useful extensions of the visiting nurses' work.

Various other measures were also begun to try to save the tenement baby. All over the country women's organizations began to organize day camps, hold classes for mothers, and sponsor health lectures. Within a few years a helpful assortment of private clinics came into being, including clinics for sick babies, prenatal clinics, health stations for well babies, and eventually preschool clinics. Before World War I, groups were organizing "Baby Weeks," with all the usual exhibits, lectures, posters, and even sermons for "Baby Sunday."

In Providence, the Health Department distributed circulars on infant care to every mother as soon as the birth of a baby was reported. Printed in Italian, Yiddish, French, and Portuguese, as well as English, these circulars of Chapin, like those on other subjects, were frequently reprinted by other health organizations both in the United States and abroad.[41] Beginning in 1908 Chapin provided mothers and hospitals with lists of all milk dealers. These showed the butterfat content and the bacteriological ratings of milk furnished by each. The Health Department began as well to distribute free silver nitrate solution to prevent gonococcal infection in newborn babies and the resulting blindness.

Chapin also took energetic steps with respect to the midwives who had come to Providence with the tide of late nineteenth-century immigration. Although Rhode Island nominally outlawed them, about a third of all Providence births before World War I were attended by midwives. Chapin tried to educate the midwives in hygienic practices by calling them to his office, arranging for district nurses to advise them, and having the latter follow up their deliveries. In spite of an eventual improvement, Chapin, in contrast to New York health officials, did not want to encourage the midwife as a permanent institution. He felt they should be tolerated only until there were enough physicians to drive them out of business. And he was sure that the forces of Americanization would speed the process. "When one sees the remarkable change in customs, clothes, food, drink, etc., among foreigners, after only a few months residence, one can be confident that the preference for a midwife must yield to the force of American public opinion." [42]

By around 1910 the baby-saving campaign was becoming well organized in the United States. The New York City Health Department had formed its Division of Child Hygiene under Josephine Baker in 1908. Chapin established a somewhat similar division four years later, with Ellen Stone as Superintendent of Child Hygiene. In 1909, the American Academy of Medicine organized its important Conference on the Prevention of Infant Mortality, held at Yale University. Chapin and Sedgwick were the two public health leaders on the Advisory Committee for the Conference, which also included Jane Addams, Irving Fisher of Yale, and a number of leading educators, sociologists, and presidents of national women's groups. The American Association for the Study and Prevention of Infant Mortality, which was organized as a result of this Conference, became one of the important educational agencies in markedly reducing the infant death rate during the next two decades. Chapin served as a Director of the Association for a number of years and contributed papers at its meetings. In 1912 the federal Children's Bureau was formed under Julia Lathrop. Among its first projects was a house-to-house inquiry as to what selected American cities were doing to prevent infant mortality. Its report indicated that little or nothing was being done in many cities, although certain places, notably New York and Providence, were doing work of great significance.[43] The bureau from this time forward gave an important impetus to the child hygiene movement all over the country.

Thus, in the years after 1900 the public health movement dramatically burst its old bounds of environmental sanitation and a limited concern with a few infectious diseases. A host of new voluntary organizations, national and local, rose beside the National Association for the Study and Prevention of Tuberculosis (later the National Tuberculosis Association) to help public health officers shape a new pattern of public health work. The rules of personal cleanliness became household words under the educational efforts of health officer, physician, nurse, and teacher. The visiting nurse became as well-known a personality around the city as the nuisance inspector, and much more useful in saving lives.

Health workers disagreed as to just what the New Public Health was, but few denied that it was a reality.[44] The radical principles of communicable disease control which Chapin had pointed out gradually began to sink into the consciousness of physicians and officials. The save-the-baby campaign, gathering momentum, brought about a drop in infant mortality which

Chapin felt was "one of the most remarkable achievements of modern medicine." [45] The decline in tuberculosis, going on for years, accelerated under effective measures. Well-cared-for schoolchildren came to form a generation that would far outlive all previous estimates of life expectancy. Vital statistics, reflecting these matters, were not long in suggesting that the twentieth century might well become the "Public Health Century."

THE PEOPLE OF THE CITY:
THE VALUE OF VITAL STATISTICS

The importance of collecting vital statistics had never been questioned ever since the earliest phases of the modern public health movement. Chadwick, Farr, Shattuck, Billings, and Snow all had used these facts about people and disease in order to weigh the effectiveness of health measures. Chapin had considerable interest in registration work for its own sake, but he had more interest in its use. Vital statistics were indispensable in investigating infectious diseases. They were equally useful when it came to weighing the changes that were occurring in the makeup of his community.

When Chapin became City Registrar at the end of 1888 he had already received a practical education in vital statistics from a top man in this field in America, the thoroughgoing Snow, who had occupied the adjoining office. The following year, Arthur Newsholme's book on *The Elements of Vital Statistics*, which admittedly leaned heavily upon Farr, came out; it provided an up-to-date guide and a good bibliography. Chapin set about to try to maintain the enviable reputation of the Providence statistical work.

In 1888, despite the work of the early pioneers, the registration of vital statistics was still a practically untouched field in most parts of the United States except in the northeast. Few cities issued reports of vital statistics. Registration was imperfect even in Providence where great care had been taken with it. Consequently, one of Chapin's continuing efforts was to bring about improvement in his own data. He also pressed vigorously for a wide extension of registration elsewhere in the country in order to ensure more of the basic information he needed if his studies of disease were to have validity.

The most immediately important of these data from the point of view of the health officer were the death returns. As one of his projects in educating his medical colleagues in Providence, Chapin drew their attention to the need for complete, accurate, and prompt reporting of deaths. It was of relatively little value to know merely that a man had died. Chapin drilled the doctors in the necessity of careful diagnoses and of adequate descriptions of the causes of death. In actual practice, every Saturday morning throughout his career he scrupulously examined each death return for the city. If one was unclear or incomplete, he kept after the delinquent practitioner until he was satisfied that it was correct. Providence physicians in the age of bacteriology could no longer get by with a guess, an approximation, or a general characterization that could be any one of a dozen specific causes of death.

In 1897 Chapin began a long and important connection with the American Public Health Association's Committee on Demography and Vital Statistics. The Committee was one of the principal bodies in the United States that were actively concerned with promoting registration activities. During the next five or six years a devoted group of men on the Committee, principally Cressy Wilbur of Michigan, John S. Fulton of Maryland, and Chapin, worked together to extend registration throughout the United States and to put it on a modern basis.

In 1898 the Committee recommended that American sanitarians and statisticians adopt the new system for the classification of diseases and causes of death devised by Jacques Bertillon.[1] The Bertillon system assigned a number to each disease, rather than classifying alphabetically or in the many other ways which had been tried since the beginning of Farr's work. It also attempted to standardize the confused terminology of disease. Chapin began to use the Bertillon system in Providence in 1900, and by 1902 it was being used by the federal government and generally by the states in the death registration area (those states in which the registration of deaths was deemed to be at or above a certain level of completeness). In the beginning, due to the system's defects, he was anything but happy.[2] But it was a useful step toward uniformity, and he tried to persuade other registrars to adopt it.[3]

The Committee on Demography and Vital Statistics also helped establish a permanent Census Bureau in the federal government beginning in 1902. This ensured a continuing governmental concern for vital statistics. Wilbur, from his work on the Committee and in Michigan, went on to follow William King as Chief Statistician of the Census Bureau. There he drew up a model registration law for the country and worked tirelessly to get additional states to accept its principles. He did more than any other individual to extend the death registration area in the United States.[4]

One of the unsatisfactory things about American vital statistics during much of this time was the frequency with which they were manipulated or misused. Ambitious health officers frequently made exorbitant claims of decreases in the death rate and exaggerated the effects of their sanitary efforts.[5] Consequently, for many years the glowing statistical reports of some of the western cities—Buffalo, Chicago, and St. Paul were examples—were suspect in the minds of experienced health officers and statisticians. Chapin, looking ahead to better times, observed philosophically: "We cannot expect that figures will ever cease to lie, but we may hope that vital statisticians will." [6]

Another source of error in the use of vital statistics to which Chapin frequently called the attention of his fellow health officers was the common practice of generalizing from uncorrected death rates. He criticized the Census Bureau for sending out figures in this form and observed that the important European bureaus never did so.[7] Crude death-rate figures meant very little, for they involved a good many factors. The mortality in Eastern cities, for instance, usually appeared to be high in relation to the rest of the country largely because the registration of deaths was far more accurate and complete.[8] Moreover, the population of each region and each city had varying characteristics of racial composition, proportions of the sexes, age distribution, and social conditions. Providence did not show up well in most of the crude death figures of the first quarter of the twentieth century, for its uncorrected death rates from tuberculosis and cancer were among the highest in the country. Chapin frequently felt obliged to explain that Providence had a relatively large number of Negroes, whose death rate was then "twice that of whites"; that there was an unusual number of old persons; that the city, like the rest of the East, had an excess of women over men, and women were much more subject to cancer; that the Irish who had poured into the city were somehow more subject to tuberculosis than those who stayed in Ireland; and that when, as in Providence, "you have industries that bring a lot of poor people in to herd together you will get a higher death rate." Corrected figures showed that Providence had no more tuberculosis or cancer for the nature of its population than any of the large Eastern cities.[9]

Chapin studied the death statistics of Providence closely. His studies had unusual value partly because the statistics themselves were unique. No other American city had unbroken series of statistical reports going back to 1856, while only New York, Boston, Baltimore, and Philadelphia had begun as early as Providence to publish any such data.[10] Looking back over these

figures in 1906, Chapin could report more accurately than anyone else just what was happening to the diseases which beset
Americans. Some of the greatest changes in causes of death
were due, he observed, to better diagnosis. Hence, many deaths
which once were widely assigned to convulsions, croup, scrofula,
teething, dropsy, or simply "old age," were now more accurately
listed as cerebral hemorrhage, bronchitis, or various diseases of
the heart, arteries, and kidneys. This was true of cancer as well,
although figures for this disease were also affected by the increased number of women at the advanced age levels which
were particularly susceptible. On the other hand, along with
these *apparent* changes, Chapin's statistics illuminated bril-
liantly a sizable *real* decrease during the previous fifty years in
the mortality from many of the ordinary communicable diseases.[11] In another ten or twenty years these figures would be
even more striking.

As City Registrar, Chapin was also concerned with birth
statistics. He worked on the physicians and midwives for years
in an attempt to have all births reported in Providence, but had
to rely on semiannual house-to-house enumerations to get even
an approximately accurate figure. Rhode Island did not pass
adequate legislation to obtain these figures until after 1920, and
throughout the United States birth registration was far less
complete than was death registration. As part of his effort to
improve this condition, Chapin sought to make birth reports
more precise. He concerned himself for years with the question
of how to count stillbirths in the birth statistics. And, as Chairman of an American Public Health Association committee in
1914 and 1915, he helped to work out a definition of stillbirth
which became the legal and statistical standard in many states.

From his office in City Hall, Chapin watched with interest
the procession of persons who came to obtain marriage licenses.
Around 1900 Providence was enjoying considerable notoriety as
the "Gretna Green" of New England. Getting married there

was easy, for no banns were published and waiting periods were shorter than in nearby Massachusetts. Public opinion was fascinated for a time by numbers of Chinese men who came from Boston with white girls, "pale-faced and nicotine-finger-stained young women," Chapin called them, "victims of the opium and cigarette smoking habits." [12]

Over the years Chapin worked steadily to obtain stricter marriage legislation. This included the licensing of clergymen, parental consent for minors, adequate waiting periods, penalties for false marriage applications, and tighter regulations of re-marriages by divorced persons. Marriage, in his mind, was one of society's most splendid institutions. He did all he could to build up respect for it.

Another fundamental source of vital statistics was the census. Chapin was sometimes called upon to make local censuses. Although most of these were school censuses and birth enumerations, in 1893 he conducted a city census which was a model for efficiency, economy, and accuracy. This did not become a prominent part of his work, yet he made it his business to watch the various national, state, and local census reports, for these were important indicators to the health officer as well as to the sociologist.

Chapin came to occupy in the field of American vital statistics a place similar to the one he occupied in municipal sanitation and communicable disease control. It was he who showed the practical way to the ordinary registration officer and set the standard for the field. The chapter on vital statistics in his volume on Municipal Sanitation described the mechanics of operating a registration system. Wilbur particularly praised Chapin's discussion there of the essentials of certificates of death, and he thought it gave considerable impetus to the standardization of such certificates from place to place.[13] Although by no means an exhaustive study, this chapter was one of the most authoritative American sources on the subject up to the detailed study by George C. Whipple in 1919.[14] Meanwhile, English health officials pointed to Chapin's success as Registrar as well as Health Officer as proof that the two positions might well be combined, for, up to 1914, in British cities they were almost always separate.[15]

In 1912 Frederick L. Hoffman, Statistician of the Prudential Insurance Company, who was probably the leading man in his field in the United States, surveyed the condition of municipal vital statistics work in America. It seemed to him that there had been "a measureable advance" in the accuracy of death reports, but in only a few cities was there any continuity of statistical material from one year to another. Although many more cities issued reports than formerly, there were often delays of years in publishing them. The outlook for better records of births was encouraging, but few cities made any attempt at all to report on the relative fecundity of the native- and foreign-born. Many registrars, Hoffman complained, were "indifferent to the larger public uses of vital statistics." They were concerned with the mechanics of recording the data and in general took "a bookkeeper's point of view" of the health and life of their communities.

As far as the country as a whole was concerned, Hoffman concluded, no American city yet matched the average British city or colony in the completeness of its vital statistics or in the usefulness of its reports. The reports of the largest cities, including Boston, New York, Chicago, and Philadelphia, had been for a long time, he asserted, virtually useless. Providence and Washington were the only cities which approached the British *mortality* statistics in quality, while Providence *morbidity* statistics appeared to Hoffman as "unquestionably the most conclusive" of their kind published in the United States.[16] Other Americans, and even English officials, agreed with his estimates.[17] As a result, Chapin's reports were read from coast to coast and abroad with a thoroughness which few statistical collections receive.

Improvement of the machinery for collecting fundamental facts about people was an essential task, but Chapin was not satisfied to let it go at that or to approach these facts with the "bookkeeper's viewpoint." On the contrary, his uses of statistics were as warmly appealing as the human beings they stood for. In the aggregate they provided him with firm answers to some of the problems that were troubling people in the changing America of his day.

Americans then were worrying over the changes taking place in the racial composition of society. They worried about how these changes would effect the great national destiny which leaders like Theodore Roosevelt, Alfred T. Mahan, and Josiah Strong were proclaiming. Immigration was perhaps the greatest worry. At the same time, it appeared that many native Americans were not marrying or having the number of children necessary to keep the Anglo-Saxon race in its dominant position in the United States.[18] When a man like Roosevelt took up the cry of "Race Suicide" and trumpeted it loudly in the context of the current discussions of natural selection, heredity, and eugenics, he was sure to have a large audience.

Irving Fisher of Yale discussed various of these matters in his great 1909 *Report on National Vitality*, a study which emerged out of Roosevelt's concern for the nation's human resources as well as for its natural resources.[19] Chapin, like such other Yankees as John Fiske, Charles Eliot, and the Adamses, however, had had to face them long before and make what adjustments he could.[20] As early as 1892 he called for improved vital statistics which could illuminate the extent of these changes and suggest trends for the future. "Not only is the increase of population as a whole of interest," he pointed out, "but the relative increase of the different races and nationalities is of paramount importance in forecasting our future and moulding political action." The absence of reliable data in American states and cities, he felt, "leaves us almost wholly at sea in regard to the relative increase of blacks and whites, or the probability of our recent foreign immigration supplanting the old stock through superior fecundity." [21]

Looking into the Providence statistics in 1892, Chapin found that there was no decline among the old American stock in the desire for or ability to have children. Its women were averaging just as many children as they had thirty-five years before. Likewise, although more of the immigrant women married and bore more children, this seemed no permanent danger, for the mortality of the children of foreign-born parents was also considerably greater than that of the natives.[22]

Providence people were not entirely reassured by Chapin's prediction, for they could point out streets in the old parts of town where there had been fewer than a dozen births in twenty years.[23] In the meantime, the Italians upon Providence's Federal Hill continued to multiply rapidly, while immigrants continued to pour in from abroad. True, with the development of the electric trolley system in the 1890's, not all of them stayed to intensify the tenement problem in the heart of the city, for many joined the rush to suburban towns.[24] Nevertheless, by 1916 some two-thirds of the Providence population was of recent foreign extraction.

Much of the older American population in Providence and elsewhere thought of the new immigrant masses largely from an economic point of view. Irving Fisher reflected this materialistic outlook in the concluding note of his report of 1909. Estimating the average money value of a person living in the United States at $2,900, he pointed out that preventable disease, much of it among the immigrants, was costing the nation over a billion dollars per year in lives lost, plus untold amounts in time lost from work or school.[25] Conservation of life and health through public health measures, he felt, would thus save large amounts and constitute a tremendous step toward realizing Roosevelt's ideal of the strenuous life and achieving the national destiny.

Chapin was much interested in the estimates of Fisher, and in similar calculations by Frederick L. Hoffman and others, but he found it difficult to accept their arguments that public health expenditures would be repaid financially. Actually, he pointed out, in America there was usually no economic loss as the result of the death of a worker so long as there was a replacement, and immigration was seeing to that. "If a weaver in the Wamskuck Mill should die tonight," he observed, "doubtless an Italian could be found in the morning to take his place." [26] Moreover, it seemed unlikely that arguments as to the money value of life resulted in higher appropriations for public health measures. In fact, workers resisted public health expenditures on the ground that the saving of lives would only increase the labor market and intensify competition for jobs. And employers, Chapin felt, could see no concrete return to themselves from better sanitation so long as there were labor surpluses.[27]

It was unwise, in Chapin's opinion, for health officials to emphasize the doubtful financial gains to be obtained from public health measures.[28] "It is proper to consider cost in relation to results and financial savings, when such can be measured with accuracy, but there is much in the world that cannot be measured in terms of money, though to so measure it is doubtless the tendency of the age. Should we not place our profession on a higher level by resisting this tendency instead of yielding to it?" Finally, he asked, "is it not enough to urge expenditures for the preservation of health because the happiness of mankind will be promoted thereby?" [29]

Chapin's high-minded view of human life was severely tested by the influx of immigrants into his community. Yet, from the beginning, he allied himself with that minority of the old element whose members recognized their responsibility to the newcomers. He realized that their condition must be raised if the desirable aspects of the old community life were to be saved. Chapin made an effort to meet this reality gracefully. He never stopped being a Yankee, and he never lost his pride of race, religion, and region; yet he never let this awareness prevent him from being a decent human being.[30]

One factor which prevented the immigrants and other poor people from raising their condition was that of their excessively large families. The answer seemed to be birth control. Chapin rejected such techniques as celibacy, late marriage, and abstinence. He thought that "the only way to successfully limit the birth rate is by methods which will not interfere, at least to any great extent, with the gratification of the sexual instinct." [31] In 1891 he deplored the fact that such methods were hardly used and that late Victorian society did not permit healthy discussion of them even by physicians. To those who objected that birth control was unnatural, Chapin replied that nearly all of civilized life was unnatural. To those who said it would promote prostitution and sexual looseness, he averred that on the contrary it would make the nation's sex life quieter and more even. Finally, to the argument of Social Darwinists who objected that birth control would diminish the struggle for existence and thereby cause a setback for progress and civilization, Chapin pointed out with Huxley that true civilization actually aimed to diminish the struggle for existence, through hospitals, medical research, and sanitary laws. It was a corollary of this civilization that it should teach the sick how to avoid sickness and the poor, through such measures as birth control, how to avoid poverty.

In 1895 Chapin presented a lecture course at the Hartford School of Sociology, on sex and the family. (The great sociologist Lester Ward was a fellow faculty member.) He first discussed the anatomy of sex and the place of the family in society. The institution of marriage was undergoing evolution in his own time. He noted the steady decrease in the marriage rate for nearly half a century, with the accompanying increase in sexual irregularity and divorce. Many things in modern society, including the public school, industrial life, and the growth of cities, were lessening the importance of the family. It seemed possible to Chapin in 1895 that both marriage and divorce would become progressively freer. He declined, however, to look ahead with Edward Bellamy or some of the Fabians to visualize a day when the family would have disappeared and the state would intervene in the sex life of society only to safeguard and help raise the children. The family was too essential in his own life for him to think far along these lines without going on the defensive.[32]

Chapin devoted a large part of the Hartford course to the implications of evolution and heredity for sex and the family. As an up-to-date evolutionist, he drew readily from the concepts of Darwin, Huxley, Spencer, and Lewis H. Morgan. At the same time, with Weismann and Galton, he rejected the Lamarckian idea that acquired characteristics could be inherited. Chapin found Darwin, who dealt with the concrete facts of biological observation, more convincing than the speculative Spencer. He loved to cite Darwin as one of three great men of science of the second half of the nineteenth century. (Pasteur and Koch were his other two choices.) Unlike many of his contemporaries Chapin never abandoned his belief in and admiration for the theory of natural selection.[33]

Evolutionary theory, and particularly natural selection, had important implications for the public health profession. Social Darwinists habitually argued that humanitarian work in general and preventive medicine in particular tended to race deterioration. By preserving the less fit, so ran the argument, health officers hindered the operation of the law of natural selection. Chapin conceded that public health work was partly antagonistic to natural selection, which, if left to itself, would slowly tend to build up immunity to infection in the human race.

Nevertheless, he felt that man had no warrant for abandoning the fight against disease in favor of some uncertain future result when the present work was tangibly saving so many lives. Moreover, he pointed out, there was every indication that science would eventually bring forth measures to immunize against additional diseases, while in the battle for survival germs themselves might well succumb or at least slowly lose their virulence. Above all, statistics showed that in the battle against communicable disease, in most cases the strong were no more exempt from attack than were the feeble, poor, or defective.[34]

Despite this and similar rebuttals of the Social Darwinists' position by other leading health officials, people continued to question the long-term effects of public health work. The English eugenicist Karl Pearson was a prominent critic. On one occasion he stated his view that the lowering of the infant death rate contributed to race degeneration. In this instance, Chapin publicly refuted Pearson. His own studies together with some by Newsholme showed that Pearson did not have a case since he had used incorrect statistics.[35] But such rebuttals could never eliminate the recurring nagging skepticism of the preventive ideal.

Under Pearson's influence, eugenics was becoming a science early in the twentieth century. In the hands of Anglo-Saxon racial alarmists in the United States, however, eugenics went beyond a science; it became a movement. It provided the basis for more and more eugenic marriage laws and for provisions for the sterilization of confirmed criminals and mental defectives.[36] Chapin expressed sympathy with the aim to improve human breeding; yet, a calm voice in the babble of the day, he opposed eugenic marriage laws as unenforceable. And heredity was so complex, he pointed out, that it would be a matter of great difficulty to decide whether a given marriage were desirable or not.[37]

Although Chapin would not venture to predict how heredity

would work in any given family, he had no hesitation in asserting the value it had had in preserving the superior qualities of the old New England stock. This stock had developed, he felt, into an elite just as real as any hereditary nobility. He was not much worried about the deterioration of this elite, but was concerned, rather, lest it neglect its responsibilities and lest its talents be overlooked in a jostling democracy where the voices of immigrants, labor unions, women, and other new groups were getting louder. As an admirer of Athenian rather than Jacksonian democracy, Chapin felt that national leadership and public office required the special ability this elite could provide.[38] This was true even while as Health Officer he bent over backwards to work within the local democratic institutions which he respected, and even while on principle he would deny large legislative powers to sanitarians.[39]

It was hardly possible to be a New Englander of the old stock amidst the tensions of these years without being interested in genealogy. Chapin turned to this interest about the time he became City Registrar, and it became a considerable source of recreation. His interest led to service on the genealogical committee of the Rhode Island Historical Society, while it led to a productive career for his son Howard as Librarian of the Society. Chapin did not agree with his historian friend, J. Franklin Jameson, that genealogy was "the most barren and contemptuous of pursuits." He shared much the same curiosity about it that had led men like Francis Galton, John Fiske, and Lemuel Shattuck to give it a position of prominence. For him, the problem of identifying an ancestor from among several persons with the same name took the place of an evening of bridge. A ramble among the old houses of Mendon, Massachusetts, or in the English countryside where his ancestors had lived was as much recreation for him as golf was for others.[40]

Genealogy was for Chapin neither an escape nor a mere mechanical exercise but an historical adventure of a personal kind which refreshed him for his encounters with reality. Few men of his generation grappled so intimately and constructively with the factors which were changing the American scene before their eyes. In Chapin's view, the human problems of the present were challenges to the best in his country. Within his local community he showed the way to practical, healthful, and humane solutions of many of the complex problems which came along with urbanism, immigration, and industrialization. Within his profession he provided an impetus of ideas and an example of work which were among the important reasons for its coming into its own by the time of the First World War.

THE AMERICAN PUBLIC HEALTH
MOVEMENT COMES OF AGE

In the decade between 1910 and 1920 it seemed to Chapin and other leaders that public health in America was finally reaching maturity. During this time the New Public Health became something more than a fit of enthusiastic energy. As the scientific method gradually caught on, public health work became more and more professional. Because the education of the public was central to the New Public Health, health propaganda poured out in new ways and in an unprecedented volume. Meanwhile, because the well-trained health officer was a necessity, proper public health schools became priority projects. By the time that America entered World War I, the public health movement in the United States could hardly be called a movement any longer, except insofar as people demanded ever more of its benefits. Scientific public health was becoming a well-established reality in the lives of Americans, a reality which was helping to create one of the highest standards of living in the world.

During this decade death took away such public health leaders as Billings, Sternberg, and Gorgas, while retirement claimed Walcott, Durgin, and Swarts. At the same time, new names were coming into prominence. There were administrators such

as Haven Emerson and W. S. Rankin, epidemiologists like
Wade H. Frost and L. T. Webster, new laboratory men of the
United States Public Health Service and the Rockefeller Insti-
tute, immensely productive financial angels connected with the
Metropolitan Life Insurance Company and the Rockefeller
Foundation. Perhaps the period of pioneering was over, but
public health still demanded men of vision, energy, and ability
to carry on toward higher potentials of achievement and service.

The coming-of-age of American public health was foreshad-
owed in 1912, when the Fifteenth International Congress on
Hygiene and Demography met in the United States, the first
time in this country. Chapin accepted the post of Vice-President
of the Section on State and Municipal Sanitation. As the time
for the Congress approached, he joined with Walcott, Biggs,
Welch, Jacobi, and several other leaders in an appeal to the
American medical profession to give it their support. The Assistant Secretary-General of the Congress, wishing to make certain that Chapin himself would be on hand, wrote to the Mayor
of Providence particularly to request that the "leading health
official in the United States" be named to represent that city.[1]

The Congress did much to promote interest in preventive
medicine. For Chapin it became an opportunity to pound home
again and more decisively some of the principles set forth in
The Sources and Modes of Infection. It was a matter of scientific honesty for him to give his colleagues further data as they
became available. As it turned out, practically all of the data,
both from the field and from the laboratory, that came to
Chapin's attention during the years after 1910 served to support
his book. They confirmed his position on fomites and filth.
They upheld his rejection of traditional disinfection as well as
of air-borne disease. They strongly reaffirmed his views on carriers, contact infection, and personal cleanliness.

Chapin was fully aware that his book, to the extent that it
rendered traditions archaic and measures obsolete, stirred up

objections and sometimes indignation. All this had been expected. The extent of the initial hostility reminded George Goler of the antagonistic reception given by America in 1876 to Lister's antiseptic surgery.[2] But, the principal effect in the long run was to start medical men and health officials thinking, to stir them, as Newsholme had predicted, out of an easy complacency about public health principles. Progressive health officers had nothing but applause. C.-E. A. Winslow had already expressed the sentiments of many enthusiastic followers when he wrote to Chapin: "It is a joy to me whenever you unmask one of your batteries, and I trust you may keep on firing until all the ghosts and spectres of Sanitary Science are completely laid." [3]

All over the United States, professors in colleges and medical schools, bacteriologists, and, above all, young physicians just starting out in public health work, were stirred by Chapin's attack on tradition and caught up by the irresistible force of his logic.[4] Hibbert W. Hill, one of his most devoted disciples, felt that publication of *The Sources and Modes of Infection* marked the "beginning of scientific public health in America." [5] Many others credited Chapin with bringing about a sanitary revolution almost single-handedly.[6] Health officers all over the land began to reprint choice passages in their bulletins.

Another outstanding text of the New Public Health was Rosenau's *Preventive Medicine and Hygiene*, which came out in 1913 to provide the authoritative detail which Chapin had not attempted to give. Following this, other writers, using the viewpoint of Chapin's book as a starting point, produced a succession of texts which spelled out in modern terms for the health worker and the public every aspect of public health work.[7] One of the more important was the American Public Health Association's 1917 manual on *The Control of Communicable Diseases*, prepared by a committee led by New York's Haven Emerson. This manual was designed to help establish standard state and local regulations for diseases common to the United States, but subsequent editions made it authoritative for all parts of the world. Chapin had an advisory role in both the first and second editions.[8]

Chapin's own book was never translated, but his ideas spread widely overseas. Medical missionaries carried them to countries such as China, where they formed the basis of much of the preventive medicine taught in the Western-sponsored medical colleges.[9] In Europe, alert doctors heard about the new ideas and sought to interest the authorities in their various countries, although for many years they were thwarted by war, bureaucracies, and an ever-conservative profession.[10] Medical and health officers in England, Scotland, and all over the British empire were particularly enthusiastic. Medical visitors from the continent in 1913 and 1914 reported that leading English medical officers of health regarded *The Sources and Modes of Infection* as the authoritative work on the principles of communicable disease control.[11] Claude B. Ker of Edinburgh, whom Chapin himself regarded as a major authority, in 1920 noted the special debt of his work to the concepts of Chapin and Park. He wrote that, "thanks largely to the illuminating and suggestive writings of Chapin," English and Scots health officials were laying "more and more stress upon the importance of infection by contact." [12] The single measure in which they were still reluctant to follow Chapin, Ker noted, was in abandoning terminal disinfection, and he wistfully wished there were someone like Chapin in Great Britain to carry on the fight against outmoded ideas.[13]

During these years Chapin's professional relations with British health officials became even closer. In addition to his earlier membership in the Incorporated Society of Medical Officers of Health, he joined the Royal Society of Medicine and the Royal Institute of Public Health. He constantly exchanged reports, reprints, and letters with the leading men. Those who came to America made a point of calling upon him. The English professional journals were as important to him as the American ones. Editors of these journals, men like George Elliston of *The Medical Officer* and Charles Porter of *Public Health*, kept Chapin's views prominently before the English profession by publishing reviews of his work, excerpts from his reports, and occasional original articles.

Exchanges of this sort were invaluable, but in democracies public health progress also depends upon enlightened legislators, heads of government, and electorates. The basic premises of the New Public Health made it a matter of concern to the whole populace. The earliest sanitarians had seen the value of health education, and their often lurid health reports served this function to some extent. Until Chapin's time, however, there was little effort among American health officers to educate the public except in time of epidemics. Now it became a strenuous continuing effort, and Chapin used every possible medium: lectures, circulars, the press, the schools, physicians, nurses, and the voluntary associations.

State health departments and those of the larger cities built up elaborate arrangements for public health education. New York City created a special bureau in 1914, but it had long been distributing regular bulletins, conducting stereopticon shows, and issuing scientific reports from its laboratories, as well as the more conventional publicity.[14] In smaller cities like Providence, tiny health department budgets permitted only limited expenditures. Chapin's chief health education expense, for example, was for printing his annual reports. For the most part he kept the Department's health education work on a personal basis throughout his career. Anyone who went into his office might expect to get educated in one way or another. The settee in the City Hall corridor outside his office became a municipal institution. On this settee, Chapin listened courteously to the complaint of any citizen about nuisances and then explained forcibly that smells were not dangers to health. Here was health education at the grass roots.[15]

When radio broadcasting began, Chapin was ready to use it. In 1922, the New York State Health Department broadcast an article of his on one of the earliest regular health programs on radio.[16] In December 1923, Chapin gave his first radio talk over a local station. A listener in Maryland wrote in: "Dr. Chapin very good, would like to hear him soon again. Your signals very loud and clear this evening." Rhode Island listeners said that they wanted more talks like this and less jazz.[17]

The most ambitious project of local health education which Chapin undertook was a weekly column in the *Providence Journal* and *Evening Bulletin,* in which he discussed almost every aspect of health and medicine. He began this column in 1917 and continued it regularly for ten years. Medical circles considered the column to be an example of the best type of popular educational work, and requests came in to syndicate it for nation-wide distribution.[18] Chapin declined several offers which promised handsome remuneration. He would not accept outside money for work which he considered to be part of his basic responsibility to his community.[19]

There was no doubt in Chapin's mind that "to advertise health work saves lives just as surely as advertising chewing gum brings in money." [20] But he had harsh criticism for health officers whose publicity was filled with sensationalism, unscientific statements, and divergence from absolute truth. Public health, he pointed out, was already inexact enough without making it more so through lurid publicity. On the other hand, just because it was true, health literature did not also have to be dull. One can hold steadfast to scientific truth, and yet avoid pedantry and scientific jargon. Chapin cautioned the members of his profession not to commit themselves to the writing of regular bulletins which might be hard to fill. "The space writer is the curse of our day and generation, and especially in our business," he wrote. "If you have nothing to write, do not write it. Better pay your publicity man for doing nothing than for writing something which is not so." [21]

Sedgwick and other leaders were as exasperated as Chapin with publicity excesses.[22] And they were discouraged when truly valuable health education work was sacrificed to local politics or economy. In 1918 Chapin joined Welch, Winslow, and a number of others in writing to Mayor Hylan on behalf of New York City's health publicity work, which was threatened by a municipal reorganization. His letter appeared in the New York newspapers along with that of Charles Hastings of Toronto, the American Public Health Association President. Chapin considered the New York City Health Department publications as not only the best of their kind, but as being so valuable to him personally that he was ready to pay for them rather than have them discontinued. "It is the publication and exchange of such bulletins and reports which make common knowledge of the successes of different cities in the saving of human life. I have always urged upon my own city the moral obligation of doing its own share in thus extending human knowledge, and I feel that such an obligation rests on all other cities as well." [23]

Although they did not approach the New York publications in quantity, the publications issued by Chapin were their equals in quality. His circulars were widely copied by other cities. His annual reports were considered to be "documents of unique value," studied by more health officers than any other set of similar reports issued in their day in the United States.[24] In writing such reports, Chapin advised other health officers to record all really important work but leave out the usual "platitudes about municipal cleanliness, the triumphs of hygiene, and the prospect of stamping out infectious disease." [25] He hoped there would develop a certain uniformity in health reports in order to make comparisons easier, but not if this meant a decline in initiative on the part of health officers.[26]

Early twentieth-century health officers especially sought to impart to the public the lesson of personal cleanliness. In Providence Chapin used every means of publicity to spread this idea among adults and children. He did not neglect the possible influence of his personal example. At his office in the City Hall, after shaking hands with visitors he would excuse himself briefly to wash his hands in a corner basin. Meanwhile, employees in other city departments would nudge each other and snicker whenever they saw Chapin, on his way down the hall to the Men's Room, reaching into his pocket for a tissue so his hand would not touch the doorknob. To them he was sometimes less the famous scientist than a "fussy old fellow" who feared germs as some people fear snakes.[27]

Chapin also preached personal cleanliness to a national popular audience. During a number of years before World War I, he was invited annually to give one of the public Sunday lectures at the Harvard Medical School. Here, Chapin explained the principles of the New Public Health and personal hygiene in terms which the intelligent layman could digest. The lectures were widely reported and quoted in the daily press. Chapin's suggestions about kissing made good copy. He pointed out that, since kissing was one of the more direct modes of infection, it should be discouraged on the part of schoolgirls and "gushing women." "Of course," he went on, "it is expected that lovers will continue to brave this course of danger." [28]

Chapin's lecture was published in 1917 as one of the authoritative "Harvard Health Talks." This small volume, *How to Avoid Infection,* had the largest sale of any of Chapin's books. It became in essence the layman's version of *The Sources and Modes of Infection.* It was translated into French in Canada and had a British edition in 1921. Reviewers liked its calm approach as well as its conciseness.[29] Along with Hibbert W.

Hill's *The New Public Health* and Samuel Hopkins Adams' *The Health Master*, it was one of the influential books in putting the new ideas of personal hygiene upon a household basis.

Still, the education of the public was only one side of the coin. A high level of health education, even a high level of health work, stood no practical chance of achievement without a high level of training for health officers. Adequate facilities for this training had to be provided before public health work could claim professional status.

Throughout his career Chapin moved on the edges of the field of medical and public health teaching, but he never went into it completely, although he had several opportunities. His stint as part-time Professor of Physiology at Brown set the pattern. His effort to educate the physicians of Providence was another aspect. If the training of physicians, during the early years of his career, left much to be desired, the preparation of health officers left even more. As late as 1899 Chapin joined Welch in expressing concern over the lack of "scientific methods of teaching hygiene." [30] Before 1910 the teaching of public hygiene in the United States developed chiefly in connection with the teaching of bacteriology in universities and medical schools. By far the most important center was the one developed by Sedgwick at the Massachusetts Institute of Technology, although Victor C. Vaughan at the University of Michigan and Alexander C. Abbott at the University of Pennsylvania also did significant work. Sedgwick's department put its teaching and research stress upon scientific sanitation of the physical environment, water, sewage, and foods. In the years after 1900, however, such courses as Personal Hygiene, Industrial Hygiene, Epidemiology, and Sanitary Statistics were also offered, although usually there were no specialists to teach them. Graduates of this department were directly responsible for bringing basic sanitary facilities to many American communities and in-

directly to even more. For over a quarter-century they constituted the largest part of those health workers who had any
special training.[31]

Before 1910 Sedgwick had started sending many of his students to Chapin at Providence every year so that they could
observe the operation of what he considered to be a "model
department" before they went out to take public health jobs of
their own.[32] "I consider it a great thing," Sedgwick wrote to
Chapin, "for young fellows meaning to go into Public Health
work to be able to sit at your feet for a couple of hours and to
imbibe some of your ideas and inspiration." [33] In 1913, in order
to formalize this arrangement, he designated Chapin as one of
his department's regular lecturers and had him listed in the
Institute's catalogue. The visits to Providence, brief as they
were, were immensely stimulating occasions for the M.I.T. students. Coming on top of Sedgwick's own enthusiastic teaching,
a day with Chapin was a heady experience which helped to
make many embryo health workers into hero-worshippers.[34]

In 1909, upon the sudden death of Professor Charles Harrington, Chapin gave the second-term lecture course on Hygiene at
the Harvard Medical School. It is tempting to speculate as to
the differences in his career which might have resulted had
Chapin accepted the school's offer to stay on permanently. But
he declined, and Harvard brought in Milton J. Rosenau to
occupy the first chair of Preventive Medicine in America.

In 1913, Sedgwick and Rosenau, joined by George C. Whipple, the Professor of Sanitary Engineering at Harvard and an
expert on vital statistics, were making the final plans for a joint
Harvard-M.I.T. School for Health Officers. This project aimed
to provide a more adequate program of public health training
than Sedgwick's department alone could provide, by making
available the combined facilities of the two institutions. Rosenau
was the one who asked Chapin to lend his name to the project

by becoming one of its expert outside lecturers.[35] Chapin accepted, and for the next two decades maintained a connection with Harvard.

In 1914 Chapin was invited to give some of the Cutter Lectures in Preventive Medicine at Harvard. His six lectures on Municipal Sanitation proved to be the largest number ever given by a guest lecturer under this appointment.[36] In them, Chapin called upon those who were going into public health work to train themselves diligently. He agreed in principle with Sedgwick that it was not always necessary for a person to be a physician in order to be a health officer, so long as he was thoroughly and scientifically trained, but he insisted upon the need for the critical outlook.[37] "All established forms of preventive medicine should be questioned," he told them. "The more established and the older they are, the more they should be questioned." Eminent authorities like Rosenau and Theobald Smith should be believed "provisionally only," even if they were their professors.

The basing of public health work upon a consensus of opinion was a matter which came in for Chapin's criticism at Harvard. There could be no justifiable criterion for action, he pointed out to the student health workers, except fact. "In fact, when consensus of published opinion is strong in support of any one method of treatment, that method should immediately be investigated," he advised. "People will say 'crank,' 'nihilist,' etc.," but it seemed far "better to do nothing than to do it wrong and waste money or effort." [38]

The problem of obtaining a sufficient supply of trained health officers was by no means solved by the establishment of the joint Harvard-Technology School for Health Officers. Practically alone in its field in the country for several years, the school was successful and useful, but it remained a kind of interim structure.

During 1912 and 1913, Chapin served on an American Medi-

cal Association Committee which considered the matter as part
of the over-all problem of medical school curriculums. With
him on the Sub-Committee on Hygiene were John S. Fulton,
Wesbrook, Vaughan, Rosenau, and Irving Fisher. The sub-
committee urged medical schools to take immediate steps to fill
the great gap in the teaching of preventive medicine by establishing undergraduate departments of hygiene as well as developing graduate courses for health officers and those in allied
fields. Looking to the long-term needs of the profession, the
sub-committee also called for independent schools or institutes
of public health, endowed and equipped to provide every need
of instruction and research.[39]

In the year following this report the Rockefeller Foundation
and the General Education Board took up the problem of training public health personnel, largely perhaps as an outcome of
some of their own projects but certainly stimulated to some
extent by the report. Wickliffe Rose, Director of the International Health Board, together with Welch, proposed concrete
action for a comprehensive institute of hygiene. Quickly accepted, the proposal became a reality with the establishment of
the School of Hygiene and Public Health at Johns Hopkins
University in 1916 and with its opening under Welch in 1918.
With the ground broken and the pattern set, more money now
became available from the Foundation for the creation of similar schools elsewhere in America and abroad.[40]

The Harvard School of Public Health, one of them, came
into being in 1922 just after the death of Sedgwick and just as
the old Harvard-Technology arrangement had to be dissolved
by court order. Harvard officials asked Chapin to take charge
of the division of Public Health Administration in the new
school.[41] The Providence work ever his first loyalty, he declined this invitation, but did consent to a connection as Lecturer similar to the one he held in the old school, and he continued in this for the rest of his career.

Chapin brought to his instruction all of his old capacity for inspiring students. He also brought a memorable teaching technique which avoided formal lectures and theorizing. Instead he spoke informally upon his own work in Providence and illustrated it by bringing in specific cases which he was then working on.[42]

Meanwhile, it was almost inevitable during these years that Brown University, too, should be interested in developing professional public health instruction. As early as June 1909 the University had honored Chapin, its former student and professor, with an honorary Sc.D. degree. Gorgas came to Providence for a similar degree at the same time. Chapin then had been serving his University modestly for some years as member of the Visiting Committee for the Department of Comparative Anatomy, later the Biology Department. In 1914, however, President William H. P. Faunce hoped to lure Chapin back to the University with a more substantial job.[43] Faunce knew that Rockefeller money was going into public health work, and he hoped to use Brown's connection with the family to get some of it. Whatever his scheme was, it came to nothing.

The idea that Faunce had in mind was possibly the same one that Chapin's associate, Gorham, elaborated upon the following year. Gorham, looking back at one of the lost glories of Brown, its long-defunct Medical School, in 1915 proposed a school of public health for the University. Like M.I.T., but on a smaller scale, Brown had already been training and sending out public health technicians. This training was predominantly in the fields of pathology and immunology. Gorham proposed to build upon the basic courses already offered and to broaden out with a variety of hygiene subjects. With the cooperation of Chapin, Swarts, Richardson, and other prominent Rhode Island men assured, he felt that "we could establish a school of health officers second to none in the country." [44]

The project to build up a public health school at Brown went ahead with considerable enthusiasm for a period. In 1917 the University began to offer the degree of Doctor of Public Health and laid out plans for additional courses. Informal overtures to the Rockefellers, however, failed to obtain the funds which such a school would need, and the project was quietly dropped.[45] Chapin took no active part in the attempted organization of this abortive school, although he promised to support Gorham so far as he was able. Meanwhile, as a favor to Gorham he continued to go up to the Brown Biology Department several times a year on an informal basis to give his "Public Health Dollar" lectures. Students who were going out into public health work long remembered the big charts showing a silver dollar cut up like a pie which illustrated Chapin's scale of values in health work.[46]

During the immediate postwar period, short-term intensive schools for practicing health officers were organized throughout the United States as a stopgap means for providing public health training. These seminars or institutes brought in the top men in the country to give a few lectures each in their specialties. Chapin participated in several of these programs. At the course conducted in 1919 by the Training School for Public Service of the New York Bureau of Municipal Research, he was the leader of the Conference on Contagious Disease Hospitals. At the United States Public Health Service's Institute in Newark in 1922, the most important of several regional seminars, Chapin gave the keynote address and had three of the leading subjects to himself: The Principles of Contagious Disease Control; Influenza and Pneumonia Control; and the Evaluation of Health Work. Chapin also participated in another such institute at Yale, but declined an invitation to give a one-man seminar in Colorado.[47]

With the multiplication of training facilities for health officers, the Chapin ideas spread even more widely than before. At Columbia University, Winslow announced to the students that the concrete knowledge in his course was from Chapin's book.[48] Professor Murray Horwood of M.I.T. told health officers in Oklahoma that they should read two books, one of them the biography of Louis Pasteur and the other *The Sources and Modes of Infection*.[49] At the new Johns Hopkins School of Hygiene and Public Health, Welch used Chapin's book for some of his lectures, while Wade H. Frost for many years never used any other text in teaching epidemiology. The latter also relied a great deal on the raw material of Chapin's Annual Reports.[50] Goler, lecturing on the communicable diseases at the University of Rochester Medical School, reread Chapin's book every year to prepare himself adequately, while he had the constantly growing feeling that Chapin had been "inspired" when he wrote it.[51] By 1920, the profession as a whole was beginning to realize just how far ahead of his times Chapin had been and to accept with some awe the revolutionary synthesis of information about disease which he had made years before.[52]

The expansion of facilities for public health training, the growth of education work among the public, and the general spread of Chapin's principles were not isolated phenomena but were parts of a general bursting out of public health work and institutions. Chapin himself saw this as a twentieth-century "Sanitary Awakening" which had started with the Spanish-American War. In 1917 he could point to work in a host of new areas, not only local or statewide but often affecting whole regional populations and involving hitherto unthought-of agencies. The Army's great achievement in Panama was a case in point. There were also the public health contributions of the foundations, among which the Rockefeller groups alone were pouring vast resources into such areas as medical research, hookworm control, medical and public health schools. And then there was the entry into active public health work of the large life insurance companies for whom saving lives was a business proposition. The Metropolitan Life Insurance Company launched its substantial health work in 1909 under the guidance of Lee K. Frankel; within a short time its projects had spread public health nursing to the far corners of the country, had made the company perhaps the chief source of health education materials, had helped local communities to build sanatoriums and health departments to expand their work, and had financed many research projects of significance. Chapin noted an enormous increase in the number of national voluntary health organizations. Likewise, he pointed out the great increase in sanitary activity at all levels of government, but especially in the federal government. With the reorganization of the United States Public Health Service in 1912, the government had taken a step which most public health workers had been urging since the demise of the National Board of Health. The establishment of the Children's Bureau in the same year had been another highly encouraging step. "The Federal Government," Chapin said, "can no longer be accused of spending millions to care for hogs and doing nothing for babies." Taking into consideration the productive work being done by 1917 in all of these various agencies, public and private, and the astounding success it was having against sickness and death, it seemed to Chapin that public health work was really coming into its own. Already, he pointed out, "the truth has been demonstrated of the dictum of the distinguished health commissioner of New York that 'Public Health is Purchaseable.' " [53]

Chapin's career touched this ever-widening Sanitary Awakening at new points almost every year. In 1913 he represented municipal health officers on a national Committee of Fifteen which the American Medical Association established to explore coordination of the activities of the many national public health organizations. Others on the Committee included Surgeon-General Rupert Blue, Livingston Farrand, Wickliffe Rose, Frederick L. Hoffman, Lawrence Veiller, Irving Fisher, and representatives of medical and educational groups. Professor Selskar Gunn of M.I.T. wrote the report. This was the first step in a movement which, in 1921, resulted in the establishment of the National Health Council.

Chapin also helped establish local chapters of some of the new voluntary health organizations. He was an incorporator and original Director of the Rhode Island Society for Mental Hygiene. He had long recognized the immensity of mental illness as a public health problem and tried as early as 1912 to get city measures for its relief. Chapin indicated his awareness of another major public health problem of the future by helping to organize the Rhode Island Committee of the American Society for the Control of Cancer.

During these years Chapin occasionally accepted jobs as an expert consultant, but he turned down many others. He did go to New York to advise the Metropolitan Sewerage Commission on the dangers of sewage disposal in New York harbor, to Fall River and Springfield to help on plans for their infectious disease hospitals, and to Washington at the request of Surgeon-General Rupert Blue to advise on the establishment of a National Lepers' Home. And he accepted appointment to the Committee on Appraisal for the Framingham (Massachusetts) Community Health and Tuberculosis Demonstration. This demonstration, begun in 1917, was sponsored and financed by the Metropolitan Life Insurance Company and was conducted by the National Association for the Study and Prevention of Tuberculosis. It sought to find out how far deaths from tuberculosis could be reduced in a given community if the known methods of prevention were applied to the fullest possible extent. The recommendations of Winslow, Chapin, and the other members of the Appraisal Committee ensured that the demonstration would be continued long enough to get meaningful data.[54]

One of the matters which the Framingham work drove home

anew to people was the old close relation of poverty to sickness and death. It was obvious that the poor could not afford the same medical care as the well-to-do. Less obvious was the answer to the question of how, in an unregimented society, the poor could get the sort of care they needed. Since about 1900, poor children had been getting some public care through school medical services, infant hygiene programs, and various district nursing activities. Yet, by and large, when either they or their parents became seriously sick they had to rely upon private physicians or hospitals for whatever treatment they received. Unfortunately, this sort of care, which had been an old and honorable tradition in rural and village America, broke down in the rapidly growing cities. Medical men, like everybody else, lost some of their community spirit with the invasion of so many foreigners into the community. In any case, it was impossible to do much charity work and still do justice to regular patients. Individual medical charity work was, as Chapin pointed out, an imposition on the physician. "It is as if the Charitable Fuel Society were supported exclusively by coal dealers, and household supplies which are distributed by the overseer of the poor were furnished by the grocers of the city." [55]

Several European countries had, by 1910, adopted some form of social insurance which included health insurance or public medical care. The individualistic United States at that time had hardly thought about the question, although there were some health plans among private groups. Serious discussion of the problem of medical care for the poor, in fact, did not get under way until after England adopted compulsory health insurance legislation in 1911. The next year, the American Association for Labor Legislators began a drive for governmental health insurance which resulted in much discussion and various proposals, but no concrete achievement. In 1913, however, Chapin obtained in Providence authorization for what was apparently the first systematic governmental health program of medical care for the sick poor in this country.

The dissolution of the Providence Dispensary, a private medical charity organization, in 1903 left the poor of that city largely neglected in medical care except for the limited and often perfunctory charity treatment by physicians and later the attention of visiting nurses. Chapin thus followed with great interest the discussions which lead to the British Health Insurance Act. His friend Arthur Newsholme, who was one of the British leaders working for such legislation, sent Chapin copies of his papers on the subject and made sure to include Fabian tracts which argued for a national medical service. There was much in the ideas of men like Newsholme that interested Chapin and reinforced his practical Yankee realization that the community had a responsibility in the matter.[56] Chapin could not himself have been a Fabian, but he was very much a part of the progressive ferment infecting Americans of both political parties soon after 1900. By 1910 his work in sanitation, housing, and local charities had earned him a reputation among New England labor circles as a public official who was more than ordinarily concerned with and sympathetic to the total welfare of the poor.[57]

In 1912, looking for an American precedent, Chapin sent out questionnaires to various large Eastern and Midwestern cities to ascertain what provisions were then made for public medical treatment.[58] The replies indicated that throughout the United States "no systematic effort is made to provide really effective medical care for the sick poor." [59] The only service which was being provided anywhere, in fact, even by public physicians, was the superficial examination of poor persons who were being sent to a hospital, almshouse, or other public institution.

It remained for Chapin himself to set the American precedent for effective public care. In 1913 he obtained city funds and began systematic medical work with the sick poor in their homes as a practical public health measure. The work was immediately successful in Providence. He reported that in the first year, because of earlier and more thorough medical care, death and suffering among the poor was greatly reduced and periods of sickness shortened. Care, of course, had to be taken to investigate the economic status of patients in order not to offend the medical profession by providing public care to patients able to pay a physician. But the community in general was convinced that public medical care was a good thing, for, as Chapin said, "it is cheaper to furnish a physician for the early case than it is to build a hospital to nurse the advanced case until death comes." [60]

Chapin became as certain as Newholme that measures for medical care could not be separated from preventive measures in an effective community health program. He also became convinced that eventually not only the poor but all of the population that wanted it should have public medical care, even if this meant socialism.[61] Chapin's view at this time was essentially the same that it had been thirty years before. It was a flexible view of state medicine, one which gave every opportunity to the workings of individual practice in a laissez-faire society, but one which expected little of that practice so far as the medical welfare of the general public was concerned.

Almost in justification of this view, bills providing for health insurance which were introduced in several state legislatures during these years were easily defeated through the opposition of insurance companies, physicians, and labor unions. Chapin discussed health insurance before the Providence medical profession in a 1917 paper which was one of the earliest on this subject in the State of Rhode Island.[62] He saw little likelihood that health insurance would be adopted in the United States in the near future. The general public, he saw, was not in the least prepared for it, while American physicians and health officers had for the most part no realization that broader medical care was a serious legitimate concern of theirs.

In fact, even the promising Health Center principle was having some difficulty. As developed in New York City, Cincinnati, Boston, and some other places, the Health Center provided, in a decentralized form, a wide range of health services, both preventive and curative, to the citizens of given districts in large cities or rural areas. In 1920 Biggs proposed a state-wide extension of the Health Center idea in New York as a compromise in place of a health insurance bill. Chapin joined with Theobald Smith, Rosenau, Winslow, Haven Emerson, Surgeon-General Hugh Cumming, and other public health leaders in endorsing the measure, but it was defeated.[63] Nevertheless, Chapin felt that Health Centers were here to stay and that public medical care would continue to expand. He cautioned his contemporaries, however, not to rush the matter too much. "It is perhaps best that progress should be slow and that we should feel our way." Preventive medicine, Chapin saw, had reached its present advanced state in the United States by a process of evolution in easy stages that the public could accept. Both compulsion and education had been employed in this upward progress over the previous seventy years or so, but, as he always said, "education is better than legislation. It is slower, but surer." [64]

In 1920 Chapin reviewed this evolution of preventive medicine in one of the Delamar lectures at the Johns Hopkins School of Hygiene and Public Health. The lecture had a certain symbolic interest in bringing Chapin back momentarily into the orbit of Welch, though this time it was as colleague rather than as student. In the lecture he indicated his belief in the virile maturity of the American public health movement. Public health work in this country was not by any means at a final plateau of achievement, but it was, he felt, finally far enough out of the slough of theory, ignorance, and error for its leaders to be able to look confidently to a future of ever greater community health.

The lecture had a fine success with the Baltimore people. Frost and Henry Barton Jacobs were among those who wrote Chapin afterward to express their pleasure. Welch confided, moreover, that "it is the best which we have had in the course of public lectures, and that is saying a good deal when we have had such lecturers as Sedgwick, Biggs, Park, Rosenau, Whipple and several foreigners." [65]

The real climax to this coming-of-age period of American public health came during the year after Chapin's Johns Hopkins address. In 1921 the public health profession met in New York to celebrate the fiftieth anniversary of the American Public Health Association. Stephen Smith, the New York sanitary reformer, now 99 years old and long retired, was the central figure. The Association had come a long way since he, with Snow, Harris, John Rauch, and the handful of others had founded it in 1872. For the postwar generation of health officers, steeped in the New Public Health and becoming thoroughly grounded in science, Smith and the era of sanitary work which he represented were hardly credible. To men like Chapin, Welch, Biggs, and Goler, however, Smith stood as a marker at the beginning of the evolutionary movement in which they all had participated. They were themselves now the statesmen of the profession, the landmarks for the next generation of health officers. Chapin and his wife took in all of the festivities for Smith and thoroughly enjoyed the occasion. As his own contribution to the anniversary volume Chapin wrote an historical essay on State and Municipal Control of Disease which remained for years the best available discussion of the subject. [66]

Chapin had been, since 1916, one of the select group of Honorary Members of the American Public Health Association, one of only a dozen or so men who had been so honored for especially great service to the Association and to American public health work. [67] In 1921, as he had a number of previous years and as he continued to do for several years afterward, he refused to accept the presidency of the Association.[68] He was a modest man who could not, in all sincerity, believe the statements of his colleagues that he was among the greatest leaders of the profession. He was, moreover, still dedicated to the idea of advancing his profession through action or research in his own community rather than through holding national offices.

Modest as he was about his own work, Chapin was far from retiring when it came to talking about the achievement of his country in sanitation. By the end of this decade, he noted, phenomenal medical progress had made American physicians and surgeons the equal of any, while American medical schools, formerly a national disgrace, had risen to a point where the best were rarely equaled abroad. In medical entomology as it related to public health, no nation had contributed more than the United States through such great demonstrations as those of Theobald Smith, Reed and Gorgas, Sedgwick, Howard T. Ricketts, Bailey K. Ashford, and Charles W. Stiles. The United States had long been ahead of Europe in the scientific study of water, milk, and sewage purification. American scientists like Smith, Park, Wesbrook, and Simon Flexner had made contributions of basic importance to bacteriology and immunology. American epidemiologists such as Sedgwick, Vaughan, and Winslow—and he should have added Chapin— were most responsible for recognizing contact infection as "the most important factor in the spread of the common infections of temperate regions." Finally, Chapin concluded, Americans were the ones who had shown "that the preventive work of the future must be centered largely on the education and care of the individual." It appeared, even before the United States entered World War I, that American public health could claim superiority over that of Germany, and perhaps over England as well.[69]

A WAR AND AN EPIDEMIC

THE involvement of the United States in World War I brought an unprecedented demand for the services of public health specialists to cope in a scientific manner with disease in the armed services. In no preceding major war had preventive medicine offered such promise of conserving manpower, keeping the fighting men out of the sick wards, and bringing deaths from disease below deaths from battle injury. Yet there were plenty of danger signals. Even before war broke out, public health leaders were aware that it would be difficult to do anything to stop pneumonia or polio, while measles or influenza, if they broke out, would be totally unmanageable.

American public health leaders served in various ways during the war. Gorgas, as Surgeon-General of the Army, was at the very center. Biggs was an Army Consultant on Tuberculosis and helped to improve the production of serums and vaccines for the troops. Welch helped Gorgas in several respects, including much inspection work in the training camps. Victor Vaughan, a veteran of the Cuban war, first helped screen doctors who applied for medical commissions, and later took charge of the Division of Communicable Diseases of the Army. Sedgwick helped on the home front by organizing courses for the laboratory workers who were needed in the camps, while he proudly kept a card catalogue of over 120 of his "boys" who were in service in one capacity or another. Chapin was torn between repeated requests by the Army for his services and his sense of responsibility to his immediate community. He compromised by doing as much as he could for the former but not getting too far away from home. In this way he was able to help his neighbors as best he could when influenza struck, just before the war ended, in the greatest epidemic of modern times.

Rumbles of the war reached Chapin almost from its beginning in 1914 from various of his European correspondents. They wrote to envy him his continued quiet labors, instead of being caught in a useless conflict between nations.[1] These labors seemed less and less quiet during 1915 and 1916 as the Coast Artillery batteries guarding Narragansett Bay stepped up their practice firings and activities at the Newport Navy Base increased. There was no question about Chapin's emotional sympathy with the Allies during the war. Essentially, however, he was close to being a pacifist and had no patience with the professional drum-beaters. When the United States finally entered the war, he turned his energies to the practical problems involved and let the ideology of the affair pretty much alone.

Chapin was the first Providence official to be called into defense work. Early in June 1917, at Welch's suggestion, the Army Surgeon-General's office asked him to criticize and correct the draft of a War Department general order on the subject of sanitation and public health procedures. A few days later Chapin went to New York as one of a Commission to discuss and complete this directive. Simon Flexner of the Rockefeller Institute for Medical Research was Chairman, while the other members, along with Chapin, were Biggs, Welch, Vaughan, and one of Gorgas' deputies, Lt. Col. Frederick P. Reynolds. It was Gorgas' idea to give this group full responsibility for communicable disease control in the big training camps in this country and also have them plan for the health of the forces sent to France.[2] Neither Chapin nor Biggs, however, could see his way clear to go into the Army for the duration of the war, so other arrangements had to be made. Chapin thus remained a civilian, although he made himself available to help out from time to time.

The Chapin doctrines, however, did see direct war service. Gorgas himself had long acknowledged the validity of his old friend's views on communicable disease. *The Sources and Modes of Infection* had been distributed by the Army as a standard guide for its medical officers as early as 1911. Routine disinfection was abandoned by the Army before the start of the war, while the aseptic technique became standard in the Army's infectious disease wards. Company Commanders became as responsible for teaching personal hygiene to their men as for instructing them in markmanship.[3] The use of modern techniques in general by the armed forces was an important educative factor for thousands of physicians and was a significant element in the further spread of the New Public Health after the war.

In the middle of June, Henry P. Davison, Chairman of the Red Cross War Council, asked Chapin to serve on the Council's Medical Advisory Committee. The other members of the Committee were Flexner, Welch, Biggs, Rosenau, Vaughan, Wickliffe Rose, Frank Billings, Richard C. Strong, and R. M. Pearce. This Committee was established to advise on European war relief and the health of the armed forces.[4] Among its other work it took over for Gorgas much of the public health inspection of the cantonments and nearby cities. During the summer of 1917 Chapin made a number of such inspections of new camps in the South. Wade H. Frost was the permanent Public Health Service officer detailed to coordinate this work for the Red Cross. Throughout the rest of the war the Committee met periodically and performed a useful service.

Meanwhile there was work on the home front. Chapin helped

out by giving lectures on personal hygiene to reserve officers. He made the City Hospital available for patients with communicable disease from nearby Fort Devens. He met with members of the French scientific mission with respect to their study of American sanitary methods.

Chapin's most important direct contribution to the war effort, both locally and nationally, was in connection with the food supply. For his own city he drew up and distributed circular-charts of foods which were healthful but cheap. He argued the merits of day-old bread and cottage cheese. Food Administrator Herbert Hoover had persuaded him that Americans should be corn-meal eaters rather than flour eaters for the duration, and Chapin enthusiastically spread this idea in Providence.

With the demand for food conservation, Chapin's long-time view on the feeding of garbage to swine came to the fore. Soon after America entered the war Chapin pointed out this ready-made measure which would release large amounts of grain for use by the Army and our allies. He emphasized that this was the most economical way to dispose of garbage, that it need not necessarily be a nuisance, and that pork from animals fed with garbage was not inferior or more diseased than any other. By 1917 many health officials had swung over to Chapin's way of thinking about this. In December 1917, Hoover asked Chapin to attend a conference in Chicago which was called chiefly to discuss the problem of utilizing inedible foodstuffs. Chapin was the only health officer in a meeting of swine experts, sanitary engineers, and government officials. The conference ended with the United States Food Administration actively promoting the feeding of garbage to hogs. Several large cities subsequently abandoned their reduction or cremation plants in favor of hog disposal of garbage.[5]

In December 1917 Gorgas wrote again to see if Chapin felt able to take on a permanent war assignment for the Army, this time to take "charge of the epidemiological work," as he put it. "But I do not urge you. I think you are doing about as good work for your country in your present position as you could do anywhere, and a short tour here would hardly answer for the position I have in view." [6] Chapin again declined. Later he also refused a commission on the General Staff itself, where he would have been in charge of medical statistics.[7]

For World War I sanitarians, such horrors of previous wars as typhoid fever, smallpox, malaria, tetanus, dysentery, and the diarrheal diseases were now in large measure controllable.[8] Nevertheless, there still remained infections which constituted great problems for the successful prosecution of the war, both among soldiers and civilians. Tuberculosis was one of these. The army physical examinations were helpful in unearthing large numbers of unsuspected cases. These became problems for civilian health officials when they were sent back to their respective communities. The New England Regional Tuberculosis Conference planned, in 1918, when Chapin was its President, to discuss how to cope with these cases. The Conference had to be postponed until the next year, however, and by then the disease had lost the urgency of wartime.

The army medical examinations also revealed the magnitude of the venereal disease problem. Chapin had recognized this disease as a serious public health problem as far back as the 1890's and had suggested the licensing of prostitution as the chief control measure.[9] Before the war, however, few places in America had done anything. Yet, a few states, beginning with California in 1911, had made these diseases at least nominally reportable, and Chapin himself had by 1913 taken the step of authorizing public treatment of venereal disease at the Providence City Hospital. The wartime manpower crisis of 1918 finally brought a vigorous federal campaign against this evil, with state and local cooperation. In Providence as elsewhere, VD clinics provided free treatment to hitherto unsuspected thousands of patients, frequent raids were made on bawdy houses and hotels, and public rest rooms were plastered with posters, while special VD films played everywhere to overflow crowds. "Fit to Fight" played to men only, while "The End of the Road" was shown to female audiences.[10]

Of the epidemic diseases, polio, which late in 1916 hit much of the United States harder than ever before, subsided and fortunately did not come back severely during the war. Meningitis, however, began to threaten in the summer of 1917. The Red Cross Medical Advisory Committee counseled the Army that prompt measures in the camps could avert serious outbreaks of the disease. But, by December, apparently because commanders did not take vigorous enough action, meningitis epidemics were raging in several of the largest Southern camps. At the same time epidemics of measles and pneumonia had broken out to an even more damaging extent. On the day after Christmas, Gorgas urgently called Chapin to Washington to advise on the problem of these epidemics. Chapin went for a short time, although he could give little direct help, for by then it was too late to do much more than care for the sick. Yet, damaging as the epidemics of meningitis, measles, and pneumonia were to the war effort, these were only a prelude to the coming influenza.

In September 1918, with the world in the last throes of the war, influenza struck western Europe and the northeastern United States. Within a month, it spread over the entire European and North American continents, and from there in every direction over practically the whole inhabited earth. Before it ran its course, hundreds of millions of persons had taken sick, while somewhere between ten and twenty-one million died, perhaps half a million in the United States. Although its death rates were much lower, it ranks with the plague of Justinian and the Black Death of the fourteenth century as among the most widespread disease outbreaks in history.[11]

Faced with their greatest challenge since the germ theory was verified, public health workers stood by impotently, in almost total ignorance of the disease. It was in varying degrees a disillusioning, embarrassing, and, above all, a sobering experience. Chapin found it more frustrating than anything else. He had had a good deal of experience with influenza. Ever since the so-called Russian influenza of 1889 and 1890, Providence had some influenza every year, with well-defined outbreaks in alternate years closely associated with pneumonia.[12] There was a damaging New England epidemic in the winter of 1915–1916. In Boston that winter the Massachusetts Association of Boards of Health devoted most of its mid-winter meeting to a Symposium on Influenza and Pneumonia, at which Chapin and Rosenau were the principal panelists.[13] A few weeks later Chapin himself almost died from an attack. Respiratory diseases were also widespread in Providence in January 1917 and again in the bitter winter of 1917–1918, when the suffering was heightened by drastic coal shortages.

In early September of 1918 the first Providence cases of the so-called "Spanish Influenza" were reported among sailors stationed near the city. As it spread, Chapin thought that the disease was much the same as the usual variety of influenza except that its course was shorter and its effects less serious. Before the month was out the epidemic took a sudden and ominous turn for the worse. Serious complications appeared in many of the cases, and deaths began to increase noticeably.

Although there was no panic as the pestilence spread, the demand grew for Chapin to do something to halt it. Unfortunately, there was nothing to be done. Little was known about the disease beyond the facts that it was highly contagious, of a very short incubation period, often hard to diagnose, closely associated with pneumonia, and that immense numbers of extremely mild cases helped to spread it. For these reasons, Chapin warned, standard preventive measures like the requiring of reports from physicians, the disinfection of houses, and the isolation of patients would be useless. Likewise, the closing of schools, churches, theaters, and other public places, which was widely demanded, would be completely futile, at least as long as stores, offices, and factories remained open and public conveyances continued in use. Since it was impossible to control influenza, even in military camps where rigid discipline could be imposed, it was even further out of the question for civilian communities. "When a community is pretty well sown with cases of the disease," Chapin noted on September 28, "as is true of our New England cities today, the disease will run its course. When the susceptible material is used, the disease will stop." [14] Under these circumstances, almost the only way that people could have any hope of avoiding the disease, he pointed out, was to take extreme precautions of personal hygiene; in other words, to stay at home. More feasibly, he asked people with colds or similar ailments not to come out into public. He advised women to do their shopping in the slack hours to lessen the crowding on streetcars. And he gave directions for caring for the disease.

The personnel problem became a critical one everywhere when the epidemic struck, since so many nurses and physicians were away with the armed forces or the Red Cross. Nurses whom Chapin had dispatched to the aid of beleaguered Boston had to be recalled hastily as the emergency increased at home. City and state emergency committees, on both of which Chapin was a member, were set up to coordinate nursing and hospital facilities, to enlist volunteer workers, and to round up more beds. Chapin himself put in many extra hours of work at the City Hospital during the epidemic after Richardson came down with the disease.[15] Despite shortage of personnel, the Providence City Hospital, at Chapin's suggestion and at the very height of the epidemic, began to experiment on immunization against influenza. They tried using blood plasma from

soldiers who had recovered from the disease as a serum to prevent the disease in others, but unfortunately had no success.[16]

Realizing that the new science was of no help, many health
officers reverted during the epidemic to the old "shotgun
methods" of epidemic control. Desperately they struck out
with every conceivable measure in the hope that one might do
some good. They prescribed strict isolation, performed disinfection, and above all took the lead in closing up the places of
assembly in their communities. Few health officers had the
courage to come out strongly, in the face of immense popular
pressures, against useless closures of public places, and fewer
still succeeded in keeping them open. Chapin protested, but
the Mayor of Providence finally gave in to public demand and
closed all schools, theaters, dance halls, and churches, except
for Sunday services. A conspicuous exception in this among
American cities was New York, where public places were kept
open, and it suffered no worse than other places. At the height
of the epidemic, Chapin joined with Welch, Rosenau, and
Vaughan in wiring the Commissioner of Health, Dr. Royal S.
Copeland, commending New York's enlightened position and
urging its officials to hold to it. In most communities, however, the scientifically correct position on handling the epidemic
was socially untenable.[17]

In the absence of officially endorsed remedies or preventives
for influenza in 1918, the quack and the patent medicine pur-
veyor rushed in to fill the vacuum. Early in the epidemic the
rumor spread from Boston to Providence that camphor hung
in a small bag around the neck would ward off influenza. This
set off a run on the drug stores, which were soon advertising,
"Camphor, one cake only to a customer." When the supply of
camphor ran out, many persons (most of them women) re-
sorted to carrying moth balls around and sniffing them when
they went into crowds. Dr. Byron U. Richards, who succeeded
Swarts as Secretary of the State Board of Health in 1917, said

that "the streetcars smelled as though everybody had got out his winter flannels at once." He went on to report that at the height of the epidemic "three papers circulated in Providence carried advertisements of thirty-two different preparations which, according to the manufacturers, would prevent or cure influenza." Almost overnight, "compounds previously advertised as remedies for indigestion, rheumatism, constipation, headaches, as general tonics, etc., suddenly became specifics for influenza. Two well-known dental preparations became grip preventatives." Disinfectants, also widely advertised as cure-alls for the disease, had tremendous increases in sales. Chapin issued broadsides attacking "such useless and superstitious means" and advising people instead to "avoid infection and keep up your strength." [18] Yet, even he hardly hoped to sway very many with a counsel of reason and little more.

The epidemic was at its worst during the first two weeks of October. It created havoc not only among the feeble and aged but to an amazing extent among those in the prime of life. Chapin observed, moreover, that the 159 deaths in Providence for the first week in October—61 of which were from influenza, 37 from pneumonia—were the largest number in the city's history. New records were set in the next two weeks. The week ending October 18 claimed 330 deaths from influenza and 18 from pneumonia. By that date, after which a decline finally set in, some 15,000 cases had been reported to Chapin, while the unreported cases were perhaps just as numerous. Although the main part of the epidemic was over in most places in the United States by late October or early November, communities had little chance to relax, because at the end of the year a new wave appeared. It came in a milder form than before, but there was enough to call volunteers back into action, to stir up talk of more closures of public places, and to cause thousands of fearful parents to keep their children out of school. Subsequent sporadic outbreaks occurred through the twenties.

In December 1918 Chapin attended the American Public Health Association's annual meeting in Chicago. Naturally, the papers and discussions were mostly on influenza, but speakers could offer few constructive suggestions. In the postwar era, therefore, several investigations were launched to try to solve some of influenza's mysteries. The American Public Health Association established a special Committee on the Statistical Study of the Influenza Epidemic, with Chapin as Chairman of the sub-committee on registration practices. Subsequently, some of the top men in the country, including Park, Rosenau, Frost, E. O. Jordan, and others, began laboratory studies of various aspects of the disease, in which they were supported by the professional associations, the United States Public Health Service, and organizations such as the Metropolitan Life Insurance Company. Even with such efforts the results were not imposing so long as the causative agent remained unidentified. And it was not until some years after Chapin retired that the first viruses of the disease were finally isolated.[19]

In several respects the achievements of preventive medicine during World War I were anything but encouraging. The unchecked ravages of influenza, pneumonia, measles, and meningitis were disheartening to many public health workers. There had been an equal lack of success with polio and whooping cough wherever those diseases turned up. In the middle of 1919 a friend on the Army Surgeon-General's staff wrote to Chapin: "If ever again I attempt to talk about the triumphs of preventive medicine my words will choke me." [20] Victor Vaughan, similarly despondent, declared that science had taken man as far as it could and that man faced a blank wall of defeat in further efforts to master disease.[21]

Chapin did not share this pessimism. He reminded his colleagues that it should have come as no surprise that these diseases had been unchecked, for medical men had agreed before the war that there were no controls for them. Looking further back, he pointed to a World War I death rate from disease of less than a quarter of that for the Civil War. For Chapin the era of productive preventive medicine was by no means over; it had just begun. He could see no end of promise either in the laboratory or in the field. There was no question of totally abandoning certain old measures such as isolation, as some argued might as well be done, but rather of using them with discrimination and not as cure-alls for every disease. Certainly there had been failures in the fight against disease, but was there not an even more impressive record of triumphs? "Medical men have no reason to be discouraged," Chapin assured his colleagues, "but should patiently work on, hoping that some day means may be found to control measles, pneumonia and influenza as effectually as typhoid fever and malaria are now controlled." [22]

Even as many, on the heels of influenza, despaired of the future of disease control, the immediate outlook for the public health had already changed dramatically. Chapin referred to the change at a dinner which Rhode Island physicians gave for their colleagues who had been in the war. Chapin was selected to welcome the physicians back to civilian life. "The medical and surgical accomplishments of the war," he reminded them, "have been marvelous. It will be a cause for your greatest satisfaction that you were part of the organization that gave these surgical results and filled the medical world with wonder." Then he spoke of an amazing change which had set in all over the United States at the end of the influenza pandemic. Instead of coming back to cities still besieged by epidemic diseases, the medical men had returned to find "a great wave of health sweeping over the country," bringing the death rates from the highest on record down to the lowest.[23] It was a phenomenon which was fully as unexpected as the pandemic itself. Health officials like Chapin and Winslow wrote back and forth about it with some excitement. This phenomenon, however, seemed to Chapin easier to explain than the sudden increase in influenza virulence which occurred during the epidemic. The healthy condition of his community all through 1919 must have been due, he supposed, to the survival of the fittest after the epidemic.[24]

In the fall of 1919 the Chapins and many of the others who participated in wartime disease prevention attended a Red Cross reception for Queen Elizabeth of Belgium at Henry Davison's Long Island estate.[25] The next year Chapin continued his Red Cross connection by accepting appointment as one of the Sanitary Correspondents of the new League of Red Cross Societies. This did not become a very important activity for him. Nevertheless, participation in this international venture reflected the new standing which American medicine and public health were beginning to enjoy.

NEW FORMS FOR OLD TECHNIQUES: PUBLIC HEALTH APPRAISAL AND EPIDEMIOLOGY

AMONG the factors in the maturation of American public health both before and after the war was the refinement and broad application of the public health survey. Although by no means the originator of the survey, Chapin contributed techniques of evaluation which made it a precise tool for public health administrators. Applying numerical and relative ratings to some major survey projects, he brought the process of appraisal from a largely subjective state to one of considerable accuracy and objectivity. As a logical outgrowth of his earlier activities, this work helped bring high standards to his profession and gave lasting shape to both state and municipal health organizations.

Notable, if limited, surveys of medical topography or of sanitary conditions had been carried out in the United States during the nineteenth century by men like Daniel Drake, Lemuel Shattuck, and John C. Griscom, while even more ambitious surveys had been projected though never fully carried out. John Shaw Billings in 1874 was firmly convinced that until some sort of systematic sanitary survey of the United States could be made, "state medicine in this country cannot rank as a science, but must rest mainly upon individual opinion and hypothesis, as it now does." [1] In the twentieth century, Chapin's own massive study of Municipal Sanitation was the most detailed and furthest reaching sanitary survey made in the country up to its time. After 1907, Franz Schneider of the Russell Sage Foundation directed surveys of various individual American cities. But none of the surveys before 1910 attempted comparative ratings or numerical evaluation.

In 1912 and 1913 the American Medical Association drew up plans for a comprehensive investigation of public health conditions in the United States. This was to include four parts: a survey of federal public health activities, a state survey, a municipal survey, and one of voluntary public health work. The state survey, as it turned out, was the only part of this ambitious project that really went very far. To make the state survey, the association wanted a single "trained sanitarian of the highest rank." [2] Chapin, after first declining, changed his mind and agreed to do the job. The report which he produced as a result of his survey had an effect on state health work comparable to that of Abraham Flexner's famous report of 1910 on medical education in the United States and Canada.

By 1913 Chapin had already been in demand as an investigator and had made a useful assessment of the Massachusetts State Board of Health.[3] He had moved beyond the factual approach to the survey which he had employed in his work on Municipal Sanitation. *Sources and Modes of Infection,* in a way a survey, was also an appraisal with a definite pattern of standards and values. Chapin had two principal criteria by which he arrived at his judgments of values. One was that of cost. Like businessmen, he argued, "we ought to spend our money so as to get the greatest benefit from it," eliminating or deemphasizing those measures that give little return.[4] Hence his persistent efforts to remove routine nuisance work from health departments. The other criterion was the scientific determination of whether a given measure was effective in reducing disease and death. "It is not possible," he conceded, "to make preventive medicine an exact science, but it is possible to use quantitative methods in many fields hitherto neglected, and to make at least approximate measurements of the value of our work." From this position, Chapin decided to present his state survey as an evaluation in terms of the relative standing of the states in their health work.

Chapin's survey was conducted at intervals snatched from his regular work from late 1913 to early 1915. In the spring of 1914, accompanied by Mrs. Chapin, he made a swing through the South. On his way he stopped in Washington to get an over-all résumé of the anti-hookworm campaign from Wickliffe Rose, Director of the Rockefeller Sanitary Commission. At the time of his visit, the South was experiencing what he called a "marked sanitary awakening." Most of this part of the country, Chapin observed, "for a long time was little affected by modern sanitary science. To the outsider it appears that the work of the Rockefeller Sanitary Commission, bringing to the front young, active men, trained in scientific methods, has proved a great stimulus" to public health work. Virginia, North Carolina, and Mississippi were showing the most marked improvement, while Alabama and other states were beginning to follow their lead. In Arkansas, the local Director of the anti-hookworm campaign moved directly from that job to the post of Secretary of the State Board of Health. In fact, the one reservation Chapin had about the work of the Rockefeller Sanitary Commission in the South was that, with its vast resources of money, it tended to interfere too much and to dictate the policies of the various states on hookworm.[5]

Although the South showed signs of sanitary regeneration, it still had a long way to go in providing basic health protection and service. South Carolina, among its many deficiencies, still made little attempt to supervise the supplies of drinking water.

Louisiana still paid far more attention to nuisance inspection than to direct disease control. In Georgia, as in many other states, laboratory work was almost nonexistent.

As Chapin swung into the Midwest and West later in the year, he found conditions generally even worse than in the South, and with no sign of reform. South Dakota, for instance, did not inspect its water supplies in any way, made no attempt to distribute antitoxins, had no statistical data on the prevalence of disease in the state, had little supervision of local health departments, and made little effort to control the communicable diseases. Yet there were seven states which did less health work than South Dakota and where the offices of the state health boards were not even open on a full-time basis. New Mexico did not make an appropriation for public health work.

By far the worst element was the involvement of many of the state health boards in state politics. Wherever this condition prevailed it was almost impossible to get qualified men as commissioners of health, and health work remained backward, unscientific, and ineffective. In a number of states, on the other hand, Chapin found that the Boards of Health were appointed and controlled by the state medical societies. He considered this delegation of power to private organizations to be a dangerous practice for, as far as he was concerned, "medical politics and medical bossism may be as pernicious as state politics." Politics of one sort or another was a potential threat to every health department in the country. In Rhode Island itself, a combination of political pressures which forced Swarts out of office in 1917 was kept from completely subverting the State Board of Health only by vigorous action on the part of Chapin and other medical leaders.

The brightest spots in the state public health picture in 1914 were in the Northeast. Massachusetts had easily done the best and most productive health work over a long period, Chapin felt. New York, since its new legislation in 1913, had a carefully organized health department. It was run by "exceed-ingly capable and earnest officials"—among whom at the time of the survey were Biggs, Wilbur, and Winslow. Maryland, guided largely by John S. Fulton, but helped immensely over the years by the active influence of Osler and Welch, also ranked high, as did Pennsylvania and New Jersey. Three states stood out in the Midwest: Kansas, which had the leadership of S. J. Crumbine; Indiana, under the direction of J. N. Hurty; and Minnesota, which was developing remarkably under the direc-tion of some of the most fervent and capable leaders of the New Public Health—Henry Bracken, Wesbrook, Hill, and A. J. Chesley.

Despite the good work in these places, as Chapin reviewed the various state health activities at the end of his survey he experienced a certain discouragement. "There is so much to be done and so little to do with," he saw, "there are so many technical problems to be solved, and there are so many difficul-ties outside of the health department, in the way of efficient administration, that one fears it will be a long time before the dreams of the enthusiasts come true." He noted a special need for public health work in all of the rural areas of the country. And yet, as he reported upon these conditions, he remembered again the really great health accomplishments of the past and pointed out that progress was accelerating so fast as to give definite hope for the future.[6]

Chapin's Report on his survey appeared in 1916. It im-mediately became an object of controversy in public health circles across the country, largely because of its relative rat-ings.[7] People in the high-ranking states naturally received it favorably. Conversely, many of the officials, physicians, and members of the press in the low-ranking states reacted with anger or hurt local pride. Sensitive health officers of Virginia, South Carolina, Louisiana, and a few other states tried to dis-credit the whole work on the basis of a few errors of fact, most of which they themselves had furnished. The health officer of Kentucky bitterly collected and burned every copy of the Report that he could lay his hands on.[8] The health officer of Florida canvassed other aggrieved officials for their criticisms of the Report and distributed them widely in an effort to save his own job, which the publishing of the Report had put in jeopardy.

For the most part, however, health officials accepted the Report as an honest, constructive, and valuable criticism. William A. Evans, the former Chicago Health Officer, whose noted weekly health column appeared in many newspapers across the country, prominently discussed the Report in the hope that the ratings might "irritate, anger, inflame the legislatures into properly providing for the protection of the people." [9] The Council on Health and Public Instruction of the American Medical Association noted a widespread interest in the Report and felt that it would prove to be of the "greatest value" to health officials.[10] Winslow, reviewing it in the *American Journal of Public Health*, gave unstinting praise to a work which was such "a careful comparative study of what has been done, and a mapping out of comparative ideals for future attainment." The report as a whole, he said, "should mark a distinct turning point in American health administration." [11] The state health officers themselves gave Chapin a standing ovation when he next talked at their annual meeting.

The direct effects of the Report were immediate and far-reaching. West Virginia, within a year after Chapin's visit, passed legislation providing for a full-time Commissioner of Health with broad powers. Florida quickly passed a modern vital statistics law and corrected several other of the deficiencies Chapin had noted. New Mexico, in order to remove the "black eye" which the Report had given the state, in 1919 finally established a State Health Department.[12] The nation's involvement in World War I, only a year or so after the appearance of the

Report, doubtless lessened its impact to some extent and delayed corrective legislative action in some states. Yet, in 1920 Chapin could report that the survey, with its ratings, had on the whole been successful and had acted as a "real stimulus." [13]

The war forced the American Medical Association to abandon plans to have Chapin issue an expanded edition of the Report and to conduct a follow-up state survey. There remained, however, in an age which wanted to survey everything, a great enthusiasm for surveys of public health work. There also remained a passion, partly the result of the Flexner and Chapin surveys, for standardization of this work. In 1920 public health standardization was the main topic at the A.M.A.'s Annual Conference on Public Health and Legislation in Chicago. Speakers on various aspects of the subject were Chapin, George E. Vincent, President of the Rockefeller Foundation, and Allen McLaughlin, Assistant Surgeon-General of the United States Public Health Service. Everybody conceded that great good was being accomplished by the standardization of medical education. Likewise, standards were essential for such commodities as drugs, milk, chemicals, weights, and measures. And Herbert Hoover, as Secretary of Commerce, in the next decade vigorously stimulated a valuable standardization in such areas as railways, agricultural processes, and the manufacture and distribution of thousands of articles of commerce.

However, Chapin warned, "We cannot standardize sanitary practice as we standardize the yard or the quart . . . We cannot fix standards of sanitary practice or prescribe methods of procedure with any thought of their being ideal, or with any hope that they will be enduring. In fact, our hope is that they will speedily yield to something better." As an alternative to fixed standards, he felt that periodic group surveys, say every five years and each based on freshly reassessed values, could ensure a progressive level of excellence for the public health profession.

Along with Chapin's Report, the other great stimulus to state public health administration in the decades after 1914 came from Hermann M. Biggs.[14] It was largely under Biggs's direction that New York State shaped its progressive new public health law of 1913. This provided for a public health council with broad powers to enact health rules, a strong single executive officer who should be an expert, and direct state supervision of local health work. Subsequently, as State Commissioner of Health (following his long and equally distinguished service in New York City), Biggs took advantage of the new law to build up the department to a point where, by the 1920's, in Chapin's view it was "the best health department in the Union." [15] By itself it provided the pattern of excellence for other states to emulate. Within a few years, varieties of the New York plan were adopted in the reorganization of health departments in Massachusetts, Maine, and other states. Rhode Island, which was working toward a reorganization of its State Board after 1925, also favored the New York plan. Chapin, then 70, refused to become a candidate for the new position of Rhode Island Commissioner of Health, although many urged it upon him.

Chapin greatly admired Biggs's integrity and devotion to the scientific ideal of public health management. He could not always approve the authoritarian actions which Biggs sometimes took, but he regarded him as "the leading health officer of the country." [16] The only real point at which Biggs failed to meet Chapin's model of the public health executive was that he never made public health work a full-time proposition. Although Biggs proved that he could get more done as a part-time health officer than most men could full time, Chapin felt that public health work could never gain recognition as a profession or maximum community support unless its officials were uniformly full time.

As a rule, during the early decades of the century city health departments were not organized any more logically than were state health departments. Municipal public health work generally stood out far ahead of most state work in quality, although there were great differences from one section of the country to another. With few exceptions, the best public health work around 1915 was in the older cities along the Eastern seaboard. New York and Providence easily would have rated best, followed by Boston, Rochester, and Baltimore. City health work was not, however, subjected to thorough appraisal until the 1920's. When it was, the appraisers built largely upon the techniques and pattern of values which Chapin had already established, and they retained him as their chief consultant.

As early as 1915 Chapin drew up a score card of suggested relative values for the health work of the average Northern city.[17] From this time on the numerical rating scale based upon these relative values came into wide use. Others who helped to establish the system included Franz Schneider of the Russell Sage Foundation, George Whipple of Harvard, and Murray Horwood of M.I.T., a Sedgwick-trained man. In almost every case, appraisers accepted Chapin's view that routine city cleanliness measures rated low or not at all as health measures.[18]

In 1920 the Metropolitan Life Insurance Company, on the initiative of its Vice-President, Lee Frankel, and its Chief Statistician, Louis I. Dublin, donated several thousand dollars to the Amercan Public Health Association to finance a detailed survey of city health departments. To conduct this survey the Association created a Committee on Municipal Health Department Practice, enlarged in scope in 1925 as the Committee on Administrative Practice. This Committee came to exert a great continuing influence, first upon city health departments and then upon state and other local health work. Winslow was Chairman of the Committee for its first fifteen years and deserves most of the credit for its success. It was Chapin, however, who set the productively probing tone for the Committee's work and provided it for around a dozen years with intellectual leadership. Besides Winslow and Chapin, the Committee included Wade H. Frost and Allen Freeman of Johns Hopkins, Donald Armstrong of the National Health Council, Lewis Thompson of the United States Public Health Service, and Haven Emerson of Columbia.

The survey conducted by this Committee in 1920 and 1921 covered the 83 largest American cities.[19] A similar survey of smaller communities a few years later by the American Child Health Association rounded out the municipal picture. The Public Health Service also entered the field and made some extensive municipal surveys. In 1923, Chapin, upon the request of the rest of the Committee, drew up a draft of a municipal Appraisal Form. After much modification, this form and its successors provided the bases for the subsequent productive work of the committee on rating procedures. Health officers began to use them to assess their own work. Those places which wanted more detailed assessment brought in the Committee's field consultant service to conduct full-fledged surveys.

In addition to its survey and appraisal work, the Committee sponsored manuals on public health administration, stimulated the modernization of health departments, and provided a point of departure for the promotion of organized health services in rural areas and small towns of the United States. In these and other ways the Committee, guided by Chapin, Winslow, and a succession of other men, helped to extend public health work, to refine it, and to provide definitive standards for the public health profession.[20] Winslow, at the end of the first decade of this work, spoke to Chapin of the Committee's success. "It must, I think, be a satisfaction to you to feel that not only the whole modern practice with regard to communicable disease control but also the entire program for quantitative evaluation of public health work is all the creation of your brain." [21]

In 1929 officials watched with interest as an extensive health survey of Providence was made. On the basis of the latest appraisal form, the community made its expected good showing and maintained a high standard of achievement for other cities to follow.[22] It showed up exceptionally well in most activities and above average in all. British observers of the Providence survey were impressed by the techniques of scientific evaluation and saw in them something valuable for other countries to use.[23]

In the middle 1920's the editors of *The Medical Officer* in London took advantage of Chapin's most recent annual reports to make an informal appraisal of their own of American public health work in comparison with British work. Since Chapin, they observed, was "better known in this country [Britain] than any other American hygienist," they took his work in Providence as more or less typical of the best American work. "We are of opinion," the article began, "that our own system is in a more advanced state of evolution, but there are certain departments where they have the advantage." Infant welfare and school health services seemed to be carried on similarly, but England appeared to be ahead in the amount of school curative work provided, except for psychiatric clinics. The British praised the consolidation of school health work within American health departments, and commended the small size of American city health committees. On the other hand, general epidemiology and notification of infectious diseases by physicians seemed more thorough in England than in America, as did sanitary inspection and food inspection. In 1925 British health officials still failed to respond to the Chapin logic as to the low relative value of these as public health functions. Conversely, the British greatly admired the extensive Providence program of immunization against smallpox and diphtheria as well as Chapin's thorough milk control program.[24] The British praised Chapin personally for the quality of his work and for having done "more than anybody else to keep in touch the public health services of the two great English speaking nations," in an effort which had lasted almost fifty years.[25]

During the 1920's, as health officers refined their administrative operations and appraised and brought new logic to them, they realized that they had been neglecting one of their most useful investigative tools. Put in the shade by the dramatic discoveries and the virtually all-encompassing hopes of the bacteriological laboratories, field epidemiology had been almost forgotten in America since 1885. Now, both in Great Britain and the United States, epidemiology came to the fore again as an increasingly exact sub-science of public health work, as one which provided a new impetus to disease investigation.[26]

In the United States, the move for greater utilization of epidemiology was partly the delayed reaction of scientifically minded leaders to the residue of archaic communicable disease controls which Chapin had been working to eliminate. It was partly a lingering on of the intense interest in the behavior and periodicity of epidemics which the World War outbreaks had stirred up. The British investigator Major Greenwood considered that the revival of epidemiology resulted also from concern over the mutations of smallpox and from concern over the emergence of postvaccinal encephalitis.[27] A positive stimulus to the development of epidemiology as a distinct discipline came with the appointment at Johns Hopkins in 1921 of Wade Hampton Frost as America's first Professor of Epidemiology. Another came from the example which Chapin set in his everyday work.

During the period after the war, investigators called for epidemiological studies at all levels of health organization. Frost pointed to Providence as the best "proof that a busy health department actually does have the resources necessary for fruitful investigation." Chapin, he observed, had so "directed, shaped and compiled his routine records that they stand today as a contribution to epidemiology of which any research institution might well be proud." [28] Probably the only health department in the country which approached Providence in its epidemiological work was the Minnesota State Board of Health, with its investigations under Hill and Chesley. [29]

Frost began to make the epidemiological material of Chapin's Annual Reports the backbone of his class work from the time of his arrival at Johns Hopkins. In so doing he brought up an entire generation of epidemiologists to think of the Providence data and Chapin's use of them as the standard of excellence. A number of his students used the data of the Reports as the bases for further productive studies. [30] Frost himself took up one of Chapin's rather incidental techniques, the secondary attack rate of infectious disease within family groups, and adopted it as one of his basic epidemiological tools. He found this to be "the simplest, most direct, most widely applicable and useful method so far devised for assembling the essential facts" about the incidence of infectious disease in households. [31]

Quite apart from his techniques and his accumulations of statistical data, Chapin's epidemiological investigations had become famous by the 1920's. Although he had paid particular attention to diphtheria and scarlet fever, his studies of typhoid fever, tuberculosis, and other diseases had been equally suggestive, if somewhat less extensive. His investigations of the relation to disease of dirt, air, food, drink, insects, and personal contact had helped make *The Sources and Modes of Infection* one of the great epidemiological treatises of all times. Now, in the 1920's, Chapin turned a few of his students—Alton Pope was one—to further studies of the Providence data. [32] More important, he himself carried through a number of new epidemiological studies which played a large role in stirring up interest in epidemiology as a science. His 1925 analysis of the incidence of measles over a sixty-five year period, for example, was a much-studied work.[33] Another was his original comparative study in 1924 of mortality among income taxpayers and non-taxpayers, an analysis of Providence data of 1865. His tentative conclusion that economic well-being caused a decided difference in mortality seemed to offer a valuable field for further study.[34]

During the several decades before 1925 some health workers watched with interest as certain of the infectious diseases changed character almost before their eyes. In some cases the change was a mysterious but welcome decline in virulence of the disease, while in others it was a sinister shift from a relatively moderate form to a malignant one. Diphtheria, once practically unnoticed, had suddenly become severe not long before the bacteriological age. Smallpox made an opposite change just at the end of the nineteenth century. Chapin noted this change in smallpox closely at the time and began to look for an explanation. He was still looking for it up to the time he retired as health officer. In the meantime he made a long and brilliant study of the phenomenon and had suggested a hypothesis which pointed up the immensity of the natural forces against which man contends in his fight to control disease.

Chapin's earliest findings in this study, published in 1913, suggested that the new strain of mild smallpox virus was probably a biological variation or mutant of the usual severe type.[35] At the time perhaps the only other person who was looking into the matter was C. O. Stallybrass of Liverpool.[36] Chapin's article set others to thinking about the problem. In Paris, Arnold Netter was reading the article in the library of the Institut Pasteur just as the first German airplane flew over at the beginning of hostilities in August 1914. He regretfully laid it aside for the duration but took up its ideas again in 1918. He thought that the war deprived the article of an early extensive European discussion and probable acceptance.[37]

With the spread of the mild type of smallpox in the twentieth century, the general population lost much of its traditional fear of the disease. It took an occasional visitation of the old severe type to remind people that it could still be dangerous. In the 1920's, at Chesley's request, Chapin prepared some popular literature for the vaccination campaign of the Conference of State and Provincial Health Authorities.[38] The need for this propaganda was apparent when Chapin pointed out that with over 35,000 smallpox cases in 1925, the United States had one of the world's poorest records against this disease. "What becomes of our boasted superiority in public health," he asked, "when we are more widely infected with the most loathsome of the contagious diseases than is any other country but Mexico, and when we have to admit our inferiority to the Soviet Republic." [39]

About this time Chapin was chosen to give the Sedgwick Memorial Lecture for 1926 at Huntington Hall in Boston. For his subject he decided to take up again his investigation of changes in type of infectious diseases. The behavior of influenza in the 1918 pandemic had convinced him anew, as he remarked to Winslow, that "the variation of bacteria is a most important field for investigation. I wish I knew when and where the influenza germ was suddenly transformed." [40] Other serious researchers wondered the same thing. Since 1919 Chapin had been trying to get someone at the Providence City Hospital to investigate the varieties of pneumonia.[41] Changes in plague, dysentery, diphtheria, and typhus fever also badly needed investigation, he felt. Of course, some researchers denied that there had been any real changes within historic times.[42] Chapin's 1925–1926 study of the types of smallpox and scarlet fever, therefore, provided the most authoritative light thus far upon the whole question of such changes.[43]

His conclusions from this study were based upon an analysis of some million and a quarter cases of smallpox and of a similarly large number of scarlet fever cases which had been reported by correspondents from all over the world. There was no doubt, Chapin pointed out, that the nature of diseases is often considerably modified by changes in immunity in the host due to inoculation, by temperature changes, or by increased bodily resistance; but the changes he observed were more fundamental than these. On the other hand, variations in disease could not be explained by any of the new but still vague forms of the theory of the epidemic constitution, as elaborated by such men as Hamer and Cruickshank in England. Likewise, the theory that symbiosis, or the intimate association of an organism like a streptococcus with disease organisms such as those of influenza, smallpox, or scarlet fever, caused such basic changes was not generally acceptable to Chapin. Eliminating these and other hypotheses, he thought it likely that "most variation in infectious disease is due to changes in the specific germs."

With smallpox, the evidence seemed strongly in favor of Chapin's former view that the mild strain was a mutant of the classical severe type. There was still no certain evidence, however, that the new strain always bred true or, in other words, that it did not ever revert to the old classical form.

Scarlet fever was another matter, for with it mild varieties had developed only gradually over several decades, whereas mild smallpox had appeared suddenly. Chapin concluded that this change in scarlet fever was the result of natural selection, that virulent strains tended to die because they killed the host in which they were parasitic. In addition, he was sure that the change in scarlet fever had been significantly influenced by human activity in the form of isolation of the severe cases. The barring of severe types of the disease from further susceptible material substantially weakened their position in the fight for existence, Chapin reasoned, so they gradually gave way to milder types.

Chapin's paper proved to be stimulating fare for health officers and investigators. E. O. Jordan used it to lead off the first issue of his new magazine, *The Journal of Preventive Medicine*, for which Chapin had agreed to be one of the four contributing editors. C. C. Pierce, Assistant Surgeon-General, hoping that every health officer in the country could read it and collect more data about Chapin's theories, abstracted the paper in the weekly *Public Health Reports*.[44] Frost felt that Chapin had set an important example. "My impression on reading the considerable number of experimental papers recently published has been that the authors generally have failed to appreciate the evidence which is already available from human experience; and I believe that papers like yours, presenting and discussing this experience would be of great help to them in the interpretation of their experimental results." [45] In London, the editors of *The Medical Officer* felt that Chapin's "novel and startling" conclusions were "argued so closely that they must be accepted." The paper, they agreed, was "one of the most interesting additions to our literature on infection with which America has favoured us." [46]

Chapin's theories as to the changes in infectious diseases remained impossible of definite proof, but they constituted the most plausible explanations yet advanced. With regard to mild smallpox, a final paper in 1932 presented additional evidence that this strain as well as the severe one continued to breed true. More than twenty years later this was still true. British health officers considered Chapin's exhaustive epidemiological study of smallpox to be about as conclusive an answer as man could get. Alton Pope, in the United States, concurred: "No one else, I am sure, would have the patience nor the wide acquaintance in the field which would make it possible to collect this type of data." [47]

With epidemiological studies finding an ever larger and more receptive audience, the middle 1920's seemed propitious for the creation of an epidemiological society in the United States. An abortive effort to establish such a group was made as early as 1920. A more productive step was taken in the spring of 1927, largely on the initiative of Dr. John Ferrell of the International Health Division of the Rockefeller Foundation. On the invitation of the Division, some forty epidemiologists and health officials met at the Johns Hopkins School of Hygiene and Public Health. Chapin called to order the two-day conference. Its combined recommendations constituted what was called "probably the first coordinated statement endorsed by a group of sanitarians on epidemiology as a fundamental branch of public health." [48]

At the Baltimore conference, Haven Emerson of New York proposed the formation of a national epidemiological association.[49] This found general approval and resulted in the establishment of the American Epidemiological Society in the fall of 1927. It was set up as an informal body which would be small enough to ensure critical discussion. Largely for this reason it was organized outside of the American Public Health Association, which began its own Epidemiological Section in 1928. At the first meeting of the Society, held November 11, 1927 at the New York Academy of Medicine, Chapin was elected its first President. Chapin, Frost, and the American pioneer in the new experimental epidemiology, Leslie T. Webster, gave the principal papers. In 1928 Frost succeeded to the presidency, while Chapin became Honorary President.[50]

With these formal and informal steps, epidemiology took its proper place as a discipline in American public health work. Chapin took great satisfaction in this development. Throughout his career he had tried to show other health officers that field studies were as important as were laboratory investigations. After all, he reminded them, "as it takes two to make a quarrel, it takes two to make a disease, the microbe and its host." [51] And one could rarely study the human host in the laboratory.

The epidemiology of the twenties became a discipline that

John Snow, Austin Flint, or August Hirsch would hardly have recognized. It was no longer concerned solely with the communicable diseases. Beginning in the period of World War I, it included studies of such other diseases as cancer and the nutritional disorders. Chapin was early to realize the promise that epidemiology offered in a wider application. Along with Haven Emerson, he was among the first to point out the desirability of making epidemiological studies of mental disease.[52]

In the postwar years new techniques coming into play promised to extend the effectiveness of epidemiology as a science. Among these, Chapin admired the new method of study known as experimental epidemiology, a method which utilized animals in controlled group situations. This was pioneered in England by William W. C. Topley and in the United States by Simon Flexner and Webster. Chapin's own use of animal experimentation years before on problems connected with the epidemiology of typhoid fever and tuberculosis showed him the possibilities of such experiments.

On the other hand, Chapin, together with Newsholme, expressed considerable skepticism of the new biometrical school of investigators, with its ultrarefined and abstruse formulas. This skepticism was for Chapin no denial of the basic nature of reliable statistical records as the "raw material of epidemiology" nor of the value of mathematics in studying these records. It was merely that he felt the early use of these techniques did not show any substantial results. It was still upon the old techniques, "the proper selection of data, the careful use of controls, and interpretation consistent with the known facts of the disease in question that the soundness of epidemiological studies really depends."[53] As he approached the end of his career, Chapin still maintained that the test of a technique, new or old, lay in the positive and direct contributions that it could make toward the healthy community.

HYGEIA: ILLUSION AND REALITY

THE prosperity decade of the 1920's brought to the United States the highest level of health the country had yet enjoyed. This happy condition suggested to some that perhaps the old dream of the ideally healthy community—Edwin Chadwick had defined this as one whose annual mortality rate would be five per thousand or less—was now not far from fulfillment.[1] Others, whose hopes had been shattered by previous public health failures, took a dim view of such an outlook and foresaw a future of ever-recurring disease and uncontrollable epidemics, a future hardly better than the past. Chapin, busy with the practical challenges of the Public Health Century, did not speculate a great deal on this subject. As a suggestive indicator, however, he brought forward the record of progress for Providence during the previous forty years or so. With these superb statistics, Providence became the natural microcosm around which such a conjecture might be discussed. Whatever the result, in the minds of professional public health workers no other city had come closer than Chapin's community to becoming the Hygeia of Chadwick and Benjamin Richardson.

Those who viewed the obstacles to such an ideal as insuperable had a strong case. This was true at any rate if the problems still awaiting solution were reliable criteria. As Chapin pointed out in 1922, "every year the field of public health widens and the problems increase."[2] Health officers no longer had the relatively simple problem of 1842, that of obtaining "pure air, a pure water, and a pure soil," nor had they the sanguinely viewed problem of 1890, that of "stamping out" infectious disease by isolation and disinfection. Greater knowledge had made more effective action possible than in those earlier eras, but it had also shown how vast and how difficult the problems really were.

Progress itself complicated and increased the work of the health officer in the twenties. Automobile accidents began to figure prominently in the vital statistics of the community. With prohibition, Chapin and his fellow health officers had to warn the public against the dangers of wood alcohol and Jamaica ginger. As flappers vied for slimness, Chapin opposed the fad of dieting except under medical supervision. Meanwhile, women, in their new-found equality were "rapidly approaching a state of nicotine addiction comparable to that of men."[3] The marriage rate continued to decline in most cities, which Chapin attributed to the prevailing "love of luxury." At the same time, he deplored the frivolity of those who made the marriage ceremony into a stunt performed in an airplane or on a beach in bathing suits.[4] "Is it unreasonable to inquire what it profits a nation to save the lives of its babies and protect its children from infection, and then allow them to grow up to treat marriage as a joke?"[5]

But these were largely problems of society. Health officers had problems which were their more exclusive concerns. In 1922 Chapin saw that man had much to do before he could establish the exact relation to health of such influences as housing, ventilation, nutrition, and dental work. There were all of the old problems created by nostrums, midwives, politicians, and often by backward medical practitioners or health officers. There were difficulties in coordinating the many new health agencies and the multifarious clinics.[6] One of the knottier problems was that of determining the limits of state medicine. Finally, two problems loomed larger every year as major concerns of the future. One of these was the vast incidence of mental illness. The other was the great increase in the diseases of old age as science found ways of keeping people alive longer.

The most pressing public health problems in the 1920's, in Chapin's opinion, were still those having to do with the causes and prevention of the infections and especially with the control of respiratory diseases. It was hardly necessary for him to point out that the causative organisms of many of the commoner diseases, such as scarlet fever, smallpox, colds, polio, measles, and influenza, were still unknown, and that no one yet knew how to handle healthy carriers.[7] These hard facts by themselves made Hygeia seem improbable to many, particularly when new infectious agents might at any time appear or harmless old ones by mutation become virulently destructive.

Faced with problems of this nature and magnitude, health officers of the 1920's still found good, scientific reasons for looking hopefully ahead. One was the triumph of the scientific method in public health work. Laboratories had multiplied, and people everywhere were worshipping their results. More and more health officers were scientifically trained, while those who were not no longer had much voice in the national public health organizations. The critical appraisal of health work was now becoming the rule rather than the exception.

Yet Chapin saw no room for complacency. He still found it necessary to rap outmoded theories and to keep the pressure on health workers to use only rational control measures against communicable disease. By the middle 1920's a large proportion of American health officials accepted his view that activities having no demonstrable effect on people's health should be removed from health departments.[8] Nevertheless, he still had to argue with health officers to stop running clean-up weeks. In his own city he continued his policy of doing as little routine cleansing work as possible. Under this policy Providence became, as he himself conceded, "dirty but healthy." [9]

The city's environment still required close attention, however, both on the grounds of health and comfort. In 1925, seventeen years after Chicago's pioneer act, Chapin obtained a new Providence milk law which provided for pasteurization and grading. A few years previously he had gained a food handlers' law. With the final success of his anti-mosquito campaign in mid-decade, Providence became one of the most favored cities in the country in that respect. As one observer remarked, "the Providence host no longer thinks to ask his guest in the morning if the latter was annoyed by mosquitoes the night before." [10] Yet, although mosquitoes decreased, industrial odors increased. In the 1920's Chapin's department was given the extra responsibility of investigating, charting, and abating the city's modern smells, although he protested that it was a job for the City Engineer, not the Health Officer. Here was another case of his being too efficient a civil servant.

Chapin did have some success in transferring routine functions out of his department. In 1920, Providence became the first city in the country to give its routine nuisance abatement functions to the Police Department, although the arrangement was not an unqualified success.[11] The new work of laundry inspection went to the police from the beginning. And, in 1928, Chapin was delighted when the responsibility for garbage collection and disposal was finally transferred to the Public Works Department.

Other cities, although similarly hesitant, began to effect the transfer of routine sanitary functions. Some began to establish separate departments of sanitation or divisions of public works departments to handle such major cleansing functions as street cleaning and garbage removal. Others organized a more or less separate Sanitary Police to take care of nuisance abatement work.[12] Chapin's ideas along these lines were not easily accepted by British health officials, since the English system had largely crystallized in the pattern laid down in the Public Health Act of 1875. His views, however, gained ever-increasing respect in Great Britain in the 1920's, and at least a start was made toward the separation of functions.[13]

The question did not come up in the twenties as to whether Chapin's doctrine of separation might not in the long run serve the public health movement badly by causing health officers to neglect the study of valid environmental factors in disease. On the contrary, acceptance of the doctrine meant a new measure of free time for health officers who wished to experiment, and Chapin himself hoped that people would conduct serious quantitative experiments on many environmental factors. Basically, Chapin's doctrine represented the high point of the so-called "etiological" viewpoint in the public health movement. This has been criticized as a narrow concept which, in its preoccupation with causative agents of disease, sacrificed the broad humanistic viewpoint of the nineteenth-century sanitarians.[14] Yet, during the period of Chapin's career, the humane sanitary scientist and administrator, increasingly the specialist under the weight of the new knowledge, could hardly escape the etiological viewpoint. As long as the ordinary infectious diseases constituted the major public health problems, and as long as specific measures against them promised so much, there was no alternative but to place first things first in the effort to overcome them. Although undoubtedly some of his students and associates lacked his breadth, Chapin himself had much of the viewpoint and many of the best traits of the humanists. He deliberately chose to pursue some of the wider humanistic concerns in his capacity as private citizen rather than in his work as health official. He taught the same thing to his profession.

Scientific method demanded that outmoded measures even more than irrelevant activities be eliminated from health departments. One of these was terminal disinfection. Few American health officers in the 1920's would admit to a belief that routine disinfection was a valuable measure, and by 1923 some 34 large cities had abandoned the practice. However, many officials still hesitated to give it up because of the continuing pressure of public demand.[15] English health officers were just beginning to discuss the merits of the practice, albeit nervously. A few places in France had eliminated disinfection, while Prussian state officials dropped it completely in 1921. Most other countries still fumigated religiously after infectious diseases.

In 1925 the Health Section of the League of Nations, in a tribute to Chapin, urged that health officers everywhere follow his pioneering step of two decades before in abandoning terminal disinfection in favor of concurrent disinfection.[16] Gradually other countries scrapped their elaborate steam autoclaves and fire-engine-red fumigation conveyances. Brazilian officials, in so doing, made a slip which was almost inevitable in the twenties when they paid their respects to the example set by "Charles Chaplin of Providence."[17] Actually, few men in history have had such success in destroying a centuries-old dogma in their own lifetimes as Chapin had in uprooting terminal disinfection.

As disinfection was abandoned, the "Chapin System" of aseptic nursing and concurrent disinfection for the management of communicable diseases spread slowly through American hospitals in the 1920's. Chapin's suggestion that these techniques were also of great value for home-treated cases came as an interesting new idea to British sanitarians.[18] Isolation, on the other hand, in Chapin's opinion, was still used too much rather than too little. He called for less severity in excluding children from school and more supervision of patients and contacts. He opposed compulsory hospital isolation and favored a more vigorous search for foci of infection. Judiciously used, isolation was a valuable tool, but Chapin still had to speak out against using it as a panacea.[19] In fact, he saved his sharpest criticism for those who would revert to general principles as the basis for public health work. After Gorgas' death in 1920, Chapin recalled one of the special contributions which his old friend had made. "Gorgas' greatest work was the demonstration of *separate* attack, not *mass* attack" on communicable disease.[20]

Another reason for looking hopefully to higher future health levels was the suggestion, from several experiments, that disease germs were not as widespread in the population as bacteriologists had thought. One possible explanation lay in the theory of nonspecific immunity advanced by A. G. Love and C. B. Davenport in 1920 and supported, "to a certain extent by some other persons in high standing," notably by Park and Winslow.[21] Seeking to explain negative Schick reactions in people who had never had diphtheria, the theory asserted that somehow one disease in a person develops an immunity against another, while in some cases general immunity against all diseases develops. Chapin, however, argued that the evidence for nonspecific immunity was entirely inadequate, and that, unless conclusive proof to the contrary could be found, a more likely explanation was in the carrier state, although it, too, was not yet proved. Microorganisms, it seemed to him, could covertly produce immunity in healthy persons as well as use them to distribute infection.[22]

Perhaps the most substantial health hope lay in immunization. Health officers could not yet afford to give up their propaganda for personal cleanliness. Yet, it was good news that some progress in immunization was again evident after a period of limited accomplishment and false leads. Early in 1917 Chapin himself suggested a pioneer experiment in immunizing against measles, by using immune serum from convalescing measles patients.[23] This experiment at the Providence City Hospital was successful both in producing temporary immunity and in contributing to the curative process. Chapin applied serum on a broad scale during the next epidemic that occurred in Providence, in 1925–1926, and achieved good results. This success led him to envision the establishment, at hospitals all over the United States, of so-called "blood banks" of this serum for use during times of large outbreaks.[24] Such an idea was never widely adopted, and measles convalescent serum has been supplanted since World War II by gamma globulin. But the serum served a useful purpose for some two decades and was an important development pending the discovery of a permanent immunizing agent against this disease.

The Providence City Hospital staff also successfully developed a convalescent serum against erysipelas, although it failed to produce one effective against influenza. Within a few years after World War I, its doctors and those of other hospitals were trying out a polio serum.[25] The most important immunization work at this time in Providence and in other American cities, however, apart from continued vaccination against smallpox, was the campaign against diphtheria. Toxin-antitoxin had just been developed and in a few places like New York and Rochester had already proved its high degree of protection. Through the 1920's Chapin made a systematic drive to immunize his city's schoolchildren and infants. As in the history of smallpox vaccination, there were sporadic attempts to discredit the use of toxin-antitoxin, as by the Medical Liberty League of Boston in 1924. In general, however, the diphtheria immunization campaign went ahead rapidly and smoothly.[26]

The extensive use of toxin-antitoxin throughout the United

States accelerated a decline in the diphtheria death rate which had been going on gradually since the disease reached its peak in the 1880's. In July 1930, for the first time since 1885, there was not a single diphtheria placard posted on a Providence house, and in 1933 the city had no deaths from this disease. Chapin was pleased with an accomplishment "greater than any I had ever expected to see." [27] This once dread scourge was well on the way to becoming an almost forgotten disease.

Remarkable as it was, the drop in diphtheria mortality was only one of several amazing decreases in the communicable diseases which were evident by the 1920's.[28] Typhoid fever, affected by the development of water filtration and chlorination, pasteurized milk, immunization, and the increased alertness of health officers against contact infection, had shown its major decline earlier than diphtheria. In 1922 Providence became the second large city in the United States to report no fatalities in a year from this disease.[29] Scarlet fever had also had an astounding decline in mortality. Largely as a result of the new infant health work, summer diarrheas, which in 1890 killed one out of every thirteen babies born in Providence, in 1925 took fewer than one out of five hundred. Chapin considered this decrease "one of the most striking epidemiological facts of the times." [30]

Tuberculosis, though still the greatest year-to-year killer among the infectious diseases, had been having a marvelously accelerated decline.[31] Chapin still supposed, much as he had forty years before, that the chief reason was "the better physical condition of the people, brought about by the progress of science, art and industry in the nineteenth century." It now appeared, however, as it had not appeared forty years or even twenty years previously, that public health work was at last also contributing to the decline. Due to scientific work in health education, "the common drinking glass and the roller towel have gone. Spitting is becoming a lost art. The consumptive keeps his fingers out of his mouth. The use of fresh air and sunlight have been popularized. The value of pure milk and fresh vegetables in building a resistant body has been learned." Much of this change, and much of the decline in tuberculosis, Chapin concluded, was due to enthusiastic reformers in the voluntary health organizations along with publicly chosen officials. "Not all of this decrease," he agreed, "has been due to these conscious community efforts, but even if only half of it had been, it would be a wonderful achievement." [32]

There was no unanimity in the twenties as to just why these communicable diseases should have shown such remarkable declines. In fact, Chapin was among those observers who pointed out that more often than not natural causes had been more effective than human efforts. He was also ready to concede that social improvements had as much or more influence than scientific public health work. Whatever the reason, the fact of these declines contributed strongly to the widespread optimism about the future. Moreover, there seemed to be every likelihood that human efforts by themselves were becoming increasingly capable of contributing toward further decreases. Bacteriology, immunology, a revitalized epidemiology —all part of a scientific ideal of unprecedented vigor—promised much for the continued success of public health work.

Chapin carefully set the mood of cautious optimism which the perpetuation of the preventive ideal of medicine demanded. "Sanitarians work toward the ideal," he reminded his colleagues, "that all people will in time know what healthful living is, and that they will in time reach that moral plane when they will practice what they know. While hopeful for the millennium we must work." [33] Then, recalling the accomplishments of health workers during the past fifty years, he asked: "Are we not justified in the hope of other great advances in the half century next to come?"

The science which can point to its achievement against smallpox, malaria, yellow fever, diphtheria, typhoid and typhus fevers, tuberculosis, and a score of other diseases, as well as to a rapid lengthening of human life, and especially to the saving of vast numbers of infants from early deaths, need not be ashamed to acknowledge that some experiments have failed; neither should it hesitate to admit that we are still merely picking up pebbles on the shore of the sea of knowledge, and that what is not known about maintaining and perfecting the health of mankind is far greater than what is known. The opportunities for discovery are as great as before the days of Harvey, Pasteur and Lister.[34]

Chapin did not look for a public health utopia or for the realization of any impossibly ideal Hygeia in the next generation. He only pointed out that a continuing patient but critical devotion to science could scarcely fail to clear away more clouds of ignorance about keeping people healthy. As he approached retirement, he urged health officers to view the future of their professional work with a realistic confidence based on the demonstrated capabilities of the scientific method.[35]

HONORS AND RETIREMENT

In the 1920's Chapin began to slow down. He welcomed Dr. Clarence Scamman, a young graduate of the Harvard School of Public Health, as his assistant and possible heir in office, and he began to consider the necessity of retiring. But he hoped he could complete fifty years in office. With advanced years, the amount, though not the quality, of innovations, ideas, and writings began to taper off. In the meantime, as if to take the place of his decreasing creative satisfactions, these years and his subsequent years of retirement were filled with a succession of honors. Health workers from all over the world did their best to persuade him that he was and had been no ordinary "hod carrier of science." Chapin was never convinced. He had, he thought, done little more than any Chapin or any New Englander worth his salt would have done. His great satisfaction, moreover, came from a final realization that his work had been of some tangible service to his own immediate community and that he enjoyed the love and good will of his neighbors for this service.

Doubtless the celebrations for Stephen Smith in 1921 reminded Chapin of how old he was getting. The death of Sedgwick that same year and of Biggs in 1923 brought it home even more forcefully. Chapin had a heartfelt tribute for Sedgwick— the "delightful, as well as ever helpful, friend." He respected

Sedgwick for his "clear thinking and brilliant way of putting things" as well as for the spontaneous enthusiasm of his teaching. Sedgwick's work had played an important part in convincing Chapin of the vast extent and importance of contact infection. "His words turned my own thoughts to more careful consideration of the modes of infection, a subject which has ever since been uppermost in my mind." [1]

Chapin admired Biggs, on the other hand, for his achievements in public health administration and also for the way in which he represented the best working of the scientific spirit in their profession. Biggs "taught others to think before acting, to devise specific measures for specific ends, to demand that public health work should be effective and that it be undertaken only on a well established scientific basis." [2] To honor this colleague, Chapin participated in organizing the informal Biggs Club in the fall of 1923. The others in this small original group were Park, Winslow, Emerson, Dr. William F. Snow of the American Social Science Association, Dr. Matthias Nicoll, Biggs's successor as State Commissioner of Health, and Dr. Linsly Williams, long Biggs's right-hand man. [3]

In 1924 Chapin completed forty years as Health Officer. To mark the anniversary, his close associates in Providence—Gorham, Richardson, and Scamman—arranged a large dinner in his honor. It provided an opportunity for the public health profession to pay tribute to its elder statesman, the man who had shown what a health officer could do. It gave the local community the chance to honor a man who represented the best type of public servant.

The toastmaster at the dinner characterized Chapin as "one of the greatest, best, and most beloved citizens of Providence." [4] But Milton Rosenau came down from Harvard to remind those who needed it that Chapin was also much more than a local personage. "We think of him," he said, "an an institution, as an inspiration and as an ideal we glory to follow" in the public health movement. W. S. Rankin, who represented the American Public Health Association, felt that the public health world was most indebted to Chapin for giving it a "sense of proportion, a sense of relative values." Charles J. Hastings, long-time health officer of Toronto, came to say that "your name is as well known in Canada as in the United States." [5] Chapin was moved by the speeches, and Winslow thought they struck the personal note Chapin preferred, although they did not begin to convey the significance of his work. He made a mental note to tell more of that story himself some day.[6]

The tributes from those who could not come to the dinner were as warming as the ones from those who did. Newsholme wrote to affirm the great influence that Chapin's work had had in Great Britain and in Europe.[7] Surgeon-General Hugh S. Cumming sent a deputy with the praises of the entire Public Health Service. Welch, paying his respects to America's "foremost sanitarian," thought back forty-five years to his association with Chapin and Gorgas at Bellevue Hospital Medical College. "I have felt more personal pride," he wrote to Chapin, "than I have any right to claim in your career and achievements and spreading reputation." He thought that Chapin and his inquiring mind "exemplify the sentiment that there lives 'more faith in honest doubt than in half our creeds.' " [8]

Lee Frankel of the Metropolitan Life Insurance Company sent personal homage, as did many state and municipal health officers. Walcott sent a note from retirement regretting that Massachusetts had not tried harder to lure Chapin away from Providence to head its reorganized State Health Department.[9] Frost seized the opportunity to tell Chapin of the great specific influence the latter had had on his own work. "But I should like to say," he added, "that I am indebted to you for much more than the epidemiological facts and principles which I have drawn from you. What I chiefly owe to you and to a few others, such men as Dr. Carter and Professor Sedgwick, is the stimulus and encouragement that come from the ideals and personality that always show through your work and theirs. So many men who stand high in science shrivel up on closer acquaintance; and the rare ones who expand are needed to keep up one's faith and ideals." [10]

The anniversary dinner was only the first of many tributes. In 1926, Halsey DeWolf, retiring President of the Rhode Island Medical Society, strongly urged his colleagues to make the most of their opportunities to consult the great mind which was so close at hand.[11] For his part, Chapin was always ready to talk with young physicians on any medical subject, and he had rare skill in bringing out their best ideas.

The medical profession had come a long way since Chapin had left medical school. He viewed with satisfaction the improvement in medical training which had come about since the Flexner Report of 1910. Yet, it was a matter of regret to him that more physicians did not bring to their profession a humanitarian spirit and a greater dedication to science. The great evil of the profession in the 1920's, Chapin often asserted, was no longer ignorance but commercialism. He was partly in earnest when he told audiences that half or more of the doctors then practicing medicine should be chloroformed.[12] Even as he worked for a new medical era, Chapin realized that medical progress had almost destroyed some good qualities of the old era. He regretted the passing of the general practitioner. "The onrush of medical knowledge," he conceded, "now demands incessant devotion to science, and one man can no longer compass the whole range of medicine. The specialist has come to stay, but there is often little time for him to learn to know and love his patients." [13]

Chapin himself had become a physician's physician, in the forefront of his profession. Recognizing this, the Rhode Island Medical Society in 1927 commissioned his portrait and arranged a special meeting for its unveiling. Such a tribute, unprecedented in the 115-year history of the Society, was the occasion for another spurge of complimentary notes and telegrams. George E. Vincent, President of the Rockefeller Foundation, delivered the address of the evening. His speech pinpointed Chapin's leadership in each of the three stages of public health work and praised him as a "hero who has safeguarded the lives of many, many people in his own city, in his own land, and in lands beyond the sea." As a public health leader, he was, "easily the first in all the world." [14]

In Warsaw, a few months later, members of the Polish Club of Rockefeller Fellows, who had received an account of the portrait ceremonies, wrote to join in the tribute. They had been working, they reported, to make Chapin's name "a synonym of revolution in public health in Poland," and added that "there is no country which has not profited from your illuminating work." [15]

Thanks largely to the International Health Board (later the International Health Division of the Rockefeller Foundation), these statements were no exaggeration. During the 1920's the Board brought large numbers of foreign medical practitioners, administrators, and specialists to the United States for the public health training which was by then second to none in the world. Many of these Rockefeller Fellows chose to visit Providence as part of their field training. Advanced American students at public health schools also came in large numbers. The Harvard people always arranged a special pilgrimage for its graduate students so they could see Chapin at work in Providence as well as hear him lecture when he went to Boston. The students inspected the model City Hospital for infectious diseases; they saw the noted Providence district nurses in action; and they observed the exemplary Health Department techniques. But above all, they came to see and talk with Chapin. Thus, as it worked out, the public health school which

Gorham tried in vain to establish in Providence came into existence anyway.[16] It rested largely on the reputation and vitality of only this one great man, however, and lacked the tangible organization to carry his teachings forward into the future.[17]

The Rockefeller Fellows and other visitors in the 1920's saw Chapin much as a Boston reporter found him to be, "a man of quiet charm in whom wisdom combines with humor." Many people noted the "sweetness and simplicity" of his character. Young laboratory men whose work failed to meet Chapin's standards found that he could express his displeasure as effectively as a drill sergeant, while employees who did not stick to business had a short career in his office. He was a warm, kindly man, despite a somewhat austere appearance. Sham or pretense rarely got by without scathing sarcasm.[18] Yet, his habit of plain-speaking seldom made him enemies, for no one was fairer or more courteous even when expressing his differences.

As he approached his seventieth birthday, Chapin was slender almost to the point of fragility. He dressed trimly and immaculately in dark blue suits. His hair had not thinned greatly, but it had silvered along with his moustache. His blue eyes were as bright as ever. Sunday afternoon visitors to the Keene Street home found him and his wife in a living room that was simple yet warm in its rich tones of red and bronze. There were flowers in the windows, and books close at hand. Saturday nights, their son Howard and his wife were expected for supper. On Sundays, if it was pleasant, the elder Chapins would return the call.

Chapin had long since given up sailing on the bay, although until the war he kept an "easy-rowing boat" for fishing. The cottage at Oakland Beach, no longer the quiet summer retreat it once was, was exchanged for one at Saunderstown, further down the bay away from the city. Just out in front of the

Saunderstown cottage were the ruins of a ferry landing. Chapin and his wife were intrigued with this relic and began asking around for its history. This interest led them to other old ferry lines until, over a seven-year period, they had uncovered information about every ferry that had ever run in the state. In 1925 they published their findings in book form, a valuable study in local history.[19]

Ferries, however, were only for spare time. During these years, as previously, Chapin was associated in one way or another with many community projects bearing on the public health in addition to his official work. He remained a consultant in the city's hospitals. He was a trustee for local philanthropic funds and various other civic institutions. Every year there were fund-raising drives of day camps, nurseries, or nurses' groups to be endorsed and pushed. His active role in the work of the voluntary health agencies of Providence helped achieve a measure of coordination that was rare in American cities. Chapin had long felt that as a matter of course much of the work of the private agencies would eventually be turned over to public health departments.[20] By the 1920's, however, many of the private health agencies had too much of a vested interest in health to want to dissolve themselves. This led to the idea that coordination of community health work should come from the meeting and discussion of all agencies, public and private, in some voluntary body, rather than from a single strong executive. Just before Chapin's retirement the Providence Health Council was created for this purpose, one of many similar organizations in cities around the country.

If Chapin was not particularly enthusiastic about this development, he was even less so about accepting the Presidency of the American Public Health Association. His refusal for many years to consider holding the office had been something of a source of wonder to his colleagues. It was thus an occasion of satisfaction for the profession when, in the fall of 1926 at the

Buffalo convention, he finally agreed to accept the post. Chapin performed the duties of his office conscientiously, but at the end of 1927 he was glad to turn over the presidency to Herman Bundesen, Health Officer of Chicago.

More honors came to Chapin, including honorary university degrees and the first honorary membership in the national public health fraternity, the Delta Omega Society. In 1928, at a Washington, D.C. ceremony, he received the rarely awarded Marcellus Hartley Honor Medal of the National Academy of Sciences for "eminence in the application of science to the public welfare." [21] The following year he was unanimously elected the first recipient of the Sedgwick Memorial Medal for "distinguished service in public health," awarded by the American Public Health Association. Surgeon-General Cumming, making the award, commented that Chapin had been "the leading figure in establishing the public health standards of this country" and that to him "we owe the entire formulation of the modern viewpoint on communicable diseases." [22]

A survey of 138 of the large American cities in 1928 showed that the average tenure of the nation's health officers was seven and a half years. Chapin, at the end of that year, had completed forty-five years of service, while the next in length of service was Goler of Rochester, with thirty-three.[23] Chapin still hoped he could round out an even fifty years before calling it quits, and it looked as if he might make it. To be sure, his plans for the succession had been upset in 1926, when his understudy, Scamman, was lured away from Providence. But Chapin engaged Joseph Smith, one of Richardson's young internes, as his new assistant and started the training process over again.

Smith and the rest of the staff did all they could to relieve Chapin of administrative details. But they could not prevent his getting old. Despite Anna Chapin's watchful care, the illnesses which attacked his slim frame almost every year took an impossible toll of Chapin's strength and vitality. Evening engagements were gradually done away with, while out-of-town trips became fewer and fewer. By 1930 he found it difficult even to get to the meetings of the Committee on Administrative Practice which he enjoyed so much and considered so important. Early in 1931 he had to pass up the White House Conference on Child Health. Even keeping up with the literature of public health had become an impossible chore.

At the end of October 1931, ill and worn out, Chapin resigned all of his positions, to be effective in January, two years short of the fifty-year goal. He did not attempt to name his successor. In any case, he was satisfied with the eventual solution which gave Richardson the Superintendency of the Health Department as well as of the Hospital. Chapin's last official act on January 15, 1932 was to have himself revaccinated.

Chapin's retirement was the end of an era. All over the country boards of health paused in their meetings to note the event, while Providence people knew they would look in vain for someone to replace him. Many Providence physicians reacted like Halsey DeWolf who, on hearing the news, said he felt the bottom had dropped out. The Rhode Island Medical Society agreed that, as a physician, Chapin was the "greatest who has yet lived" in Rhode Island.[24] The city itself, mindful of its debt, made Chapin Emeritus Superintendent of Health with a desk in City Hall for as long as he should live. The honor which Chapin felt perhaps the most deeply of any, however, was the action of the city in changing the name of the now-famous Providence City Hospital to the Charles V. Chapin Hospital. A few years later, Brown University conferred its highest honor, the Rosenberger Medal, upon the man who perhaps had made the greatest contribution to humanity of any of its graduates.

For Chapin, retirement as City Health Officer meant a complete break from serious work of any kind. He canceled his subscriptions to professional journals and resigned from every organization to which he belonged. As he wrote to Winslow, "I shall be easier in my mind if my name is dropped from all committees. Those who cannot work deserve no honor. The worst thing about failing health and strength is inability longer to work with my old tried and dear friends." [25]

It was hard to think of Chapin in retirement, no longer letting his inquiring and critical mind play upon public health matters. E. B. Wilson of Harvard hoped that Chapin would use his new leisure to outline some of the pressing health research problems that needed attention. George Goler, among others, urged him to write the story of American public health work. Other friends had other suggestions. But Chapin was exhausted. After resigning from office he wanted only, as he told his friends, to "rest and not even think much." [26] He informed his London book agent that he doubted he should ever feel like buying another book.[27] To Goler he replied, "I have no pep or ambition. My hand shakes badly and I guess too that my head shakes." As for writing his memoirs, he added, Mrs. Chapin "would be glad to be a perfect secretary for me but she has earned rest more than I have." [28]

Even before he left office Chapin began to break up his magnificent library on medicine, infectious diseases, and other public health subjects. He gave the larger parts to the state medical society, Brown University, Rhode Island Historical Society, and the Harvard School of Public Health. His prized autographed copy of the Shattuck Report went in 1930 to Winslow, his equal as a bibliophile.[29] Chapin's token of friendship was, perhaps, a symbolic gesture for the public health profession, one which signified the passing of the mantle of leadership to other capable hands.

At the time Chapin retired, the depression already had a deep grip on the United States. It forced a cutback of public health work everywhere, although the need actually increased.

Winslow wrote in discouragement of the lack of funds for the Committee on Administrative Practice and the American Public Health Association generally. In Providence, with hundreds of apple vendors on the streets by late 1930, Chapin had tried to stimulate apple sales by emphasizing their health value.[30] And, with more and more persons unable to afford a physician for communicable diseases, he urged all such persons to call the Health Department. In 1932, the Report on the Costs of Medical Care (sponsored by the American Public Health Association) emphasized what everyone knew about a deep-rooted social and economic problem. During the New Deal years, interest in this problem intensified, and the controversy over health insurance and other forms of state medicine became increasingly vituperous. Chapin, now following these discussions from the sideline, observed that "I never was one who believed in chewing the rag over socialized medicine. When it is needed it will eventually work out. I see no good in pushing it or fighting it, either." [31]

The depression did not affect the Chapins personally very much. His city pension was enough to live on adequately, if not luxuriously, even although Emerson considered it to be the next thing to penury. "Fortunately," Chapin wrote Winslow, "Mrs. Chapin and I are finding that we are less and less dependent on what money is needed to purchase." [32] This was one of the compensations of old age.

Chapin settled easily and gratefully into his unaccustomed rest. He and Anna now spent a good deal of time reading mystery stories to each other. Chapin delighted in observing the scientific structure of the better ones. For exercise, there were walks around the neighborhood when the weather was good and occasional ventures over to the University or down to the City Hall. But Chapin did not want to be a burden, so such visits became fewer. Out-of-town trips were too much effort, so they stopped completely. Even Emerson and Winslow could not find a way to lure Chapin out into the world again from this final Providence seclusion.

Although he had stopped working for the public health, the profession continued to honor Chapin and to seek him out. A succession of presidents of the American Public Health Association made pilgrimages to Providence. The American Epidemiological Society made Chapin an emeritus member, while the Committee on Administrative Practice designated him as a permanent consulting member. On the initiative of Walter B. Cannon, the American Academy of Arts and Sciences voted to exempt him from paying dues in order to keep him as a Fellow. In London, the Society of Medical Officers of Health unanimously elected Chapin to its seldom awarded Honorary Fellowship, an extraordinary honor which had come to few other Americans.[33]

Apart from such honors, faithful friends kept Chapin in touch with the public health world. Colleagues or disciples sent copies of their work or data relating to his interests. Out-of-town friends stopped by his house. There were always more letters and photograph requests than he and Anna could keep up with, although they loved to read them. Winslow and his successors on the Committee on Administrative Practice saw to it that Chapin received regular notes of information and appreciation from the Committee. Chesley sent at least yearly greetings from the Conference of State and Provincial Health Authorities. Pope and other friends reported that no national public health meeting occurred without frequent reference to Chapin's work. From England, Newsholme still sent an occasional letter to pass on the news and to describe his labors on his latest book. He regretted that he and Chapin would never meet again on earth, but he was sure "that kindred spirits will meet hereafter." [34] Chapin himself did not speculate a great deal upon this eventuality.

A loyal Emerson went out of his way to make flying visits

to Providence from time to time and in between sent chatty notes about people and events. He made it his special business to report on the meetings of the American Epidemiological Society. In 1935 he wrote of the presentation before that society of significant papers by W. F. Wells and G. W. McCoy, which, he felt, forced the renewal of the ancient discussion of air transmission of communicable disease under certain conditions.[35] Additional experiments during the next few years left the impression that the air played a considerably larger role than Chapin had assigned to it. With many health workers accepting these new findings, a shadow fell over that part of Chapin's great thesis on the transmission of infection. Chapin himself noted this new work on air-borne infection with interest. He saw, however, what many did not, that there was not yet sufficient quantitative evidence to justify again changing public health concepts.[36] Public health investigators worked upon this matter for nearly twenty years more of research before they realized that Chapin's skepticism was warranted and that quantitative evidence of extensive disease transmission through the air, even of viruses, was not forthcoming. The basic principles of his work on the infections thus still remain fundamentally unchallenged.[37]

Yet for Chapin such work was all in the past. The only scientific activity in which he now engaged was to observe his reactions to the process of growing old. As he watched this process, the familiar local scene was changing around him, and the remaining old faces were dropping from view. Mary Gardner ended her notable career of public health nursing work in Providence when she retired in 1931. In the summer of 1933 the brilliant Gorham died. Dr. King, Chapin's deputy for many years, retired soon after Chapin himself and died in 1934. Meanwhile, the reunions of the Brown University Class of 1876 became smaller year by year, and Chapin, the class's long-time Secretary, became almost the last surviving member.

Tragedy struck Chapin's family in 1938 when his daughter-in-law ended her own life, while two years later Howard also died. Of the immediate family, no children or grand-children were left to carry on the line; only Anna survived her husband for a few years.

By the late thirties, almost all of those great national figures who had pioneered with Chapin in shaping the patterns of modern American public health work and making it the admiration of the world had gone. Chapin outlived virtually the last of them, including Vaughan, Wilbur, Durgin, Frankel, Welch, Theobald Smith, and Park. A later generation, one made up of men like Winslow, Emerson, Maxcy, Reed, Chesley, and Wolman, to name a few, now had the profession's leadership.[38]

Chapin died January 31, 1941 after two years of increasingly poor health. The funeral services at the Central Congregational Church were as he wanted them, brief and simple. His grave in Swan Point Cemetery, in Providence's East Side, was marked with the plainest of stones.

* * * * *

EPILOGUE

THE contribution of Chapin's generation of public health scientists cannot be overstated. Measured by creative results, there has never been a time in history when medical progress was so rapid and so tangible. There has never been greater justification, perhaps, than during that period, for a solid faith in the perfectability of the human race and for a belief that science could do much to bring this about, at least so far as its health was concerned.

The optimism of that day about continued medical and sanitary advances may never again be equaled. Public health problems are still formidable. Man now must cope with such new environmental factors as more complex industrial processes and the hazards of radioactive fallout. He must, with his new and rational understanding of disease, face the prospect that chemotherapeutic agents may not be the permanent cures or preventives of the communicable diseases they were thought to be. He must recognize that, ironically, the very successes of Chapin's generation have led to immense new public health problems today. The save-the-baby campaign and the world-wide drive against communicable diseases have been key factors in the population explosion. The significant lengthening of human life through such means as better nutrition, disease control, and higher standards of living has led to large increases in the diseases of old age. Perhaps, as Dubos argues, we may now be getting too much medical and public health care. Perhaps, as a result of this, the human race is getting soft and is deteriorating genetically to an extent that threatens its ability to survive.[1] Perhaps, indeed, the humanitarian ideal of preventive medicine no longer serves humanity well.

In his lifetime, Chapin could not foresee all of the problems which suggest such a possibility. If he were living today, he would be among the first to point out that the science which has finally produced successful vaccines against polio and influenza has no warrant in now forsaking the preventive ideal. Yet he knew from experience that the public health measures of one generation cannot be sufficient for the next.

> Science can never be a closed book. It is like a tree, ever growing, ever reaching new heights. Occasionally, the lower branches, no longer giving nourishment to the tree, slough off. We should not be ashamed to change our methods; rather we should be ashamed never to do so. We should try new things, but should show common sense about it.[2]

Public health problems are no longer the somewhat compartmentalized concerns either of reforming sanitary engineers, of dedicated medical health officers like Biggs or Chapin, of the hosts of voluntary health organizations, or of foundations and governments. More and more, health is the concern of the whole society. When every segment of society and science finally participates in this concern there can be a true social medicine. And surely, as Chapin would want to add, this condition cannot be either rushed or delayed. It will come about when the need becomes great enough.

* * * * *

APPENDIXES

BIBLIOGRAPHY

LIST OF ABBREVIATIONS

NOTES · INDEX

* * * * *

* * * * *

APPENDIX A

Values of Municipal Health Work

I. Communicable Diseases:

Medical Inspection and Nursing	13.0
Hospital	6.0
Antitoxin	2.0
Immunization	2.0
Venereal Disease	2.0
Ophthalmia	1.0
Tuberculosis: Nurses	4.0
Dispensaries	3.0
Hospital	3.0

II. Child Hygiene:

School Inspection	8.0
Infant Mortality: Nurses	10.0
Midwife Supervision	2.0
Boarding Houses	1.0
Milk Stations	1.0
Consultations	4.0
Prenatal Clinics	2.0

III. Sanitation:

Privy Sanitation	3.5
Housing	2.5
Plumbing	1.0
Nuisances	1.0
Fly and Mosquito Control	1.0
Garbage Removal	0.0
Cleanups	0.0

IV. Food:

    Adulteration   0.0

    Sanitation   1.0

V. Milk:

    Adulteration   0.5

    Sanitation   7.5

VI. Other:

    Care of Sick Poor   5.0

    Laboratories   5.0

    Education   8.0

                Total: 100.0

This chart was a part of CVC, "Effective Lines of Health Work," *Providence Medical Journal,* 17 (January 1916), 12–22. The percentages indicate both the shares of the health department budget which each activity should be allocated and the relative amount of time that the health officer could profitably spend on each. Where vital statistics work also was an integral function of the health department, the scale of relative values would have to be revised to include that function.

* * * * *

APPENDIX B

THE DECLINE IN CERTAIN OF THE MOST COMMON COMMUNI-
CABLE DISEASES IN PROVIDENCE, 1856–1925

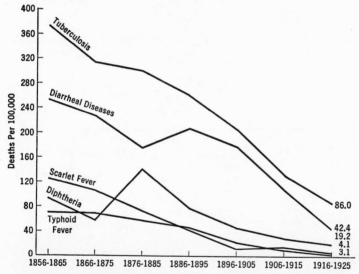

This chart was compiled from data in *Providence Health Report, 1925,*
p. 10. It indicates a consistent decline in three of the five diseases. Chapin
considered the increase in deaths from diarrheal diseases between 1885 and
1895 to be more apparent than real, however, due to particularly poor
reporting of total births during that period. The diphtheria increase, on
the other hand, was a real one, due to a sudden increase in virulence in the
decade after 1875.

* * * * *

A SELECTED BIBLIOGRAPHY

I. PRIMARY SOURCES

MANUSCRIPTS AND OTHER COLLECTIONS

Chapin material at the Rhode Island Medical Society Library. This constitutes the most valuable collection of unpublished material by or about Chapin. It includes four principal categories:
    1. Twenty-four large scrapbooks of clippings, letters, programs, and miscellaneous items covering the period from 1880 to 1941. These were assembled largely by Anna A. Chapin.
    2. Manuscripts of many unpublished lectures and papers.
    3. Manuscript notes and drafts for some published works.
    4. Miscellaneous manuscripts relating to epidemiological investigations and major publications.
A list of this material, by title and date where possible, is on file with the Librarian of the Rhode Island Medical Society.

Chapin material at the John Hay Library of Brown University. This includes four file boxes, chiefly of correspondence.

Chapin material at the Rhode Island Historical Society Library. This includes letters, family records, unpublished lectures and reports, and printed circulars and pamphlets distributed by Chapin's Department.

Chapin material at the Harvard School of Public Health. This represents the only sizable segment remaining intact of Chapin's personal library. It includes several hundred volumes, together with around 5,000 reprints of articles.

My own correspondence and interviews with living public health leaders was another valuable primary source.

NEWSPAPERS AND PERIODICALS

American Journal of Public Health, The, 1911–1959.

Annual Report Upon the Births, Marriages and Deaths in the City of Providence, 1855, 1856, 1883–1931.

Atlantic Medical Weekly, The (Providence), 1895–1898.

Bellevue Hospital Medical College, *Catalogue*, 1877–1881.

Brown University, *Catalogue*, 1872–1896, 1914–1940.

Brown University, *President's Report*, 1882–1896.

College of Physicians and Surgeons (New York), *Catalogue*, 1876–1879.

Evening Bulletin, The (Providence), 1880–1941.

Harvard School of Public Health, *Announcement*, 1922–1932.

Harvard University and Massachusetts Institute of Technology School for Health Officers, *Catalogue*, 1913–1922.

Journal of the Massachusetts Association of Boards of Health, The, 1890–1910. From 1907 to 1910 the journal was called the *American Journal of Public Hygiene*.

Monthly Bulletin of the Rhode Island State Board of Health, The, 1888–1921.

Providence District Nursing Association, *Annual Report*, 1900–1932.

Providence Journal, The, 1880–1941.

Providence Medical Journal, The, 1900–1916.

Public Health: Papers and Reports presented at the meetings of the American Public Health Association, 1875–1908.

Report of the Superintendent of Health of the City of Providence, 1856–1935.

Rhode Island Medical Journal, The, 1917–1942.

Rhode Island Medical Science Monthly, The, 1893–1894.

Rhode Island Medical Society, *Transactions*, 17v, 1859–1916.

Rhode Island State Board of Health, *Annual Report*, 1878–1932.

Sanitary Protection Association of Newport, The, *Annual Report*, 1879–1890.

Trustees of the Rhode Island Hospital, *Annual Report*, 1880–1887.

PUBLISHED WORKS BY CHAPIN

A list of Chapin's published writings was compiled by Professor Frederic P. Gorham and Doctor Clarence L. Scamman for the volume of selected *Papers of Charles V. Chapin, M.D.* (New York, 1934). Since that book is readily available, it has not been deemed necessary to repeat the list here. The list is substantially complete except for about forty reviews, editorials, and more or less ephemeral works.

PROFESSIONAL WORKS AND MEMOIRS BY PUBLIC HEALTH LEADERS

Abbott, Samuel W., *The Past and Present Condition of Public Hygiene and State Medicine in the United States*. #19 of *Monographs on American Social Economics*, ed. Herbert B. Adams. Boston, 1900.

American Public Health Association, *The Control of Communicable Diseases*. 1st and 2d eds., New York, 1917 and 1925. American Public Health Association, *Control of Communicable Diseases in Man*. 9th ed., New York, 1960.

Biggs, Hermann M., W. H. Park, and A. L. Beebe, *Report on Bacteriological Investigations and Diagnosis of Diphtheria, from May 4, 1893 to May 4, 1894*. New York City Department of Health, Scientific Bulletin No. 1, New York, 1895.

Billings, John S., "Report of Committee on the Plan for a Systematic Sanitary Survey of the United States," *Public Health: Papers and Reports*, II (1875), 47–54.

Bowditch, Henry I., *Public Hygiene in America*. Boston, 1877.

Chadwick, Edwin, *Report on the Sanitary Condition of the Labouring Population of Great Britain*. London, 1842.

Children's Bureau, United States Department of Labor, *Baby-Saving Campaigns*. Washington, 1913.

Crumbine, Samuel J., *Frontier Doctor*. Philadelphia, 1948.

Downie, A. W., and A. Macdonald, "Smallpox and Related Virus Infections in Man," *British Medical Bulletin*, IX (1953), 191–195.

Emerson, Haven, "The Story of the American Epidemiological Society," mimeographed paper, April 1951. Property of Dr. Phillip Sartwell.

Flexner, Abraham, *I Remember*. 1st ed., New York, 1940; 2d ed., 1961.

—— *Medical Education in the United States and Canada*. New York, 1910.

Folks, Homer, *Public Health and Welfare*. New York, 1958.

Frost, Wade Hampton, *Papers of Wade Hampton Frost, M.D.*, ed. Kenneth Maxcy. New York, 1941.

Fulton, Frank T., "The Detection and Treatment of Cases of Tuberculosis Among Factory Employees in Providence," *Transactions*, Annual Meeting of the National Association for Study and Prevention of Tuberculosis (1907), pp. 123–129.

Gardner, Mary S., *Public Health Nursing*. New York, 1916.

Godfrey, Edward S., Jr., "As I Recall It," mimeographed paper, April 1952. Property of Dr. Phillip Sartwell.

Gray, Samuel H., *Proposed Plan for a Sewerage System and for the*

Disposal of the Sewage of the City of Providence. Providence, 1884.

Hague, Ernest W., "Modern Tendencies in Public Health Work," *AJPHealth*, XV (February 1925), 137–140.

Hill, Hibbert Winslow, *The New Public Health*. New York, 1920.

Hiscock, Ira V., ed., *Community Health Organization*. New York, 1932.

Horwood, Murray P., *Public Health Surveys*. New York, 1921.

Janeway, Edward G., "Post Mortem Examinations in Relation to Public Health," *Public Health: Papers and Reports*, V (1880), 75–83.

———— "Remarks," *Public Health: Papers and Reports*, V (1880), 44–54.

Levy, Ernest C., "Present Views of the Importance of Municipal Sanitary Inspection for the Abatement of Nuisances," *AJPHealth*, II (January 1912), 7–13.

Medical Department of the United States Army in the World War. Washington, 1923–1928.

Newsholme, Arthur, *Fifty Years in Public Health*. London, 1935.

———— *The Last Thirty Years in Public Health*. London, 1936.

Pettenkofer, Max von, *The Value of Health to a City*, translation and introduction by Henry E. Sigerist. Baltimore, 1941.

Pope, Alton S., "Studies in the Epidemiology of Scarlet Fever," *American Journal of Hygiene*, VI (May 1926), 387–430.

———— and Clarence L. Scamman, "Diphtheria Immunization in Providence," *JAMA*, 88 (Feb. 19, 1927), 563–565.

Providence Sanitary Documents. A bound but unpublished selection of assorted city documents from 1840 to 1884, mostly by Snow. At RIMSL and other Providence libraries.

Reed, W., V. C. Vaughan, and E. O. Shakespeare, *Abstract of Report on the Origin and Spread of Typhoid Fever in United States Military Camps During the Spanish War of 1898*. Washington, 1900.

Report of the Committee on Appraisal for the Framingham Community Health and Tuberculosis Demonstration. Framingham, 1919.

Richardson, Dennett L., *Infectious Diseases and Antiseptic Nursing Technique*. Philadelphia, 1927.

———— and Hilary Connor, "Immunization Against Measles," *JAMA*, 72 (April 12, 1919), 1046–1048.

———— and H. P. B. Jordan, "Measles Immunization," *AJPHealth*, XVII (June 1927), 607–613.

Rosenau, Milton J., *Preventive Medicine and Hygiene*. New York, 1913. Eighth edition edited by Kenneth F. Maxcy under title of Rosenau: *Preventive Medicine and Public Health.* New York, 1956.

Rush, Benjamin, *Medical Inquiries and Observations.* 4 vols., Philadelphia, 1815.

Schneider, Franz, Jr., "Relative Values in Public Health Work," *AJPHealth,* VI (September 1916), 916–925.

Sedgwick, William T., "Investigations of Epidemics of Typhoid Fever," in State Board of Health of Massachusetts, *24th Annual Report.* Boston, 1893, pp. 667–742.

Shattuck, Lemuel et al., *Report of the Sanitary Commission of Massachusetts—1850,* edited by C.-E. A. Winslow. Cambridge, Mass., 1948.

Simon, John, *English Sanitary Institutions.* London, 1890.

—— *Filth Diseases and Their Prevention.* 1st American ed., Boston, 1876.

Trudeau, Edward L., *An Autobiography.* Philadelphia, 1916.

Vaughan, Victor C., *A Doctor's Memories.* Indianapolis, 1926.

Veiller, Lawrence, *A Model Housing Law.* New York, 1914.

Wald, Lillian D., *The House on Henry Street.* New York, 1915.

Wallace, James, *A Survey and Appraisal of the Health Activities of Providence, 1929.* Providence, 1930.

Waring, George E., Jr., *The Sanitary Drainage of Houses and Towns.* New York, 1876.

Webster, Noah, *A Brief History of Epidemic and Pestilential Diseases.* 2 vols., Hartford, 1799.

Welch, William Henry, *Papers and Addresses,* edited by Walter C. Burket. 3 vols., Baltimore, 1920.

—— *Public Health in Theory and Practice.* New Haven, 1925.

Wells, William F., *Airborne Contagion and Air Hygiene.* Cambridge, Mass., 1955.

Weston, Edmund B., *Report of the Results Obtained with Experimental Filters.* Providence, 1896.

Whipple, George C., *Vital Statistics.* New York, 1919.

Wolman, Abel, "Values in the Control of Environment," *AJPHealth,* XV (March 1925), 189–194.

II. SECONDARY WORKS

WORKS DEALING WITH CHAPIN

There is no previous full-length biography or study. A number of articles and contemporary testimonials, however, apart from obituaries, have discussed Chapin or his work. Among the most useful of these are the following:

Belcher, Horace G., "Dr. Charles V. Chapin," *Sunday Tribune* (Providence), March 17, 1912.

Cassedy, James H., "Dr. Charles V. Chapin and the Impact of the Scientific Method Upon American Public Health," M.A. Thesis, Brown University, 1950.

———— "Dr. Charles V. Chapin and the Modern Public Health Movement," Ph.D. Thesis, Brown University, 1959.

"Charles Value Chapin," *Men of Progress*, compiled by Richard Herndon. Boston, 1896, pp. 265–266.

Donley, John E., "Charles Value Chapin—The Man and His Work," *RIMJ*, XXXVII (June 1954), 311–316.

Emerson, Haven, "Foreword," *Papers of Charles V. Chapin, M.D.* New York, 1934, pp. vii-xii.

Fontaine, L. E. A., "Dr. Chapin Sees it Through," *Providence Sunday Journal*, magazine section, Nov. 8, 1931, pp. 1–2.

Frost, Wade H., "The Familial Aggregation of Infectious Diseases," *AJPHealth*, 28 (January 1938), 7–13.

Metropolitan Life Insurance Company, *Charles Value Chapin*. Health Bulletin for Teachers, vol. XV, no. 3. New York, April 1944.

Newsholme, Arthur, *The Last Thirty Years in Public Health*. London, 1936, pp. 261–263.

Scamman, Clarence L., "Charles V. Chapin," *Papers of Charles V. Chapin, M.D.*, pp. xiii-xxiv.

Simmons, James S., "Medicine of the Future," *RIMJ*, XXXV (July 1952), 361–367, 370, 404.

Vincent, George E., Address at the unveiling of the Chapin portrait, *RIMJ*, X (March 1927), 35–45.

Winslow, Charles-Edward Amory. *The Conquest of Epidemic Disease*. Princeton, 1943, chapter XVIII.

(There are a number of other discussions of Chapin and his work in the annual Chapin Orations of the Rhode Island Medical Society, all of which may be found in the *Rhode Island Medical Journal*. Among the most interesting of these is the oration by John R. Paul, "Chapin and Modern Epidemiology," *RIMJ*, XLII (June 1959), 375–379.)

GENERAL: THE LOCAL SCENE

Balch, G. B., *Genealogy of the Balch Families in America*. Salem, Mass., 1897.

Bicknell, Thomas W., *History and Genealogy of the Bicknell Family*. Providence, 1913.

Bronson, Walter C., *The History of Brown University, 1764–1914*. Providence, 1914.

Bumpus, Hermon Carey, Jr., *Hermon Carey Bumpus, Yankee Naturalist*. Minneapolis, 1947.

Cady, John H., *The Civic and Architectural Development of Providence*. Providence, 1957.

Chapin, Gilbert W., *The Chapin Book of Genealogical Data*. 2 vols., Hartford, 1924.

Clark, Franklin C., "History of the Development of Sanitary Science in Rhode Island," unpublished MS at RIHS, dated 1904.

Comstock, John A., *A History and Genealogy of the Comstock Family in America*. Los Angeles, 1949.

Fleming, Donald, *Science and Technology in Providence, 1760–1914*. Providence, 1952.

"Gardner T. Swarts," obituary in *RIMJ*, VIII (December 1925), 208.

Goldowsky, Seebert J., "The Beginnings of Medical Education in Rhode Island," *RIMJ*, XXXVIII (September, October, and November 1955).

Gorham, Frederic P., "The Old Medical School in Brown University," *Providence Medical Journal*, XVI (July 1915), 218–227.

Historical Catalogue of Brown University. Providence, 1905.

Ihlder, John, *The Houses of Providence*. Providence, 1916.

"Joshua Bicknell Chapin," *The Biographical Cyclopedia of Representative Men of Rhode Island*. Providence, 1881, p. 404.

Kirk, William, *A Modern City—Providence, R.I.* Chicago, 1909.

Mead, A. D., "Episodes and Personalities in the Development of Biology at Brown," *Science*, 91 (March 29, 1940), 301–305.

Nelson, Mary Cobb, "The Influence of Immigration on Rhode Island Politics, 1865–1910," Ph.D. Thesis, Radcliffe College, 1954.

Providence Medical Association, *History and Centennial Observance*. Providence, 1948.

Sherman, Frederick Fairchild, "Newly Discovered American Miniaturists," *Antiques*, 8 (August 1925), 96–99.

[Swarts, Gardner T.], "History of the Providence Clinical Club," unpublished pamphlet, Nov. 10, 1915, at RIHS.

Taylor, Robert J., "The Providence Franklin Society," *Rhode Island History*, IX (July and October 1950), 73–83, 119–129.

Wilson, George G., *Town and City Government in Providence*. Providence, 1889.

Winslow, C.-E. A., *The Tuberculosis Problem in Rhode Island*. Providence, 1920.

GENERAL: THE LARGER SCENE

Ackerknecht, Erwin H., "Anticontagionism Between 1821 and 1867," *Bulletin of History of Medicine*, XXII (September–October 1948), 562–593.

―――― "Elisha Bartlett and the Philosophy of the Paris Clinical School," *Bulletin of History of Medicine*, XXIV (January–February 1950), 43–60.

―――― "Hygiene in France, 1815–1848," *Bulletin of History of Medicine*, XXII (March–April 1948), 117–155.

―――― *Rudolf Virchow*. Madison, Wisconsin, 1953.

Adams, Samuel Hopkins, "Doubling the Guards on Health," *The World's Work*, May 1923, p. 96.

―――― "Guardians of the Public Health," *McClure's Magazine*, XXXI (July 1908), 241–252.

―――― *The Health Master*. Boston, 1913.

Anderson, Oscar E., *The Health of a Nation*. Chicago, 1958.

Blake, John B., "The Origins of Public Health in the United States," *AJPHealth*, 38 (November 1948), 1539–1550.

Bolduan, Charles F., *Illustrious Contributors to Public Health*. New York, 1936.

―――― *Over a Century of Health Administration in New York City*. New York, 1916.

Bulloch, William, *The History of Bacteriology*. London, 1938.

Bunker, John W. M., "Frederic Poole Gorham," obituary in *AJPHealth*, 23 (July 1933), 716.

Burnet, [F.] Macfarlane, *Natural History of Infectious Disease*. 2d ed., Cambridge, 1953.

―――― *Viruses and Man*. London, 1953.

Carlisle, Robert J., *An Account of Bellevue Hospital*. New York, 1893.

Cassedy, James H., "Edwin Miller Snow: An Important American Public Health Pioneer," *Bulletin of History of Medicine*, XXXV (March–April 1961), 156–162.

Cavins, Harold M., "The National Quarantine and Sanitary Conventions of 1857 to 1860 and the Beginnings of the American Public Health Association," *Bulletin of History of Medicine*, XIII (April 1943), 404–426.

Chagas, Carlos, *Remarques sur la Valeur de la Desinfection Terminale*. CH363, Société des Nations, Organisation d'Hygiène. Génève, Suisse, 1925.

Clark, James Bayard, *Some Personal Recollections of Dr. Janeway*. New York, 1917.

Clark, Paul F., *Pioneer Microbiologists of America*. Madison, 1961.

"Conference of Epidemiologists, The," report in *AJPHealth*, XVII (August 1927), 777–782.

Crum, Frederick S., "Results of Preventive Medicine in Providence, R.I., 1885–1892," *Medical Record*, June 6, 1903.

Dalton, J. C., *History of the College of Physicians and Surgeons.* New York, 1885.

Defries, R. D., *The Development of Public Health in Canada.* Toronto, 1940.

DeKruif, Paul, *Microbe Hunters.* New York, 1935.

Denny, F. P., R. F. Feemster, and S. C. Prescott, *Fifty Years of Public Health in Massachusetts.* Boston, 1940.

Dictionary of American Biography. Especially the sketches of Abraham Jacobi, Austin Flint, Edward G. Janeway, and George E. Waring, Jr.

Dublin, L. I., et al., "Fifteen Years of the Committee on Administrative Practice," *AJPHealth*, XXV (December 1935), 1296–1320.

Dubos, René J., *Louis Pasteur: Free Lance of Science.* Boston, 1950.

——— *Mirage of Health.* New York, 1959.

"Edwin Miller Snow," *The Biographical Cyclopedia of Representative Men of Rhode Island.* Providence, 1881, pp. 455–456.

——— *National Cyclopedia of American Biography*, XIII (1906), 285.

Emerson, Haven, ed., *Administrative Medicine.* New York, 1951.

Evans, Alfred S., "Austin Flint and His Contributions to Medicine," *Bulletin of History of Medicine*, XXXII (May–June 1958), 224–241.

Finer, S. E., *The Life and Times of Sir Edwin Chadwick.* London, 1952.

Fisher, Irving, *Report on National Vitality.* Bull. #30, Committee of One Hundred on National Health, National Conservation Commission, Washington, 1909.

Fisher, Ronald A., *The Genetical Theory of Natural Selection.* 2d rev. ed., New York, 1958.

Fleming, Donald, *William H. Welch and the Rise of Modern Medicine.* Boston, 1954.

Flexner, Simon, "Experimental Epidemiology," *Journal of Experimental Medicine*, 36 (1922), 9–14.

——— and James T. Flexner, *William Henry Welch and the Heroic Age of American Medicine.* New York, 1941.

Ford, William W., *Bacteriology.* New York, 1939.

Fosdick, Raymond B., *The Story of the Rockefeller Foundation.* New York, 1952.

Frazer, W. M., A *History of English Public Health, 1834–1939.* London, 1950.

Galdston, Iago, "Humanism and Public Health," *Annals of Medical History,* third series, III (November 1941), 513–523.

———— ed., *Social Medicine.* New York, 1949.

Garrison, Fielding H., "Abraham Jacobi," obituary in *Annals of Medical History,* series I, II (June 1919), 194–205.

———— *John Shaw Billings.* New York, 1915.

Gerhard, William P., "A Half-Century of Sanitation," *The American Architect and Building News,* LXIII (Feb. 25, 1899 and March 4, 1899), 61–63, 67–69.

Gibson, John M., *Physician to the World: The Life of William C. Gorgas.* Durham, North Carolina, 1950.

Gilbert, Bentley B., "The British Government and the Nation's Health, 1890–1952," Ph.D. Thesis, Univ. of Wisconsin, 1954.

Gordon, John E., and Marjorie Hemming, "The Cutter Lectures on Preventive Medicine," *New England Journal of Medicine,* 258 (May 1, 1958), 896–898.

———— and Theodore H. Ingalls, "Contact and Air-Borne Transmission of Infectious Agents," *American Journal of the Medical Sciences,* 233 (March 1957), 334–357.

Gorgas, Marie D., and Burton J. Hendrick, *William Crawford Gorgas.* Garden City, New York, 1924.

Greenwood, Major, *Epidemiology, Historical and Experimental.* Baltimore, 1932.

Halverson, Wilton L., "A Twenty-Five Year Review of the Work of the Committee on Administrative Practice," *AJPHealth,* 35 (December 1945), 1253–1259.

Heaton, Claude Edwin, *A Historical Sketch of New York University College of Medicine, 1841–1941.* New York, 1941.

Hoffman, Frederick L., "The Present Position of Municipal Vital Statistics in the United States," *Transactions,* 15th International Congress on Hygiene and Demography, Washington, 1912, pp. 113–120.

Hofstadter, Richard, *The Age of Reform.* New York, 1955.

———— *Social Darwinism in American Thought.* Rev. ed., Boston, 1955.

Housing Problems in America. Proceedings of the Fifth National Conference on Housing. Providence, 1916.

Howard, W. T., *Public Health Administration and the Natural History of Disease in Baltimore, 1797–1920.* Washington, 1924.

Hume, Edgar Erskine, *Max von Pettenkofer.* New York, 1927.

———— "Sternberg's Centenary, 1838–1938," editorial in *Annals of Medical History*, n.s., X (May 1938), 266–272.

Jackson, James, *Memoir of James Jackson, Jr., M.D.* Boston, 1836.

Jordan, E. O., "The Relations of Bacteriology to the Public Health Movement Since 1872," *AJPHealth*, XI (December 1921), 1042–1047.

———— G. C. Whipple, and C.-E. A. Winslow, *A Pioneer of Public Health: William Thompson Sedgwick*. New Haven, 1924.

Jordan, Philip D., *The People's Health*. St. Paul, 1953.

Kelley, Howard A., *Walter Reed and Yellow Fever*. 3d ed., Baltimore, 1906.

Knopf, S. A., *A History of the National Tuberculosis Association*. New York, 1922.

Koren, John, ed., *History of Statistics*. New York, 1918.

Kramer, Howard D., "Agitation for Public Health Reform in the 1870's," *Journal of History of Medicine*, III (1948), 473–488; IV (1949), 75–89.

———— "The Beginnings of the Public Health Movement in the United States," *Bulletin of History of Medicine*, XX (May–June 1947), 352–376.

———— "Early Municipal and State Boards of Health," *Bulletin of History of Medicine*, XXIV (November–December 1950), 503–529.

———— "The Germ Theory and the Early Public Health Program in the United States," *Bulletin of History of Medicine*, XXII (May–June 1948), 233–247.

———— "History of the Public Health Movement in the United States, 1850–1900," Ph.D. Thesis, State Univ. of Iowa, 1942.

Lampson, Robin, *Death Loses a Pair of Wings*. New York, 1939.

Legge, Thomas Morison, *Public Health in European Capitals*. London, 1896.

"Let Us Stop Guessing in Health Work," editorial in *AJPHealth*, XI (May 1921), 247–249.

Lewis, R. A., *Edwin Chadwick and the Public Health Movement*. London, 1952.

Lewis, Sinclair, *Arrowsmith*. New York, 1925.

Mann, Arthur, *Yankee Reformers in the Urban Age*. Cambridge, Mass., 1954.

Marti-Ibañez, Felix, ed., *History of American Medicine*. New York, 1959.

Metropolitan Life Insurance Company, *An Epoch in Life Insurance*. New York, 1924.

———— *Sixteen Health Heroes*. New York, 1950.

Meyer, Ernst C., "Methods for the Defense of Public Health Appropriations," *AJPHealth*, X (March 1920), 201–209.

Mumford, Lewis, *Sticks and Stones*. 3d rev. ed., New York, 1955.

Mustard, Harry S., *An Introduction to Public Health*. New York, 1935.

Newsholme, Arthur, *Evolution of Preventive Medicine*. London, 1927.

———— *The Story of Modern Preventive Medicine*. Baltimore, 1927.

Next Steps in Public Health, The. Proceedings of the 14th Annual Conference of the Milbank Memorial Fund. New York, 1936.

Norwood, William Frederick, *Medical Education in the United States Before the Civil War*. Philadelphia, 1944.

Oliver, Wade H., *The Man Who Lived for Tomorrow*. New York, 1941.

Osler, William, *An Alabama Student and Other Biographical Essays*. New York, 1909.

Palmberg, Albert, *A Treatise on Public Health*, edited and translated by Arthur Newsholme. London, 1895.

Pearl, Raymond, *Introduction to Medical Biometry and Statistics*. Philadelphia, 1930.

———— "Some Notes on the Contribution of Dr. John Shaw Billings to the Development of Vital Statistics," *Bulletin of Institute of History of Medicine*, VI (May 1938), 387–393.

Prudden, Lillian E., *T. Mitchell Prudden, M.D.* New Haven, 1927.

Ravenel, Mazyck P., ed., *A Half Century of Public Health*. New York, 1921.

"Revival of Shot-Gun Methods in Epidemic Control, A," editorial in *AJPHealth*, VI (September 1916), 932–933.

Richardson, D. L., "Care of Communicable Diseases in General Hospitals," *AJPHealth*, XIX (April 1929), 401–406.

Richmond, Phyllis Allen, "American Attitudes Toward the Germ Theory of Disease, 1860–1880," *Journal of History of Medicine*, IX (October 1954), 428–454.

———— "Some Variant Theories in Opposition to the Germ Theory of Disease," *Journal of History of Medicine*, IX (July 1954), 290–303

Riggs, C. E., *Preventive Medicine at Training Camps and Stations*. Washington, 1919.

Rosen, George, *A History of Public Health*. New York, 1958.

———— "Problems in the Application of Statistical Analysis to Questions of Health: 1700–1880," *Bulletin of History of Medicine*, XXIX (January–February 1955), 27–45.

Sand, René, *The Advance to Social Medicine*. London and New York, 1952.

Scanlon, Dorothy, "The Public Health Movement in Boston, 1870–1910," Ph.D. Thesis, Boston University, 1956.

Schlesinger, Arthur Meier, *The Rise of the City*. Vol. X in *A History of American Life*, A. M. Schlesinger and D. R. Fox, eds. New York, 1933.

Schlesinger, Arthur M., Jr., *The Crisis of the Old Order*. Boston, 1957.

Shryock, Richard H., *American Medical Research*. New York, 1947.

———— *The Development of Modern Medicine*. 2d ed., New York, 1947.

———— *National Tuberculosis Association, 1904–1954*. New York, 1957.

———— "The Origins and Significance of the Public Health Movement in the United States," *Annals of Medical History*, I (1929), 645–665.

———— *The Unique Influence of the Johns Hopkins University on American Medicine*. Copenhagen, 1953.

Sigerist, Henry E., *American Medicine*. New York, 1934.

Smillie, Wilson G., *Public Health: Its Promise for the Future*. New York, 1955.

———— et al., "Lemuel Shattuck—Still a Prophet," *AJPHealth*, 39 (February 1949), 135–162.

Smith, Geddes, *Plague on Us*. New York, 1941.

Solomon, Barbara Miller, *Ancestors and Immigrants*. Cambridge, Mass., 1956.

Steiner, Walter R., "Dr. Pierre-Charles-Alexander Louis, A Distinguished Parisian Teacher of American Medical Students," *Annals of Medical History*, 3d series, II (November 1940), 451–460.

Taylor, Ian, and John Knowelden, *Principles of Epidemiology*. Boston, 1957.

Terris, Milton, "Hermann Biggs' Contribution to the Modern Concept of the Health Center," *Bulletin of History of Medicine*, XX (October 1946), 387–412.

Tobey, James A., *Riders of the Plague*. New York, 1930.

Top, Franklin H., ed., *The History of American Epidemiology*. St. Louis, 1952.

Walker, M. E. M., *Pioneers of Public Health*. New York, 1930.

Walker, William B., "The Health Reform Movement in the United States, 1830–1870," Ph.D. thesis, Johns Hopkins University, 1955.

Whipple, George C., *State Sanitation*, 2 vols., Cambridge, Mass., 1917.

Wilbur, Cressy L., "The Census and the Public Health Movement," *Annals of American Academy of Political and Social Science*, 37 (1911), 286–304.

———— "The Development of Vital Statistics in the United States Since 1900," *Transactions*, 15th International Congress on Hygiene and Demography. Washington, 1912, pp. 11–24.

Willcox, Walter F., et al., "The Past and Future Development of Vital Statistics in the United States," *Journal of American Statistical Association*, XXI, n.s. (September 1926), 257–281.

Williams, Huntington, "The Influence of Edwin Chadwick on American Public Health," *Baltimore Health News*, XXXIII (December 1956), 97–112.

Winslow, Charles-Edward A., "The American Public Health Association," *AJPHealth*, 37 (November 1947), 1467–1476.

———— *The Conquest of Epidemic Disease*. Princeton, 1943.

———— *The Evolution and Significance of the Modern Public Health Campaign*. New Haven, 1923.

———— "A Half-Century of the Massachusetts Public Health Association," *AJPHealth*, 30 (April 1940), 325–335.

———— *The Life of Hermann M. Biggs*. Philadelphia, 1929.

Zinsser, Hans, "Theobald Smith," National Academy of Sciences, *Biographical Memoirs*, XVII, 261–303.

* * * * *

NOTES

ABBREVIATIONS USED IN NOTES

AJHyg.: *American Journal of Hygiene.*
AJPHealth: *American Journal of Public Health and the Nation's Health.*
AJPHyg.: *American Journal of Public Hygiene.*
AM: *American Medicine.*
AMA: American Medical Association.
APHA: American Public Health Association.
BHM: *Bulletin of the History of Medicine,* or its predecessor, *Bulletin of the Institute of the History of Medicine.*
CVC: Charles Value Chapin.
JAMA: *Journal of the American Medical Association.*
JMABH: *Journal of the Massachusetts Association of Boards of Health.*
J. Prev. Med.: *Journal of Preventive Medicine.*
MABH: Massachusetts Association of Boards of Health.
Medical Officer: The Medical Officer (London).
PHR: *Report of the Superintendent of Health of the City of Providence.*
PMA: Providence Medical Association.
PMJ: *Providence Medical Journal.*
RIHS: Rhode Island Historical Society.
RIMJ: *Rhode Island Medical Journal.*
RIMS: Rhode Island Medical Society.
RIMSL: Rhode Island Medical Society Library.
RISBH: Rhode Island State Board of Health.
TRIMS: *Transactions of the Rhode Island Medical Society.*

PROLOGUE

1. The estimates summarized in this paragraph are found in: "Dr. Chapin's Fortieth Anniversary," unsigned editorial in *AJPHealth,* XIV (April 1924), 338; "Charles Value Chapin," unsigned editorial in *AJPHealth,* XXXI (March 1941), 265; "Charles Value Chapin," memorial presented by Haven Emerson et al., *JAMA,* 116 (June 28, 1941), 2870; and C.-E. A. Winslow, review of *The Papers of Charles V. Chapin, M.D.,* in *AJPHealth,*

XXIV (September 1934), 989–990. Winslow's quotation refers to the German Johann Peter Frank, the English reformer Edwin Chadwick, the English administrator John Simon, and the American pioneer Lemuel Shattuck, in addition to Sedgwick and Biggs.

CHAPTER I. THE NEW ENGLAND BACKGROUND

1. Published respectively in Philadelphia in 1842 and 1844.

2. See L. E. Rogers, ed., *The Biographical Cyclopedia of Representative Men of Rhode Island* (Providence, 1881), p. 404; and George Thurber, letter to Joshua B. Chapin, April 29, 1853 (in Chapin Papers, RIHS). Thurber soon turned up in Texas as a botanist working with the Mexican boundary survey commission. See A. Hunter Dupree, *Asa Gray* (Cambridge, Mass., 1959), p. 205.

3. Information on Louise Value Chapin and her parents comes chiefly from three sources: F. F. Sherman, "Newly Discovered American Miniaturists," *Antiques*, 8 (August 1925), 96–99; recollections and files of William Alden Brown of Providence; and J. N. Arnold, *Art and Artists in Rhode Island* (Providence, 1905).

4. CVC, quoted in the *Providence Journal*, December 24, 1922.

5. See Thomas W. Bicknell, ed., *History and Genealogy of the Bicknell Family* (Providence, 1913), p. 311; and Charles Carroll, *Public Education in Rhode Island* (Providence, 1918), pp. 183–185.

6. Rogers, *Representative Men*, p. 404.

7. 1842: "What are the Causes, Character, Nature and Best Mode of Treatment of Asthma?" 1843: "Tenotomy: Its Comparative Advantages and Disadvantages."

8. CVC, "Medical Facts and Theories," *Evening Bulletin* (Providence), March 30, 1918.

9. *Evening Bulletin*, August 20, 1872.

10. CVC, "Cholera, A Vanished Terror," in CVC, "Achievements of Medicine," 56 (unpublished and undated ms. at RIMSL), p. 1.

11. John Hutchins Cady, *The Civic and Architectural Development of Providence* (Providence, 1957), p. 132.

12. CVC, quoted in *Providence Journal*, February 19, 1922.

13. Unpublished mss. at RIHS, Chapin Papers, dated respectively May 9, 1870, February 18, 1870, and December 31, 1869.

14. CVC, "Misrepresentation of Indian Character," unpublished ms. at RIHS, dated June 20, 1872.

15. CVC, quoted by Selig Greenberg, in *Evening Bulletin*, April 4, 1936.

16. See *Liber Brunensis* (Providence, 1876) *passim*.

17. CVC, "Samuel Adams and American Independence" (unpublished ms., 1876, at RIHS).

CHAPTER II. IN PURSUIT OF MEDICAL KNOWLEDGE

1. Donald Fleming, *William H. Welch and the Rise of Modern Medicine* (Boston, 1954), has an excellent discussion of the German creative tradition and of the Bellevue Hospital Medical College while Chapin was there.

2. William H. Welch, letter to CVC, January 27, 1924 (RIMSL, Chapin Scrapbook 17).

3. See, for instance, the editorial in *Medical Record* (New York), March 8, 1879, p. 229.

4. Robert J. Carlisle, ed., *An Account of Bellevue Hospital* (New York, 1893).

5. CVC, 'Typhus, An Almost Forgotten Disease,' "Achievements of Medicine," 25 (RIMSL).

6. CVC, "The Development of Modern Nursing," *Reports of the Trustees and Superintendent of the Butler Hospital* (Providence, January 22, 1913), p. 19.

7. Claude E. Heaton, A *Historical Sketch of New York University College of Medicine, 1841–1941* (New York, 1941), p. 20.

8. CVC, *Sources and Modes of Infection* (New York, 1910), pp. 65, 67. This book had a second edition in 1912 and a revised and enlarged edition in 1916. Unless specifically noted, all subsequent citations will refer to the 1910 edition of the book.

9. CVC, "Medical Facts and Theories," *Providence Journal*, July 26, 1924.

10. CVC, quoted in *TRIMS*, VII, 455. Dr. Alfred Loomis was a celebrated diagnostician connected with the New York University Medical School.

11. Noted by Clarence L. Scamman in his essay, "Charles Value Chapin," in *Papers of Charles V. Chapin, M.D.* (New York, 1934), p. xv.

12. Edward G. Janeway, "Remarks," in *Public Health: Papers and Reports*, V (1880), 48; see also pp. 46–51, *passim*.

13. *Ibid.*, pp. 48–49.

14. CVC, "The Air as a Vehicle of Infection," *The Harvey Lectures, 1913–1914* (New York, 1915), IX, 55.

15. Chapin does not identify this surgeon. For his own accounts of this event see: *ibid.*, p. 55; CVC, 'Our Debt to Lister,' in "Some Achievements of Medicine," 28; a reporter's account in *Providence Journal*, February 13, 1912; and press interview in *Sunday Tribune*, March 17, 1912.

16. CVC to Louise Chapin, August 9, 1880 (Chapin Papers, RIHS).

CHAPTER III. BEGINNING A CAREER: PHYSICIAN, TEACHER, AND HEALTH OFFICER

1. CVC, *The Sympathetic Nerve: Its Relations to Disease* (Providence, 1881). See also, *Boston Medical and Surgical Journal*, May 5, 1881.

2. There follow the dates and titles of Chapin's Fiske Fund prize essays. (No prizes were awarded in several of the interim years.)

1880: "The Sympathetic Nerve: Its Relations to Disease"

1884: "The Origin and Progress of the Malarial Fever now Prevalent in New England"

1885: "The Present State of the Germ Theory of Disease"

1886: "The Methods and Practical Results of Treatment of the Malarial Diseases Now Prevalent in New England"

1888: "What Changes has the Acceptance of the Germ Theory Made in Measures for the Prevention and Treatment of Consumption?"

1889: "The Role of Ptomaines in Infectious Diseases"

1900: "State Control of Tuberculosis"

1909: "The Mode of Infection and Duration of the Infectious Period in Scarlet Fever"

3. See "Medical Practice in Connecticut," editorial in *Monthly Bulletin of RISBH*, IV (May 1892), 81–82.

4. [G. T. Swarts], "History of the Providence Clinical Club," mimeographed paper at RIHS, November 10, 1915, p. 1.

5. "Annual Reports of the Secretary," PMA, 1883–1937 (at RIMSL). See also, Roland Hammond, John E. Donley, and Peter Pineo Chase, "The Providence Medical Association," *History and Centennial Observance of the Providence Medical Association* (Providence, 1948), p. 8.

6. See PMA, Minutes of PMA meetings, May 1880.

7. O. C. Wiggin, remark at meeting of RIMS, September 18, 1884, *TRIMS*, III, 81.

8. *TRIMS*, II, 321, 331.

9. Secretary of the PMA, abstract of CVC's remarks, in minutes of PMA meeting, May 2, 1881.

10. Swarts, "Providence Clinical Club," p. 3.

11. See CVC, "The Persistence of Superstition" (unpublished ms., 1909, at RIMSL). Dr. Frank T. Fulton and Dr. Alexander M. Burgess, Sr., of Providence, both pointed out this shortcoming in Chapin.

12. CVC, "Asheville, N.C.," *Providence Journal*, August 28, 1883.

13. Quoted in Erwin H. Ackerknecht, *Rudolf Virchow* (Madison, 1953), p. 34.

14. CVC, "Education" (unpublished and undated ms., probably about 1890 at RIMSL), p. 19. See also *Providence Journal*, February 8, 1903.

15. CVC, "Education," p. 19.

16. CVC, "Education," p. 31.

17. See CVC, "Latin and Greek," *Providence Journal*, December 8, 1883; CVC, "Hints for Educational Reform" (unpublished ms., n.d., at RIMSL), pp. 2–3; and CVC, "Education," p. 25.

18. CVC, reply to questionnaire on "Desirable Requirements for those Entering Medical Studies," *Bulletin of the American Academy of Medicine*, VII, no. 6 (April 1906), 371.

19. CVC, "Medical Delusions" (unpublished ms., 1887, at RIMSL), p. 30.

20. CVC, "Report," *Annual Report of the President to the Corporation of Brown University, June 21, 1883* (Providence, 1883), p. 32.

21. CVC, "Report," *Annual Report—President of Brown, June 18, 1886*, p. 39.

22. CVC, "Report," *Annual Report—President of Brown, June 20, 1895*, pp. 62–63; and Brown University, *Catalogue*, 1889–90, p. 66.

23. Hermon C. Bumpus, letter to CVC, May 8, 1932 (Chapin Scrapbook 21, RIMSL).

24. See *Rhode Island Medical Science Monthly*, I (May 1893), 264.

25. See Hermon C. Bumpus, Jr., *Hermon Carey Bumpus, Yankee Naturalist* (Minneapolis, 1947).

26. E. O. Jordan, G. C. Whipple, and C.-E. A. Winslow, *A Pioneer of Public Health: William Thompson Sedgwick* (New Haven, 1924), pp. 28–30.

27. William Osler had a more optimistic view on this only a few years later. Speaking to the Rhode Island Medical Society on December 7, 1899, he commented: "The existing conditions are singularly favourable for a small first-class school. Here are college laboratories of physics, chemistry, and biology, and here are well-equipped hospitals with some three hundred beds. What is lacking? Neither zeal, persistence, nor ability on the part of the physicians, but a generous donation to the University of a million of dollars with which to equip and endow laboratories of anatomy, physiology, pathology, and hygiene. These alone are lacking; the preliminary scientific school is here; the clinical school is at your doors; the money should be the least difficult thing to get in this plutocratic town. The day has come for small medical schools in university towns with good clinical facilities." William Osler, "Elisha Bartlett," *An Alabama Student and Other Biographical Essays* (New York, 1909), p. 110.

28. CVC, 'Looking into the Body,' "Achievements of Medicine."

29. A. D. Mead, "Address" to Brown Graduate Convocation, June 17, 1939 (unpublished ms. at John Hay Library), p. 2.

30. CVC, "Report," *Annual Report—President of Brown, June 20, 1895*, p. 63.

31. There is a discussion of this schism and of Chapin's role in it in Donald Fleming, *Science and Technology in Providence, 1764–1914* (Providence, 1952), pp. 46–49.

32. See William Gammell to CVC, January 29, 1924 (Scrapbook 17, RIMSL); also *Providence Journal*, November 25, 1883, and *Providence Star*, November 25, 1883.

33. CVC, "Malaria in Providence," *TRIMS*, II, 372–379; and CVC, "Malaria in Rhode Island," *RISBH, 4th Annual Report, 1881*, pp. 217–229.

34. Chapin never followed up this concern with alcohol in an active way. Yet he was one of many physicians who saw, with the lay reformers, the magnitude of drinking as a social problem and who argued on medical grounds for abstinence. Among the other public health leaders who wrote on this problem were Benjamin Rush, John Shaw Billings, Sir Arthur Newsholme, and Haven Emerson. Chapin's works on the subject include: "Stimulants and Narcotics," Worthington Hooker, *A First Book in Physiology* (New York, 1883), pp. 195–217; and *Alcohol* (Providence, 1884). In 1906 Chapin observed that "although it is well recognized that the abuse of alcohol is an important factor in the causation of sickness and death, American health officers have held aloof from temperance work." CVC, "American Sanitation," *AJPHyg.*, XVI (February 1906), 543.

35. For a fuller discussion of Snow and his career, see James H. Cassedy, "Edwin Miller Snow: An Important American Public Health Pioneer," *BHM*, XXXV, no. 2 (March–April 1961), 156–162.

36. Boston, 1850 (reprinted Cambridge, Mass., 1948).

37. For a convenient short history of bacteriology, see William W. Ford, *Bacteriology* (New York, 1939).

38. F. P. Gorham, "History of Bacteriology and its Contributions to Public Health Work," M. P. Ravenel, ed., *A Half Century of Public Health* (New York, 1921), pp. 66–93.

39. CVC, *The Present State of the Germ Theory of Disease* (Providence, 1885), p. 24.

40. CVC, "The Sanitary Administration of Cities" (unpublished ms., February 8, 1889, at RIMSL), pp. 56–64.

41. From 1856 to 1883 the Providence population jumped from 45,000 to about 117,000. See CVC, *Census of the City of Providence, January 1, 1893* (Providence City Document No. 17, 1893).

42. CVC, "Sanitary Administration of Cities," p. 65.

CHAPTER IV. ENVIRONMENTAL SANITATION

1. CVC, *Second Annual PHR: Year Ending December 31, 1884* (Providence, 1885), p. 21.

2. CVC, "Sanitary Science" (unpublished lecture, 1906, at RIMSL), p. 12.

3. CVC, "The Sewerage of Providence," in PMA, minutes of meeting of December 1, 1884 (unpaged ms. at RIMSL).

4. C. H. Fisher, "Remarks" at APHA meeting, October 1884, reported in *Public Health: Papers and Reports*, X (1885), 404. Throughout Chapin's career, most other Rhode Island communities lagged far behind Providence in their public health work, although Newport and Pawtucket occasionally took some sanitary initiative.

5. *Providence Journal*, April 28, 1885. See also various unidentified clippings in Chapin Scrapbooks A and 1 (at RIMSL).

6. CVC, "Sanitary Administration of Cities," p. 45.

7. *Ibid.*, p. 43.

8. For details of this problem, see *PHR*, 1884–1912.

9. G. T. Swarts, "Statistics of an Investigation of Typhoid Fever," *TRIMS*, III, 152.

10. For Chapin's account of the vault problem, see *PHR*, 1884–1905; see also *Providence Journal*, May 25, 1893 and October 14, 1895.

11. CVC, *PHR*, 1889, pp. 33–34; G. T. Swarts, "Recent Progress in Hygiene," PMA, minutes of meeting, June 4, 1888.

12. CVC, *Municipal Sanitation in the United States* (Providence, 1901), p. 220.

13. See CVC, "Sewer Gas and Plumbing," *Providence Journal*, October 25, 1924; and CVC, *Municipal Sanitation*, p. 252. For Chapin's full discussion of plumbing, see *ibid.*, pp. 250–261; also *PHR*, 1884–1893.

14. The prize essay was entitled, "May the Cause of Typhoid Fever in the Human Species Originate in Animals Other Than Man?" The essay was not published and the manuscript could not be located with other prize manuscripts at the Harvard Medical School Library. There is, however, an incomplete draft at RIMSL.

15. The quotations in this paragraph are from CVC, *The Role of Ptomaines in Infectious Diseases* (Providence, 1889), pp. 64, 69. Chapin also discussed the subject of ptomaines in several other places, including "Recent Progress in Anatomy and Hygiene," a talk to PMA in 1886 (unpublished ms. at RIMSL), and "Ptomaines," a paper given in 1889 to the Providence Clinical Club (unpublished ms. at RIMSL). Also see W. T. Sedgwick, *Principles of Sanitary Science and Public Health* (New York, 1902), p. 59. (This use of the word "ptomaine" bears little if any resemblance to present usage.)

16. For further information upon this experiment, see: CVC, "The Disposal of Garbage in the City of Providence, Rhode Island," *Public Health: Papers and Reports*, XVIII (1892), 259–264; I. M. Simonin, "The Simonin Process for Treatment of Infected Articles," *JMABH*, II, no. 4 (November 1892), 14–18; CVC, *Municipal Sanitation*, pp. 701–714; CVC, *PHR*, 1889, pp. 28–29; CVC, *PHR*, 1902, pp. 11–16.

17. CVC, "The Collection and Disposal of Garbage in Providence, R.I.," *Public Health: Papers and Reports*, XXVIII (1903), 48.

18. RISBH, *14th Annual Report* (1891); see also CVC, quoted in *Sunday Tribune*, March 31, 1907. See also C.-E. A. Winslow and P. Hansen, "Some Statistics of Garbage Disposal for the Larger American Cities in 1902," *Public Health: Papers and Reports*, XXIX (1903), 141; and *Engineering News*, November 5, 1903 and December 10, 1903. Much of Chapin's reputation in this field of sanitation came from his thorough treatment of the subject in ch. XIII of his *Municipal Sanitation in the United States*, pp. 665–764. Chapin, in turn, acknowledged that much of the data in that chapter was furnished him from a report prepared by the sanitary engineer Rudolph Hering for the American Public Health Association but never published. For garbage work in Providence, see *PHR*, 1884–1928.

19. William Budd is remembered for his notable epidemiological studies of typhoid fever in mid-nineteenth-century England, studies which strongly supported, before Koch's discovery of 1876, a germ theory of disease.

20. CVC, *PHR*, 1888, p. 17.

21. Chapin's account of the epidemic is in *PHR*, 1888.

22. The establishment of the Providence laboratory is referred to in CVC, *Municipal Sanitation*, p. 556. Swarts's experiments are described in *PHR* for 1887 and 1888, and in G. T. Swarts, "Purification of Water for Drinking Purposes," *TRIMS*, III.

23. Samuel M. Gray, City Engineer of Providence, was one of the five or six most influential sanitary leaders in Rhode Island during the latter part of the nineteenth century. (The others were Snow, Chapin, and the two Secretaries of the State Board of Health, Charles Fisher and Gardner T. Swarts. George E. Waring, the engineer, also lived during part of this time in Newport.) Gray, after a thorough study of sewerage systems both in Europe and the United States, drew up an excellent pioneering plan for a comprehensive system for Providence, including intercepting sewers to carry sewage out of the city and a disposal plant for its precipitation and clarification. Principally on the basis of this work in Providence, he

acquired a national reputation as a sanitary engineer, and in 1889 President Harrison appointed him one of a commission of three to examine and report on the sewerage of Washington, D.C. RISBH, *Monthly Bulletin*, II (September 1889), 18. Besides his city post, Gray was also a member of the State Board of Health from 1882 to 1912.

24. CVC, "The Filtration of Water," *Medical News*, 66 (January 5, 1895), 13.

25. See A. J. Provost, Jr., "Water Supplies," ed. W. H. Park, *Public Health and Hygiene*, 2d ed., rev. (Philadelphia, 1928), pp. 454, 459; and L. E. A. Fontaine, "Dr. Chapin Sees It Through," *Providence Journal*, November 8, 1931.

26. G. C. Whipple, *Vital Statistics*, 2d ed. (New York, 1923), p. 509.

27. W. T. Sedgwick and J. S. MacNutt, "On the Mills-Reincke Phenomenon and Hazen's Theorem," *Journal of Infectious Diseases*, August 1910, pp. 489–564.

28. CVC, *Sources and Modes of Infection*, 2d rev. ed. (New York, 1916), pp. 329–335.

29. *Sanitary Era*, July 20, 1889.

30. See report of informal discussion at the American Public Health Association meeting, *Public Health: Papers and Reports*, XXI (1895), 161.

31. The account of the Providence water purification problem and experimentation is drawn largely from the *PHR*, 1885 to 1893. See also CVC, "The Purification of Public Water Supplies," *TRIMS*, IV, 514–535; CVC, "The Filtration of Water," pp. 11–14; E. B. Weston, *Report of the Results Obtained with Experimental Filters* (Providence, 1896); Cady, *Development of Providence*, pp. 201, 234; and *Providence News*, January 21, 1896. For a short general account of the development of water purification methods, see George C. Whipple, "Fifty Years of Water Purification," Ravenel, *Half Century of Public Health*, pp. 161–180. See also G. C. Whipple, *State Sanitation* (Cambridge, Mass., 1917), 2 vols., I, 80–87, 136–150; and Wilson G. Smillie, *Public Health: Its Promise for the Future* (New York, 1955), pp. 340–347.

32. CVC, *PHR*, 1915, p. 34.

CHAPTER V. THE OPTIMISTIC VIEW: "STAMPING OUT" INFECTIOUS DISEASES

1. CVC, *PHR*, 1884, p. 4. During the several decades before 1900, the terms "infectious" and "contagious" were used rather more loosely than today. Chapin, for instance, often spoke of "contagious disease" where the usage of the 1960's is usually "communicable disease." Likewise, all of these terms were sometimes used interchangeably with the word "zymotic," although the latter term usually referred to diseases thought to arise *de novo* from dirt, fermenting vegetation, and so on.

2. L. Pasteur, quoted in I. Fisher, *Report on National Vitality* (Washington, 1909), p. 14.

3. CVC, "The Sanitary Administration of Cities," p. 12.

4. This antivaccinationist activity is reviewed in *Providence Journal*,

April 20, 1894 and December 4, 1895, and in the *Boston Sunday Herald,* April 15, 1894.

5. CVC, "If Smallpox Comes," *Providence Journal,* November 22, 1924.

6. *Providence Journal,* July 20, 1902, and CVC, quoted in *Providence Journal,* May 8, 1894.

7. CVC, PHR, 1885, p. 29.

8. For the details of this controversy and of vaccination practice in Providence, see *Boston Medical and Surgical Journal,* December 10, 1885 through February 6, 1886; also, CVC, PHR, 1885, pp. 25–38, and CVC, PHR, 1901, p. 15.

9. Measles got little attention at first because control measures seemed ineffective. Tuberculosis was a vast problem by itself; see Chapter IX.

10. CVC, Comments at meeting of RIMS, March 18, 1886, *TRIMS,* III, 268.

11. Samuel Hopkins Adams, "Guardians of the Public Health," *McClure's Magazine,* XXXI (July 1908), 241–252.

12. See PHR, 1888, pp. 11–13.

13. CVC, *Municipal Sanitation,* p. 542; *Evening Telegram,* March 10, 1889.

14. See various newspaper clippings in Chapin Scrapbook 1 (at RIMSL), including *Evening Telegram,* March 10, 1889, and others for May 8, 1891.

15. George Sternberg, quoted in report of discussion on sulfur fumigation, *Public Health: Papers and Reports,* XV, 285.

16. CVC, "Disinfection in American Cities," *Public Health: Papers and Reports,* XXI, 217–223.

17. Smillie, *Public Health,* p. 367.

18. E. S. Godfrey, "Epidemiology," W. H. Park, *Public Health and Hygiene,* p. 258.

19. The practice of intubation, which was introduced in the late 1880's, had already proved its value in helping serious cases to pull through.

20. RISBH, *Monthly Bulletin,* VI (October–December 1894), 10–12; PHR, 1895, p. 24; PHR, 1896, p. 25.

21. PHR, 1903, p. 32; PHR, 1915, p. 91.

22. See C.-E. A. Winslow, *The Life of Hermann M. Biggs* (Philadelphia, 1929), pp. 91–130; Smillie, *Public Health,* pp. 392–394.

23. CVC, PHR, 1895, p. 14; PHR, 1896, p. 35.

24. For Chapin's account of some of these institutional outbreaks, see PHR, 1899, pp. 22–23; 1900, pp. 25–27.

25. CVC, PHR, 1899, p. 17.

26. Sidney Rider, quoted in *Providence News,* August 23, 1898.

27. CVC, PHR, 1900, p. 27.

28. For further discussion of this organization, see Chapter VI.

29. F. F. Wesbrook to CVC, March 8, 1902 (Chapin mss., John Hay Library).

30. Details of this investigation are found in CVC, "Preliminary Report of the Committee on Diphtheria Bacilli in Well Persons," *JMABH,* XI (January 1901), 1; CVC, "Report on Diphtheria Bacilli in Well Persons," *JMABH,* XII (July 1902), 3; CVC, *Sources and Modes of Infection,* pp.

55–56; and F. P. Denny, R. F. Feemster, and S. C. Prescott, *Fifty Years of Public Health in Massachusetts* (Boston, 1940), pp. 10–12.

31. See, for example, *American Medicine*, September 6, 1902; *Philadelphia Medical Journal*, September 20, 1902; *Medical News* (New York), October 11, 1902; and *Boston Medical and Surgical Journal*, September 4, 1902.

32. See Francis P. Denny to CVC, April 20, 1902 (Chapin mss., John Hay Library).

33. CVC, *Sources and Modes of Infection*, 2d ed., pp. 156–158.

34. CVC, *Sources and Modes of Infection*, pp. 100–101.

35. Except as indicated, this chapter is drawn from *PHR*, 1884 to 1903. See also CVC's account of this phase of his work in *Sources and Modes of Infection*, pp. 91–121.

36. CVC, "The Restriction of Contagious Diseases in Cities," *AM*, X (December 9, 1905), 995.

CHAPTER VI. TOWARD THE MAKING OF AN AUTHORITY

1. George L. Collins, "State Control of Medical Practice," *TRIMS*, IV, 37.

2. CVC, "Presidential Address," reported in PMA, minutes for meeting of March 4, 1895 (at RIMSL).

3. CVC, "Public Hygiene" (unpublished ms., ca. 1903, at RIMSL), pp. 10–11.

4. CVC, "Notes on Medical and Sanitary Science" (unpublished lecture ms., 1914, at RIMSL), pp. 5–6.

5. CVC, "Talk to Nurses" (unpublished ms., May 1907, in Scrapbook 7, RIMSL); and CVC, "Address to Nurses" (unpublished ms., May 8, 1918, Scrapbook 13).

6. Abraham Flexner, *Medical Education in the United States and Canada* (New York, 1910).

7. PMA, report of meeting of January 3, 1910, in *PMJ*, XI, no. 2 (January 1910), 82.

8. CVC, "Edwin Miller Snow, M.D.," *TRIMS*, IV, 96.

9. *The Chronicle* (Brookline, Mass.), November 8, 1902. See also remarks of Samuel H. Durgin, *Public Health: Papers and Reports*, XXV (1899), 493.

10. Related to me by Professor S. C. Prescott of Massachusetts Institute of Technology.

11. See *AJPHealth*, II (May 1912), 357–358.

12. S. H. Durgin to CVC, December 1, 1912 (Scrapbook 11, RIMSL).

13. This section on the Massachusetts Association of Boards of Health is drawn chiefly from the *JMABH* and its successors, *AJPHyg.* and *AJPHealth*, from 1891 to 1915. The pamphlet by Denny, Feemster, and Prescott, *Fifty Years of Public Health*, gives more detail about the Association than is appropriate here. See also C.-E. A. Winslow, "A Half-Century of the Massachusetts Association of Boards of Health," *AJPHealth*, XXX (April 1940), 325–335.

14. The quotations and discussion on these personal aspects of Chapin's

life come chiefly from his paper, "Epicurean Notions" (unpublished ms., March 5, 1897, at RIMSL). See also "A Day's Sail" (unsigned newspaper article by CVC, in Scrapbook A, RIMSL).

15. S. H. Durgin, quoted in *JMABH*, XII, no. 4, 189.

16. W. H. Allen, review in *Journal of Political Economy*, December 1902. See also *Interstate Medical Journal*, July 1901, and *Annals of the American Academy*, December 1901.

17. *Municipal Engineering*, May 1902.

18. C. Wilbur, *Michigan Bulletin of Vital Statistics*, June 1901.

19. *Public Health* (London), January 1902, pp. 255–256. See also *Sanitary Inspector* (Augusta, Ga.), June 1901. This note refers to Albert Palmberg, *A Treatise on Public Health*, ed. and trans. Arthur Newsholme (London, 1895).

20. See S. S. Rider, review in *Book Notes*, XVIII, no. 14 (July 6, 1901), 106.

21. CVC, *Sanitary Legislation in the United States Enacted During the Year 1905* (Providence, 1906); *Sanitary Legislation in . . . 1906* (Providence, 1906). See also RISBH, *28th Annual Report for 1905*; H. B. Hemenway, *Legal Principles of Public Health Administration* (Chicago, 1914); and J. A. Tobey, *Public Health Law* (Baltimore, 1926); CVC, Foreword, Tobey, *Public Health Law*, p. xvii.

22. Dr. Wilson G. Smillie made this observation to me. Other outside observers, however, felt that Chapin's intimate acquaintance with every phase of his Department's work was a prime reason for his achievements (see *Medical Officer*, February 16, 1935).

23. The Mayor of Providence, quoted in *Providence Journal*, October 9, 1896.

24. See R. B. Comstock to CVC, April 13, 1903 (Scrapbook 5, RIMSL).

25. Details and quotations relating to this trip in Europe are from H. M. Chapin, "Travel Diary" (unpublished ms. at John Hay Library).

26. CVC, "Pleasures and Hopes of the Health Officer," *JAMA*, 52 (February 27, 1909), 686–687, reprinted in *Papers of Charles V. Chapin*, pp. 6, 8, 10.

CHAPTER VII. MUNICIPAL CLEANLINESS:
THE PUBLIC HEALTH AND THE PUBLIC COMFORT

1. CVC, *PHR*, 1891, p. 9.

2. Howard A. Kelly, *Walter Reed and Yellow Fever* (New York, 1907), pp. 145–150, provides a vivid account of these experiments.

3. CVC, *Sources and Modes of Infection*, p. 203.

4. CVC, "Dirt, Disease, and the Health Officer," *Public Health: Papers and Reports*, 28 (1902), 296–299, reprinted in *Papers of CVC*, p. 20.

5. CVC, "Letter from Havana," *PMJ*, 3 (May 1902), 103.

6. CVC, "The End of the Filth Theory of Disease," *Popular Science Monthly*, 60 (January 1902), 239.

7. CVC, "Dirt, Disease and the Health Officer," p. 22.

8. CVC, *Sources and Modes of Infection*, p. 28.

9. CVC, "Sanitary Administration of Cities," pp. 28, 29, 37–38.

10. CVC, "Sanitary Inspection," *JMABH*, 12, no. 4 (January 1903), 170–175; and CVC, "Dirt, Disease, and the Health Officer," pp. 20–26.

11. W. T. Sedgwick to CVC, October 26, 1902 (Chapin mss., John Hay Library).

12. J. C. Coffey, quoted in *JMABH*, XII, no. 4, 180.

13. W. T. Sedgwick, quoted in *JMABH*, XII, no. 4, 175–176.

14. W. T. Sedgwick to CVC, October 31, 1902 (Chapin mss., John Hay Library).

15. S. H. Durgin, quoted in *JMABH*, XII, no. 4, p. 189.

16. M. J. Rosenau, *Preventive Medicine and Hygiene*, 1st ed. (New York, 1913).

17. See *Engineering News*, October 12, 1911, for articles by these last three persons on this subject.

18. W. H. Welch, "Considerations Concerning Some External Sources of Infection in their Bearing on Preventive Medicine," in *Papers and Addresses of William H. Welch*, ed. W. C. Burket, 3 vols. (Baltimore, 1920), I, 567. See also, Fleming, *William H. Welch*, p. 141.

19. J. Niven to CVC, October 20, 1908 (Chapin mss., John Hay Library).

20. E. C. Levy, "Present Views of the Importance of Municipal Sanitary Inspection for the Abatement of Nuisances," *AJPHealth*, II (January 1912), 7–13.

21. CVC, "Sanitary Science," p. 9; and CVC, "Dirt, Disease, and the Health Officer," p. 3.

22. CVC, "The Evolution of Preventive Medicine," *JAMA*, 76 (January 22, 1921), 217.

23. CVC, *For a Clean City* (Providence, 1916).

24. *Ibid.*, p. 5; also CVC, reported in *Evening Tribune*, April 2, 1930.

25. CVC, "Nuisance Prevention a Hindrance to Disease Prevention," *AJPHealth*, XIV (January 1924), 1–4.

26. CVC, "The Relative Values of Health Problems," *Proceedings of North Carolina Health Officers Association*, 1920, pp. 31–39.

27. See John Ihlder, *The Houses of Providence* (Providence, 1916).

28. CVC, "Malaria in Providence," *TRIMS*, II, 374; CVC, "Malaria in Rhode Island," *Report* of RISBH, 4 (1881), 217–229; CVC, *The Origin and Progress of the Malarial Fever Now Prevalent in New England* (Providence, 1884); and CVC, *The Methods and Practical Results of Treatment of the Malarial Diseases now Prevalent in New England* (Providence, 1886).

29. In recording this, Chapin acknowledged that the same fact had been observed independently by two Brookline, Mass., physicians (*PHR*, 1901, p. 23).

30. Sedgwick had shown vividly the relation between "dirt, diarrhea and dinner" as made even closer by the presence of swarms of flies, and Chapin himself delighted in quoting Sedgwick's phrase, although he used it in a somewhat different context, to illustrate contact infection. CVC, *Sources and Modes of Infection*, 2d ed., pp. 169–170.

31. CVC, *Sources and Modes of Infection*, pp. 352–354.

32. CVC, PHR, 1909, p. 7.
33. CVC, *Sources and Modes of Infection*, pp. 366, 367; see also pp. 351–365; PHR, 1909, pp. 14–27; and *Boston Transcript*, July 28, 1909.
34. CVC, cited and quoted in the *Morning Herald* (Sydney, Australia), October 23, 1926.
35. CVC, PHR, 1906, p. 30.
36. Quoted by CVC, PHR, 1902, p. 28.
37. For details of quarantine administration in Providence, see PHR, 1884, 1885, 1892, 1893, 1902, 1903, 1911, 1912.
38. CVC, letter to Providence Board of Aldermen, August 4, 1887 (Scrapbook 1, RIMSL).
39. CVC, *Sources and Modes of Infection*, p. 314.
40. CVC, quoted in *Providence Journal*, November 7, 1891.
41. See CVC, *Sources and Modes of Infection*, p. 318; also PHR, 1902, pp. 35–36; 1903, pp. 54–55; 1904, p. 38; and 1905, p. 39.
42. CVC, "The Management of Milk-Borne Outbreaks of Typhoid Fever," *AJPHyg.*, XX (February 1910), 36–37.
43. *Medical Officer*, September 23, 1911.
44. CVC, "Milk Control in Providence, USA," *Medical Officer*, 22 (December 13, 1919), 221–222.

CHAPTER VIII. THE SOURCES AND MODES OF INFECTION

1. This is discussed further in Chapter IX.
2. Winslow, *Life of Biggs*, p. 141.
3. PHR, 1905, p. 7; and *Providence Journal*, September 9, 1907.
4. W. T. Sedgwick, "Investigations of Epidemics of Typhoid Fever," State Board of Health of Mass., *24th Annual Report* (Boston, 1893), pp. 667–742.
5. CVC, PHR, 1903, pp. 107–108.
6. CVC, *Sources and Modes of Infection*, pp. 54, 107.
7. *Ibid.*, pp. 37, 108–109.
8. This is a slightly modified version of the original rules and is the form in which they were issued in the Providence schools in May 1901. See *Sources and Modes of Infection*, pp. 167–168; see also PHR, 1901, pp. 58–61, and 1902, p. 61.
9. See *Atlantic Medical Weekly*, vols. IV to VII, *passim*.
10. CVC, *Sources and Modes of Infection*, p. 166.
11. CVC, PHR, 1903, p. 115.
12. In 1901 every sizable city in the United States except Providence, Washington, and St. Paul made terminal disinfection a compulsory measure. See CVC, *Municipal Sanitation*, p. 550.
13. CVC, PHR, 1903, pp. 112, 111, 16–17. Also, CVC, PHR, 1905, p. 18. He remained willing to disinfect after diphtheria, however, "when the family were willing to wait for the removal of the warning sign until two successive negative cultures could be obtained from every member of the family." This was virtually never.
14. CVC, "The Fetich of Disinfection," *JAMA*, 47 (August 25, 1906), 574–577, reprinted in *Papers of CVC*, pp. 74–75.

15. Quoted in *AM*, XII (October 1906), 1–2. This refers to the Christian Science teachings of Mary Baker Eddy.

16. *Chicago Clinic and Pure Water Journal*, October 1906; see also *Bulletin*, Illinois State Board of Health, October 1906.

17. Noted by CVC, *Evening Tribune*, June 6, 1906.

18. Editorial in *JAMA*, September 22, 1906.

19. Editorial in *AM*, XII (October 1906), 1–2.

20. C.-E. A. Winslow to CVC, June 7, 1906 (Chapin mss., John Hay Library).

21. S. Greenberg, "Dr. Charles V. Chapin," *Evening Bulletin*, April 4, 1936.

22. Noted by H. Emerson, "Charles Value Chapin," *JAMA*, 116 (June 28, 1941), 2870; and in H. W. Hill to CVC, May 14, 1934 (Chapin mss., John Hay Library).

23. CVC, *Sources and Modes of Infection*, pp. 206–207.

24. *Ibid.*, pp. 209–210; and *PHR*, 1909, p. 41.

25. CVC, *Sources and Modes of Infection*, p. 211.

26. CVC, "The Value of Terminal Disinfection," *AJPHealth*, I (January 1911), 32–42.

27. G. W. Goler, "The Proper and Efficient Disinfection of a House," *New York State Journal of Medicine*, January 1917.

28. CVC, "The Disinfection of Schoolrooms—Is it Necessary?," *Transactions* of 4th International Congress on School Hygiene, 4 (1913), 570–575, reprint, p. 5; see also *St. Louis Post-Dispatch*, December 21, 1913.

29. J. T. Ainslie-Walker, "Routine School Disinfection," *JAMA*, September 27, 1913.

30. *New York Times*, December 21, 1913.

31. CVC, "Studies in Air and Contact Infection at the Providence City Hospital," *AJPHealth*, II (March 1912), 135–140, reprinted *Papers of CVC*, p. 97.

32. *Ibid.*

33. H. M. Chapin, "Travel Diary," p. 150.

34. *Ibid.*, pp. 167, 168.

35. See *ibid.* for further details of this European trip.

36. CVC, "Some Sanitary Problems," *TRIMS*, VII, 610–623, reprint, pp. 4–8. See also CVC, *Sources and Modes of Infection*, p. 151.

37. Quoted in *Boston Herald*, September 12, 1910. See also *International Hospital Record*, December 1911, and *Boston Transcript*, August 16, 1911.

38. See Philadelphia Department of Health, *Monthly Bulletin*, VI (August 1921), 124; and N.Y. State Department of Health, *Health News*, December 13, 1926.

39. Richardson wrote a standard text on this subject, *Infectious Diseases and Antiseptic Nursing Technique* (Philadelphia, 1927).

40. H. Jordan, "Treatment of Syphilis at Providence City Hospital," *PMJ*, 17 (July 1916); D. L. Richardson, "The Providence City Hospital," *PMJ*, 14 (November 1913); and *Providence Journal*, February 24, 1935.

41. About half of the cases of scarlet fever and diphtheria in Providence went to the hospital, along with a third of the measles cases, as opposed to

around 90 per cent of all diseases which some English hospitals took in.

42. See *Evening Tribune*, November 15, 1917; CVC, "Contagious Disease Hospitals and the Community," unpublished lecture ms., 1927, at RIMSL; and D. L. Richardson, "Care of Communicable Diseases in General Hospitals," *AJPHealth*, XIX (April 1929), 401–406.

43. First edition, New York, 1910. The phrase is used in C.-E. A. Winslow, *The Conquest of Epidemic Disease* (Princeton, 1944), p. 363.

44. CVC, *Sources and Modes of Infection*, pp. 176, 178–179.

45. *Ibid.*, p. 106.

46. *Ibid.*, p. v. See also CVC, "The Need of Quantitative Methods in Epidemiological Work," *AJPHyg.*, XX (May 1910), 306–310.

47. Charles Harrington, *A Manual of Practical Hygiene* (Philadelphia, 1901); and W. T. Sedgwick, *Principles of Sanitary Science*. See also, G. C. Whipple, review in *The Surveyor* (London), September 23, 1910; A. K. Chalmers to CVC, August 31, 1910 (Chapin Scrapbooks, RIMSL); and A. Newsholme to CVC, September 22, 1910 (Chapin Scrapbooks, RIMSL).

CHAPTER IX. THE NEW PUBLIC HEALTH

1. Winslow, *Life of Biggs*, pp. 85–88, prints the New York circular and relates the details of its issuance. Chapin's circular is printed and discussed in *PHR*, 1889, pp. 6–8

2. CVC, *PHR*, 1887, p. 5.

3. CVC, "Etiology and Prevention of Tuberculosis," *PMJ*, VII, no. 2 (March 1906), 58.

4. See CVC, Review of A. Newsholme's *The Prevention of Tuberculosis* (London, 1908), in *AJPHyg.*, XVIII (November 1908), 488–489; and CVC, "Notes and Reviews," *AJPHealth*, I (July 1911), 512–514.

5. F. T. Fulton, "The Detection and Treatment of Cases of Tuberculosis Among Factory Employees in Providence," *Transactions* of Third Annual Meeting of National Association for the Study and Prevention of Tuberculosis (Washington, 1907); see also, "Circular of the Committee to Enlist the Cooperation of Manufacturers in the Anti-Tuberculosis Campaign," November 25, 1907 (in Scrapbook 7, RIMSL); G. M. Kober, "History of Industrial Hygiene and its Effect on Public Health," Ravenel, *Half Century of Public Health*, p. 396; and Smillie, *Public Health*, p. 438.

6. *Providence Journal*, April 28, 1907.

7. See *PHR*, 1907, 1908, 1909, 1923. Also, J. Perkins, "Fresh Air Schools," *PMJ*, 13 (January 1912), 40; and J. Perkins, "The Providence Fresh Air School," discussion in *Transactions* of Fifth Annual Meeting of the National Association for the Study and Prevention of Tuberculosis (1908).

8. CVC, "The Need of Family Histories for the Study of Tuberculosis," *Transactions* of 6th International Congress on Tuberculosis, 4, part 1 (1908), 381–385.

9. CVC, *Sources and Modes of Infection*, p. 260.

10. "Tuberculosis in Providence," unsigned note in *Journal of the Outdoor Life*, December 1912.

11. C.-E. A. Winslow to CVC, August 25, 1910 (Scrapbook 24, RIMSL).

12. CVC, "The Friedman Cure," *Evening Bulletin*, April 13, 1918.

13. This incident is discussed in *ibid.*; also Hammond, Donley, and Chase, "Providence Medical Association," p. 13; and *PMJ*, 14 (May 1913).

14. CVC, *Municipal Sanitation*, pp. 782–783.

15. *Ibid.*, pp. 782–783; PHR, 1886, pp. 20–45; and PHR, 1896, pp. 83–93.

16. CVC, "Sanitary Administration of Cities," p. 46.

17. PHR, 1904, pp. 13–14.

18. CVC, "State and Municipal Control of Disease," Ravenel, *Half Century of Public Health*, p. 152.

19. *Evening Tribune*, September 19, 1909.

20. Report of the Committee on Medical School Inspection, *PMJ*, XI (1910), 32.

21. CVC, *Medical Inspection of Schools in Providence* (Ansonia, Conn., 1910), p. 13.

22. CVC, PHR, 1910, pp. 38, 39.

23. CVC, "Public Health is Purchaseable," *Providence Journal*, May 7, 1921.

24. CVC, *Medical Inspection of Schools in Providence*, p. 8.

25. J. C. Colton, PHR, 1912, p. 27.

26. PHR, 1891, p. 14.

27. CVC, PHR, 1903, pp. 112–115; and PHR, 1908, pp. 20–22; and PHR, 1910, p. 46. See also, CVC, *Medical Inspection of Schools in Providence*, pp. 9–12.

28. CVC, PHR, 1910; and CVC, "The Disinfection of Schoolrooms— Is it Necessary?"; see also, T. A. Story to Mayor Joseph H. Gainer, April 10, 1913 (Scrapbook 11, RIMSL); and E. O. Jordan, "School Diseases," *JAMA*, February 8, 1913.

29. *St. Louis Post-Dispatch*, December 21, 1913.

30. PHR, 1888, pp. 5, 28.

31. Smillie, *Public Health*, pp. 415–419.

32. Bolduan states that the New York City Health Department distributed such a circular in 1874. C. F. Bolduan, *Over a Century of Health Administration in New York City* (New York, 1916), p. 34.

33. CVC, PHR, 1888, pp. 28–30. A copy of Chapin's first circular, dated July 1, 1885, is found in Scrapbook A, RIMSL. Chapin's advice followed Jacobi closely in most particulars.

34. PHR, 1897, pp. 28–29; and PHR, 1898, p. 11.

35. *Evening Telegram*, March 31, 1897.

36. CVC, "Report of the Committee on Clean Milk for Babies," *PMJ*, VIII (January 1907), 3–6; and *PMJ*, IX (January 1908), 1–4; PHR, 1908, p. 35.

37. CVC, reported in *Providence Journal*, May 2, 1918.

38. Mary S. Gardner, *Public Health Nursing* (New York, 1916).

39. CVC, quoted in *Providence Journal*, May 2, 1918.

40. *Providence Journal*, January 21, 1912.

41. See, for example, *Bulletin Sanitaire*, Conseil d'hygiène de la Province

de Québec, II (May 1902); and Children's Bureau, U.S. Department of Labor, *Baby-Saving Campaigns* (Washington, D.C., 1913), pp. 44, 74–78.

42. CVC, "The Control of Midwifery," *Standards of Child Welfare*, Publication No. 60, Children's Bureau (Washington, D.C., 1919), p. 158.

43. Children's Bureau, *Baby-Saving Campaigns, passim.*

44. C.-E. A. Winslow felt that education of the individual in personal hygiene was the dominant element in the New Public Health. (*The Evolution and Significance of the Modern Public Health Campaign* [New Haven, 1923], p. 53). Welch, on the other hand, felt that the characteristic element was the widening of the public health program, with its recognition of the general physical well-being of people as a new vital concern of organized public health work. (*Public Health* [New Haven, 1925], pp. 47–48). A. W. Hedrich, for some time an editor of *AJPH*, stated that the "dominant note in the new public health is that things do not spread disease as much as persons." (Quoted in "The New Public Health," editorial in *The Ohio Public Health Journal*, June 1917, pp. 257–258.) H. W. Hill saw the New Public Health to be interested primarily in careful supervision of the infected individual and in carrying out where possible what he called "concurrent epidemiology," abolition of the sources of infection. (*The New Public Health, passim.*)

Chapin himself regarded the phenomenon fairly closely to Welch's view, and much more broadly than Hill and Hedrich. He commented that "the new public health concerns itself with all disease," instead of confining itself to a small group of infectious diseases. Moreover, "the guiding idea now," he wrote in 1924, "is to foster health rather than to prevent disease." (CVC, Review of Allan J. McLaughlin, *The Communicable Diseases, How They Spread and How They May be Controlled* [New York, 1923], in *AJPHealth*, XIV [February 1924].) In addition, he pointed out that "one of the features of the 'New Hygiene,' is that it is concerned far more with the individual than it is with the environment. This changed viewpoint has given rise to the saying that 'education is more important than legislation.'" (CVC, "The Sanitary Awakening," *Providence Journal*, October 13, 1917.)

45. CVC, "Saving the Babies," p. 1.

CHAPTER X. THE PEOPLE OF THE CITY: THE VALUE OF VITAL STATISTICS

1. Jacques Bertillon was a long-time head of the Statistical Bureau of Paris. In this position he followed his father, Alphonse Bertillon, who is famous for developing criminal identification by fingerprinting.

2. See C. L. Wilbur to CVC, April 16 and April 30, 1902 (Chapin mss., John Hay Library).

3. See CVC, "The Writing of Health Reports," *JMABH*, XV, no. 4 (November 1905), 441–442.

4. See W. T. Fales, "Vital Statistics," in Haven Emerson, *Administrative Medicine* (New York, 1951), pp. 475–500; also "Cressy L. Wilbur," obituary in *AJPHealth*, XVIII (November 1928), 1401–1402.

5. E. M. Hartwell, quoted in *AJPHyg.*, XVI (February 1906), 538.

6. CVC, "Pleasures and Hopes of the Health Officer," p. 12.

7. CVC, quoted in *Providence Journal*, March 9, 1909.

8. F. S. Crum to CVC, June 4, 1904 (Chapin mss., John Hay Library).

9. CVC, interviewed in *Providence Journal*, March 9, 1909. See also CVC, "The Incidence of the Different Causes of Mortality in Providence During 55 Years, 1856 to 1910," *Proceedings of 2nd Pan-American Scientific Congress* (1916), IX, 403–411; and CVC, "Causes of Deaths in Providence," *AJPHyg.*, XVI (February 1906), 532.

10. CVC, *76th Annual Report of the City Registrar* (Providence, 1930).

11. See CVC, "Causes of Death in Providence," and CVC, "The Incidence of Different Causes of Mortality in Providence." See Chapter XIV for more on the decline of specific communicable diseases.

12. CVC, quoted in *Providence Journal*, December 16, 1907.

13. C. Wilbur, *Michigan Bulletin of Vital Statistics*, June 1901.

14. C. Wilbur, *Michigan Bulletin of Vital Statistics*, May 1903; and George C. Whipple, *Vital Statistics*.

15. See *Medical Officer*, March 29, 1914.

16. Frederick L. Hoffman, "The Present Position of Municipal Vital Statistics in the United States," *Transactions of 15th International Congress on Hygiene and Demography* (1912), pp. 113–120. Hoffman made an even more devastating criticism in 1902. See his article, "The Vital Statistics of the Census of 1900," *Quarterly Publication of the American Statistical Association*, VIII (December 1902).

17. *Quarterly Publication of American Statistical Association*, VIII (March 1903), 287–288; and *Medical Officer*, December 17, 1921.

18. See, for example, John Ellis, *Deterioration of the Puritan Stock* (New York, 1884). An excellent analysis of these matters is Barbara Solomon, *Ancestors and Immigrants* (Cambridge, Mass., 1956).

19. Irving Fisher, *Report on National Vitality* (Washington, D.C., 1909).

20. CVC, "Some Birth Statistics of Providence" (unpublished ms., March 1892, at RIMSL). Francis A. Walker had noted the native birth decline in 1873 (see Solomon, *Ancestors*, p. 71). Billings observed it in 1893 from more extensive statistics. (See Raymond Pearl, "Some Notes on the Contributions of Dr. John Shaw Billings to the Development of Vital Statistics," *BHM*, VI (May 1938), 387–393.

21. CVC, "Vital Statistics" (unpublished ms., 1892, at RIMSL), p. 4.

22. CVC, "Some Birth Statistics of Providence," p. 12.

23. *Providence Journal*, August 29, 1909.

24. CVC, "Rhode Island Towns in the Twelfth Census," *PMJ*, I (October 1901), 51.

25. I. Fisher, *Report on National Vitality*, pp. 117–120.

26. CVC, "The Value of Life" (unpublished ms., 1908, RIMSL).

27. CVC, "The Value of Life."

28. Christopher Easton, Executive Secretary of the Minnesota Association for the Prevention and Relief of Tuberculosis, echoed Chapin's position on this. See C. Easton to CVC, August 18, 1910 (Chapin mss., John Hay Library).

29. CVC, "The Value of Life," pp. 20–32. Also see a similar pub-

lished essay, "The Value of Human Life," *AJPHealth*, III (February 1913), 101–105.

30. I am indebted to Dr. Joseph Smith, Superintendent of Health of Providence, for reminiscences on this matter.

31. CVC, "The Limitation of Births" (unpublished ms., February 1891, RIMSL), pp. 5, 13–14.

32. CVC, "The Family—Biologically Considered" (Series of 12 unpublished lecture mss., 1895, RIMSL); see also, CVC, "Marriage" (unpublished ms., 1895, RIMSL); and CVC, "Recent Progress in Physiology" (unpublished ms., 1891, RIMSL).

33. For the current standing of this great hypothesis, see Ronald A. Fisher, *The Genetical Theory of Natural Selection*, 2d rev. ed. (New York, 1958); also, Donald Fleming, "The Centenary of the *Origin of Species*," *Journal of the History of Ideas*, XX, no. 3 (June–September 1959), 437–446.

34. CVC, "Preventive Medicine and Natural Selection," *Journal of American Social Science Association*, 41 (August 1903), 54–60.

35. CVC to Editor of *AJPHealth*, February 28, 1916, in *AJPHealth*, VI (March 1916), 302. This was not the first time that leading sanitarians had been skeptical of the validity of Pearson's statistics. James Niven of Manchester, for example, expressed to Chapin his doubts as to data used by Pearson in a tuberculosis study (J. Niven to CVC, June 24, 1908, Chapin mss., John Hay Library).

36. See Solomon, *Ancestors*, pp. 145–151.

37. CVC, quoted in *Providence Journal*, April 17, 1912.

38. See CVC, "Whistles and Pigs Tails" (unpublished ms., 1895, RIMSL).

39. CVC, "Sanitation in Providence," p. 325.

40. See CVC, "In Praise of Folly" (unpublished lecture ms., 1907, RIMSL).

CHAPTER XI. THE AMERICAN
PUBLIC HEALTH MOVEMENT COMES OF AGE

1. Quoted in *Evening Bulletin*, August 15, 1912.

2. George Goler to CVC (undated but probably early October 1933, Chapin mss., John Hay Library).

3. C.-E. A. Winslow to CVC, January 3, 1906 (Scrapbook 4, RIMSL).

4. See, for example, R. G. Perkins to CVC, December 22, 1920 (Scrapbook 14, RIMSL); F. N. Hilliard to CVC, November 9, 1915 (Scrapbook 24); and Col. William Stephenson to CVC, March 14, 1913 (Scrapbook 24). Professor E. B. Wilson also noted this in a letter to me.

5. H. W. Hill, *The New Public Health* (New York, 1920), pp. iii, 7, 14, 165.

6. R. G. Perkins to CVC, December 22, 1960 (Scrapbook 14, RIMSL).

7. See, for example, J. Scott MacNutt, *A Manual for Health Officers* (New York, 1915), and Allan J. McLaughlin, *The Communicable Diseases* (New York, 1923). Another important text was the one edited by William H. Park, *Public Health and Hygiene*, 1st ed. (Philadelphia, 1920).

8. See Haven Emerson to CVC, March 8, 1935 (Chapin mss., John Hay Library).

9. See R. M. Atwater to CVC, January 14, 1923 (Scrapbook 24, RIMSL).

10. See, for example, M. W. Pijnappel to CVC, November 8, 1912, April 7, 1913, and November 12, 1913 (all in Scrapbook 11, RIMSL).

11. M. W. Pijnappel to CVC, August 20, 1913 and August 15, 1914 (Scrapbook 24).

12. C. B. Ker, *Infectious Diseases* (London, 1920), p. 3 and preface.

13. C. B. Ker to CVC, June 13, 1921 (Scrapbook 15).

14. See C. F. Bolduan, *Over a Century of Health Administration*, pp. 34–35.

15. Related by Dr. Clarence L. Scamman.

16. See CVC, "The Easiest Way," *Providence Journal*, December 30, 1922. The station was WGY in Schenectady, New York.

17. These and other letters relating to this radio program are in Scrapbook 16, RIMSL.

18. "Medical Facts and Theories," editorial in *RIMJ*, II (May 1918), 79.

19. The owners of the papers in 1927 sent Chapin a check for $2,000 in appreciation for his voluntary services.

20. CVC, quoted in *Evening Bulletin*, April 10, 1914.

21. CVC, "Truth in Publicity," *AJPHealth*, V (June 1915), 501, 502.

22. See G. C. Whipple, "The Public Health Work of Professor Sedgwick," *AJPHealth*, XI (April 1921), 366.

23. CVC, quoted in *New York Evening Post*, April 25, 1918.

24. "Charles Value Chapin," editorial in *AJPHealth*, XXXI (March 1941), 265; and "Dr. Charles Value Chapin," obituary in *RIMJ*, 24 (June 1941), 121.

25. CVC, "The Writing of Health Reports," *JMABH*, XV, no. 4 (November 1905), 440.

26. For Chapin views on reports, see *ibid.*; also MABH, "Report of the Committee on Uniform Health Reports," *AJPHealth*, III (June 1913), 595–631; and "Annual Health Department Reports," *AJPHealth*, XX (January 1930), 34–40.

27. These incidents were related to me by Mr. William Alden Brown of Providence and by the late Professor Murray Horwood of Cambridge.

28. CVC, *How to Avoid Infection*, 1st ed. (Cambridge, Mass., 1917), p. 40. For typical news accounts, see *New York Tribune*, March 27, 1911; *Boston Evening News*, March 27, 1911; *Portsmouth (N.H.) Herald*, March 28, 1911; *Philadelphia Public Ledger*, May 5, 1916; and Baltimore *American*, May 7, 1916.

29. For representative comments, see *Survey*, November 17, 1917; *Des Moines Register-Leader*, May 5, 1917; *Presbyterian Journal* (New Orleans), May 30, 1917; *Hartford Courant*, March 14, 1917; Cleveland *Plain Dealer*, May 13, 1917; and *Medical News*, July 14, 1917.

30. CVC, remarks, quoted in *Public Health: Papers and Reports*, XXV (1900), 490.

31. See Jordan, *Life of Sedgwick*, pp. 56–80, 173–186.

32. W. T. Sedgwick to CVC, October 8, 1910 (Scrapbook 24, RIMSL).

33. W. T. Sedgwick to CVC, April 3, 1913 (Scrapbook 11).

34. See, for example, F. Schneider to CVC, January 27, 1932 (Chapin mss., John Hay Library). Dr. Clare E. Turner also related this to me in a letter.

35. M. J. Rosenau to CVC, April 3, 1913 (Scrapbook 11).

36. J. E. Gordon and M. Hemming, *The Cutter Lectures on Preventive Medicine* (Boston, 1958), pp. 4–5, 11; reprinted from *N.E. Journal of Medicine*, 258 (May 1, 1958), 896–898.

37. See report of the Cutter Lecture in *Boston Herald*, April 3, 1914. Sedgwick eventually conceived of the training of physicians and health officers in terms of his famous "Y Plan." For a discussion of this, see Jordan, *Life of Sedgwick*, pp. 76–79.

38. CVC, quoted in *Boston Journal*, March 21, 1914; also, CVC, "Cutter Lectures on Public Health" (outline mss., 1914, RIMSL), Lecture 1. Chapin's views on the concensus of opinion or "common experience" were subsequently backed by Wade H. Frost. Winslow and many others did not fully agree on this. See W. H. Frost, "Rendering Account in Public Health," *AJPHealth*, XV (May 1925), 394–398, and subsequent pages of discussion of this paper.

39. "Report of the Sub-Committee on Hygiene, Jurisprudence and Medical Economics," Council on Medical Education, AMA, *Report of the Committee of One Hundred on a Standard Curriculum for Medical Colleges*, Sec. 10 (Chicago, 1913).

40. See Fleming, *Life of Welch*, pp. 180–184; and Smillie, *Public Health*, pp. 448–449.

41. D. L. Edsall to CVC, March 20, 1922 (Scrapbook 15, RIMSL).

42. Related to me by Professor E. B. Wilson of Brookline, Mass.

43. W. H. P. Faunce to CVC, January 7, 1914 (Scrapbook 12, RIMSL).

44. F. P. Gorham, "The Old Medical School in Brown University," *PMJ*, XVI (July 1915), 218–227.

45. See Brown University, *Catalogue* from 1917 through 1927. Recollections of this proposed school were supplied to me by Professor J. Walter Wilson and Professor Charles A. Stuart of Brown University, and by Dr. Edgar J. Staff of the R.I. State Department of Health.

46. Related to me by Professor Charles A. Stuart. For another way in which Chapin expressed these values, see the chart, Appendix A.

47. Programs of various of these institutes are found in the Chapin Scrapbooks 14 and 15, at RIMSL.

48. W. L. Fitzpatrick to CVC, August 5, 1919 (Scrapbook 14, RIMSL).

49. *Ibid.*

50. Welch's use was related to me by Dr. Huntington Williams, Commissioner of Health of Baltimore. For Frost's indebtedness, see Frost to CVC, January 27, 1924 (Scrapbook 17).

51. G. W. Goler to CVC, January 31, 1931 (Scrapbook 21).

52. R. T. Legge, "The Relation of Industrial Medicine to Public Health," *AJPHealth*, XI (January 1921), 62.

53. CVC, "The Sanitary Awakening," *Providence Journal*, October 13, 1917. For a summary of the work of the Metropolitan Life Insurance Company, see "Lee K. Frankel," obituary in *AJPHealth*, XXI (September 1931), 1028–1030; and "Welfare Work for Policy Holders," a chapter in the Metropolitan Life Insurance Company's official history, *An Epoch in Life Insurance* (New York, 1924), pp. 204–242.

54. See CVC, "The Framingham Experiment," *Evening Bulletin*, October 5, 1918; also, *Report of the Committee on Appraisal*, C.-E. A. Winslow, chairman (Framingham, Mass., 1919); and CVC to C.-E. A. Winslow, June 27, 1919 (Winslow papers, Yale).

55. CVC, PHR, 1914, p. 49.

56. A Newsholme, "A Discussion of the Coordination of the Public Medical Services," *British Medical Journal*, September 14, 1907; also see CVC, "Municipal Hygiene," *AJPHyg.*, XVII (February 1908), 90.

57. "Hon. Charles V. Chapin, M.D.," editorial in *Wage Earner* (Boston), April 8, 1911.

58. CVC, circular letter dated December 10, 1912 (copy with Chapin mss., RIMSL).

59. CVC, PHR, 1914, p. 51.

60. *Ibid.*, pp. 49–53; and PHR, 1915, pp. 83–85.

61. CVC, "The Relative Values of Public Health Procedures," *JAMA*, LXIX (July 14, 1917), 90–95. See also CVC, "Efficient Medical Service the Chief Health Problem After the War," *Medical Officer*, 20 (November 9, 1918), 162–163.

62. CVC, "Health Insurance" (outline of unpublished lecture ms., April 2, 1917, RIMSL).

63. See M. Terris, "Hermann Biggs' Contribution to the Modern Concept of the Health Center," *BHM*, XX, no. 3 (October 1946), 387–412.

64. CVC, "The Evolution of Preventive Medicine," *JAMA*, 76 (January 22, 1921), 215–222. For further discussions of health insurance, health centers, and medical care programs, see Shryock, *Development of Modern Medicine* (New York, 1947), 2d ed., pp. 381–430; George Rosen, *A History of Public Health* (New York, 1958), pp. 439–478; and B. B. Gilbert, "The British Government and the Nation's Health," unpublished Ph.D. thesis, University of Wisconsin, 1954.

65. W. H. Welch to CVC, November 27, 1920 (Scrapbook 14). Also see W. H. Frost to CVC, December 1920, and H. B. Jacobs to CVC, November 19, 1920 (Scrapbook 14).

66. CVC, "History of State and Municipal Control of Disease," pp. 133–160.

67. The only other persons who received this distinction up to 1916 were: Stephen Smith, Gorgas, Sternberg, Ex-President Taft, Durgin, Wilbur, Henry Holton of Vermont, George Eastman of Rochester, and six foreigners. In the next few years Herbert Hoover, John J. Hurty of Indiana, and Henry P. Walcott were similarly honored.

68. M. P. Ravenel to CVC, January 11, 1923 (Scrapbook 16).

69. CVC, "Germany Yields to America in Sanitation," *Evening Bulletin*, February 2, 1918; see also, CVC, "American Triumphs in Preventive Medicine," reported in *Evening Bulletin*, December 6, 1920.

CHAPTER XII. A WAR AND AN EPIDEMIC

1. Dr. M. W. Pijnappel to CVC, August 15, 1914 (Scrapbook 12, RIMSL).

2. See F. P. Reynolds to CVC, June 1, 1917 (Scrapbook 13); and *Providence Journal*, June 6, 1917.

3. W. C. Gorgas to CVC, March 12, 1917 (Scrapbook 24); John Wiley and Sons to CVC, January 16, 1911 (Scrapbook 24); CVC, "Control of Acute Contagious Diseases" (unpublished lecture outline, undated but probably between 1919 and 1924, at RIMSL); one excellent statement of the thorough acceptance by and direct influence on the military services of Chapin and his work is C. E. Riggs, *Preventive Medicine at Training Camps and Stations* (Washington, 1919), reprinted from *U.S. Naval Medical Bulletin*, vol. 13, no. 3 (1919).

4. Henry P. Davison to CVC, June 19, 1917 (Scrapbook 13).

5. See CVC, "Hogs, Health and Howitzers," *Providence Journal*, October 27, 1917; CVC, "Pork Barrels from Garbage Cans," unsigned article in *Municipal Facts* (May 1918), pp. 13–14; and CVC, "Disposal of Garbage by Hog Feeding," *AJPHealth*, VIII (March 1918), 234–235.

6. W. C. Gorgas to CVC, December 20, 1917 (Scrapbook 13).

7. Col. Leonard P. Ayres to CVC, October 30, 1918 (Scrapbook 13).

8. See CVC, "The Prevention of Disease in the Army," *Evening Bulletin*, June 21, 1919.

9. CVC, "The Prevention of Venereal Disease" (unpublished lecture ms., March 7, 1894, RIMSL).

10. See RISBH, *Biennial Report for 1918–1919*, pp. 35–45.

11. See accounts in Geddes Smith, *Plague on Us* (New York, 1941), pp. 25–31; and James Doull, "The Bacteriological Age," in F. Top, ed., *The History of American Epidemiology* (St. Louis, 1952), pp. 84–86.

12. CVC, "Influenza," *Evening Bulletin*, September 28, 1918; and CVC, "Former Outbreaks of Influenza," *Providence Journal*, February 14, 1920.

13. *Providence Journal*, January 6, 1916; also M. J. Rosenau, F. X. Mahoney, J. C. Coffey, and CVC, "Influenza and Pneumonia," *AJPHealth*, VI (April 1916), 307–322.

14. CVC, "Influenza."

15. Related to me by Dr. Hilary Connor, Superintendent of the Chapin Hospital.

16. CVC, "Serums and Their Uses," *Providence Journal*, October 26, 1918.

17. CVC, "What Have We Learned from Influenza?," *Providence Journal*, February 11, 1922; CVC, "A Bad General," editorial in *AJPHealth*, IX (October 1919), 785; CVC, "Will Influenza Return this Winter?," *Providence Journal*, January 1, 1921; *New York Tribune*, October 12, 1918; and *New York Sun*, October 31, 1918.

18. B. U. Richards, "The Epidemic and the Profiteer," RISBH, *Bulletin*, IV, no. 4 (November 1918), 5, 6; "Advertising of Disinfectants," unsigned editorial in *AJPHealth*, X (April 1920), 357; and CVC, quoted in *Evening Tribune*, October 9, 1918.

19. Except where otherwise noted, the factual information on the local aspects of the influenza epidemic has been drawn from Providence newspapers for the period. For more on the national discussions, see *AJPHealth*, vols. VIII, IX, X. Additional writings by Chapin which bear upon the subject include: "Pneumonia" (unpublished lecture ms., 1895, RIMSL); "Treatment of Influenza with Human Serum," *Evening Bulletin*, March 15, 1919; "Influenza" (unpublished outline of lecture ms., 1922, RIMSL); and "Pneumonia" (unpublished outline of lecture ms., 1922, RIMSL). For more on the epidemic and subsequent influenza research, see F. Burnet, *Viruses and Man* (London, 1953), pp. 103–120.

20. Quoted by CVC, "The Prevention of Disease in the Army," *Evening Bulletin*, June 21, 1919. Chapin does not identify his correspondent.

21. Referred to by CVC in two unpublished lecture mss., both entitled "Principles of Contagious Disease Control," dated 1921 and 1922, at RIMSL.

22. CVC, "The Prevention of Disease in the Army."

23. CVC, quoted in *Providence Journal*, November 12, 1919.

24. CVC to C.-E. A. Winslow, February 19, 1920 (Winslow papers, Yale).

25. After the ceremonial of the receiving line, the Queen reportedly made a special point of summoning Chapin back to discuss public health matters with her. (This incident was related first by Howard M. Chapin to Mrs. Donald Cowell and subsequently was passed on to me by her. See also, *New York Post*, October 27, 1919.)

CHAPTER XIII. NEW FORMS FOR OLD TECHNIQUES: PUBLIC HEALTH APPRAISAL AND EPIDEMIOLOGY

1. J. S. Billings, "Report of Committee on the Plan for a Systematic Sanitary Survey of the United States," *Public Health: Papers and Reports*, II (1875), 44.

2. Henry B. Favill, remarks reported in *JAMA*, LXI (1913), 20. The Association's Council on Health and Public Instruction, which made the selection, was composed of Henry B. Favill, Walter B. Cannon, Henry M. Bracken, William C. Woodward, and Frederick R. Green.

3. CVC to Governor Eugene N. Foss, June 1911 (copy of typed ms. at RIHS).

4. CVC, "Justifiable Measures for the Prevention of the Spread of Infectious Diseases," N.J. State Board of Health, *Circular*, 119 (July 1907), 5–11.

5. CVC, quoted in *Boston Herald*, April 3, 1914.

6. Unless otherwise indicated, the facts and quotations of the last several pages are taken from CVC, A *Report on State Public Health Work* (Chicago, 1916).

7. The five highest-ranking states, in order, were: Massachusetts, New York, Pennsylvania, Minnesota, and New Jersey. The lowest-ranking states, in reverse order, were: New Mexico, Wyoming, Arizona, Nebraska, and Arkansas.

8. Related to me by Dr. Wilson G. Smillie.

9. W. A. Evans, "Ratings of State Boards of Health," *Public Health* (Bulletin of Michigan State Board of Health), October 1916.

10. Report of Council on Health and Public Instruction, *JAMA*, LXVI, no. 25 (June 17, 1916), 1947–1948.

11. C.-E. A. Winslow, review in *AJPHealth*, VI (March 1916), 284, 286.

12. *The Herald of the Well Country* (Bulletin of New Mexico Public Health Association), 4 (November 1918); and 5 (March 1919). See also *JAMA*, March 22, 1919, and CVC to Governor O. A. Larrazola, February 14, 1919 (Scrapbook 14, RIMSL).

13. CVC, "The Standardization of State Public Health Organizations" (unpublished lecture ms., March 4, 1920, RIHS).

14. For details see Winslow, *Life of Biggs, passim.*

15. CVC, "A State Board of Health," *The Rhode Island Elephant*, April 1926, pp. 4–5.

16. *Ibid.*

17. CVC, "Effective Lines of Health Work," *PMJ*, XVII (January 1916), 12–22. See Chart, Appendix A.

18. See F. Schneider, Jr., "Relative Values in Public Health Work," *AJPHealth*, VI (September 1916), 916–925; E. C. Meyer, "Methods for the Defence of Public Health Appropriations," *AJPHealth*, X (March 1920), 201–209; M. P. Horwood, *Public Health Surveys* (New York, 1921); and G. T. Palmer, "The Evaluation of Community Health Programs," in H. Emerson, *Administrative Medicine* (New York, 1951).

19. *Report of the Committee on Municipal Health Department Practice*, United States Public Health Service Bulletin, 136 (Washington, 1923).

20. Among these leaders were W. S. Rankin of North Carolina; A. L. Bishop of Tennessee; Henry F. Vaughan, long-time Health Officer of Detroit; and Carl E. Buck, long-time Field Director for the Committee. For more on the work of this committee, see C.-E. A. Winslow, "The American Public Health Association," editorial in *AJPHealth*, 37 (November 1947), pp. 1467–1476; W. L. Halverson, "A Twenty-Five Year Review of the Work of the Committee on Administrative Practice," *AJPHealth*, 35 (December 1945), 1253–1259; A. W. Freeman, *A Study of Rural Public Health Service* (New York, 1933); I. V. Hiscock, *Community Health Organization*, 1st and 2d eds. (New York, 1927, 1932). I am also indebted to Dr. Louis I. Dublin for his personal observations on the importance of the Committee on Administrative Practice and of the leading role which Chapin played in it.

21. C.-E. A. Winslow to CVC, June 15, 1931 (Winslow papers, Yale).

22. The appraisal score was 817.2 out of a possible 1,000. James Wallace, *Providence Health Survey* (Providence 1930); also see H. F. Vaughan, "Providence, R.I. Survey," *AJPHealth*, XX (July 1930), 769–770. In 1927, under an earlier score sheet, Providence rated 851.6 (PHR, 1927).

23. "The Appraisal of Health Work," editorial in *Medical Officer*,

February 28, 1931; and "Appraisal of Public Health Administration," editorial in *Medical Officer*, August 23, 1930.

24. "American Health Administration," editorial in *Medical Officer*, October 17, 1925, p. 170.

25. "Dr. Chapin's Annual Report," editorial in *Medical Officer*, November 6, 1926.

26. Epidemiology is usually defined as being the science of the study of epidemic diseases. Useful background discussion for this chapter may be found in *The History of American Epidemiology*, ed. F. H. Top (St. Louis, 1952).

27. Major Greenwood, *Epidemiology, Historical and Experimental* (Baltimore, 1932), p. 19.

28. W. H. Frost, "The Importance of Epidemiology as a Function of Health Departments," *AJPHealth*, XIII (January 1923), 36.

29. In his service upon the Minnesota Board, Hill had been the first specifically designated American epidemiologist. Chapin for a long time considered Chesley, who succeeded Hill in this Minnesota post, to be "America's best epidemiologist." (Quoted by Mrs. Chesley in a letter to me.) By the middle 1920's, however, Chesley had graduated from low-paying epidemiology to largely administrative work, so Frost took over this distinction.

30. See, for example, J. A. Doull, "Factors Influencing Selective Distribution in Diphtheria," *Journal of Preventive Medicine*, 4 (September 1930), 371–404; and I. M. Stevens, "An Analysis of 3,122 Diphtheria Case Histories," *AJHyg.*, XIII (March 1931), 392–414.

31. W. H. Frost, "The Familial Aggregation of Infectious Diseases," in K. F. Maxcy, ed., *Papers of Wade Hampton Frost, M.D.* (New York, 1941), p. 544.

32. See A. S. Pope, "Studies on the Epidemiology of Scarlet Fever," *AJHyg.*, VI (May 1926), 389–430. See also the work by E. B. Wilson, Constance Bennett, Margaret Allen, and Jane Worcester, "Measles and Scarlet Fever in Providence, R.I., 1929–1934, With Respect to Age and Size of Family," *Proceedings of American Philosophical Society*, 80, no. 3 (February 1939), 357–476.

33. CVC, "Measles in Providence, R.I., 1858–1923," *AJHyg.*, V (September 1925), 635–655.

34. Chapin's observations in this study with respect to cancer were the first American epidemiological considerations of this disease along economic lines. See R. S. Taylor, L. S. Snegireff, and J. E. Gordon, "Cervical Cancer as a Mass Disease," *American Journal of the Medical Sciences*, 229 (March 1955), 319; and see CVC, "Deaths Among Taxpayers and Non-Taxpayers, Income Tax, Providence, 1865," *AJPHealth*, XIV (August 1924), 651.

35. CVC, "Variation in Type of Infectious Disease as Shown by the History of Smallpox in the United States, 1895–1912," *Journal of the Infectious Diseases*, XIII (September 1913), 171–196.

36. CVC to C. O. Stallybrass, April 2 and May 2, 1912; and Stallybrass to CVC, April 18, 1912 (Chapin mss., John Hay Library).

37. A. Netter to CVC, October 1925 and November 1925 (Chapin mss., John Hay Library).

38. CVC, "What Price Smallpox?" and CVC, "Good Citizenship Will Stamp Out Smallpox," Press Releases 8 and 9 in series against smallpox issued by Conference of State and Provincial Health Authorities of North America, 1926.

39. CVC, "What Price Smallpox?," p. 1.

40. CVC to Winslow, April 22, 1922 (Winslow papers, Yale).

41. Related to me by Professor Charles A. Stuart.

42. Among those was the Englishman S. W. Goodall. See Goodall to CVC, December 26, 1926 (Chapin mss., John Hay Library).

43. CVC, "Changes in Type of Contagious Disease, With Special Reference to Smallpox and Scarlet Fever," *J. Prev. Med.*, I (September 1926), 1–29. For a concise summary of the latest views on these phenomena, see F. M. Burnet, *Viruses and Man* (London, 1955), pp. 69–70, 193–195.

44. C. C. Pierce to CVC, December 7, 1926 (Scrapbook 24).

45. W. H. Frost to CVC, November 5, 1926 (Scrapbook 24).

46. Review in *Medical Officer*, January 1927.

47. CVC and Joseph Smith, "Permanency of the Mild Type of Smallpox," *J. Prev. Med.*, VI (July 1932), 273–320; A. W. Downie and A. Macdonald, "Smallpox and Related Virus Infections in Man," *British Medical Bulletin*, 9, no. 3 (1953), 191–195; "Does Smallpox Breed True?" editorial in *Journal of Public Health* (England), December 1932; and A. S. Pope to CVC, November 12, 1932 (Scrapbook 21).

48. "The Conference of Epidemiologists," unsigned report in *AJPHealth*, XVII (August 1927), 777–782.

49. For more on this Conference, see *Providence Journal*, May 11, 1927; *Evening Tribune*, May 16, 1927; and Edward S. Godfrey, Jr., "As I Recall It," unpublished paper, presented to American Epidemiological Society, April 4, 1952 (loaned to me by Dr. Phillip Sartwell).

50. See Haven Emerson, "The Story of the American Epidemiological Society," unpublished paper, April 13, 1951 (loaned to me by Dr. Phillip Sartwell).

51. CVC, "The Science of Epidemic Diseases," *Scientific Monthly*, 26 (June 1928), 490.

52. Pointed out to me by Dr. Arthur Ruggles, former Superintendent of the Butler Hospital, Providence.

53. CVC, "The Science of Epidemic Diseases," pp. 491–492. See also, CVC, review of A. Newsholme, *The Elements of Vital Statistics*, 3d ed. (New York, 1923), in *AJPHealth*, XIV (May 1924).

CHAPTER XIV. HYGEIA: ILLUSION AND REALITY

1. See B. W. Richardson, *Hygeia*, p. 17.

2. CVC, "The Problems of the Health Officer," p. 322.

3. CVC, quoted in *Providence News*, December 2, 1927.

4. CVC, quoted in *Evening Tribune*, December 8, 1926.

5. CVC, quoted in *Evening Bulletin*, August 21, 1927.

6. In 1924 Chapin noted nine different types of clinics in Providence besides those for general medical care: baby, heart, polio, mental, dental, eye, diabetes, obstetrical, and tonsil, and new clinics were being founded every year. See CVC, "The Relations of Hospitals to Public Health" (unpublished ms., May 21, 1924, RIMSL).

7. CVC, "The Problems of the Health Officer," pp. 322–325.

8. CVC, reported in *Providence News*, December 12, 1923.

9. CVC, "The Filth Theory" (unpublished ms., March 20, 1923, RIMSL).

10. *Providence Journal*, August 8, 1926.

11. CVC, PHR, 1916–1922, p. 19; see also W. L. Chapman, "Pro Bono Publico," *RIMJ*, VI (December 1923).

12. René Sand has reported that in many cities by 1952, "the health services have turned over to local cleansing departments the collection of household rubbish, street-cleaning and elimination of refuse and 'effluvia,' no longer regarded as the source of disease." R. Sand, *The Advance to Social Medicine* (London, 1952), p. 279.

13. Part of this paragraph is based upon an editorial in *Medical Officer*, February 16, 1935.

14. See the argument of Iago Galdston, "Humanism and Public Health," *Annals of Medical History*, 3d series, III (November 1941), 513–523.

15. CVC, "Disinfection in American Cities," *Medical Officer*, 30 (November 17, 1923), 232–233; also, "Terminal Disinfection," editorial in *AJPHealth*, XVII (September 1928), 1132–1134.

16. Carlos Chagas, *Remarques Sur la Valeur de la Désinfection Terminale*, C. H. 363, Société des Nations, Organisation d'Hygiène (Génève, 1925).

17. Quoted by F. M. Read to CVC, March 25, 1926 (Scrapbook 18, RIMSL).

18. CVC, "Disinfection in American Cities," p. 233.

19. CVC, "Isolation, Its Value and Limitations," *Public Health Journal* (Toronto), 13 (January 1922), 1–9.

20. CVC, "Principles of Contagious Disease Control" (unpublished ms., 1922, RIMSL). See also, CVC, "A Bad General."

21. A. G. Love and C. B. Davenport, *Defects Found in Drafted Men* (Washington, D.C., 1920).

22. See CVC to C.-E. A. Winslow, January 26, February 7, 16, and 19, 1920; also, Winslow to CVC, February 5, 10, and 17, 1920 (Winslow papers, Yale).

23. The only previous experiments along this line were those by Herman in New York in 1915, Nicolle in Paris in 1916, and Park and Zingher in New York in 1916. Herman's limited and inconclusive experiment was the only one that had been published when Chapin made his suggestions, and the Providence investigators were not aware of the other experiments. See D. L. Richardson and H. Connor, "Immunization Against Measles," *JAMA*, 72 (April 12, 1919), 1046–1048; H. P. B. Jordan, "Measles Immunization," *RIMJ*, IX (May 1926); Richardson and Jordan, "Measles Immunization," *AJPHealth*, XVII (June 1927), 607–613;

W. W. Oliver, *The Man Who Lived for Tomorrow* (New York, 1941);
and *PHR*, 1926, pp. 35–37.

24. This was related to me by Professor Charles A. Stuart.

25. *Providence Journal*, August 28, 1931.

26. See *Providence Journal*, October 2, 12, and 19, 1924.

27. CVC, quoted in *Providence Journal*, January 4, 1931.

28. See Appendix B, Chart of the Decline in the Ordinary Communicable Diseases in Providence. The crude death rate of Providence dropped from 22.16 per thousand in 1856 to 20.18 in 1883 and to 12.88 in 1930. (Figures furnished by Superintendent of Health of Providence.)

29. Spokane (population 109,000) had no typhoid fever deaths in 1919 (*Providence Journal*, January 3, 1923). Also see *PHR*, 1916–1922, pp. 41–42.

30. CVC, *PHR*, 1925, p. 11.

31. For Rhode Island tuberculosis work of the 1920's, see CVC, "Tuberculosis" (unpublished ms., undated but probably ca. 1920, RIMSL). See also CVC to Winslow, February 19, 1920 (Winslow papers, Yale); and Winslow, *The Tuberculosis Problem in Rhode Island* (Providence, 1920).

32. CVC, 'Why Tuberculosis Has Decreased,' "Achievements of Medicine," 20 (RIMSL).

33. CVC, "Foreword," in Tobey, *Public Health Law*, p. xvii.

34. CVC, "Science of Epidemic Diseases," p. 493; CVC, "Science and Public Health," p. 1115.

35. For a critical view of the ideal of perfect health in the light of modern knowledge, see René Dubos, *Mirage of Health* (New York, 1959); and R. Dubos, "Medical Utopias," *Daedalus* (Summer 1959), pp. 410–424.

CHAPTER XV. HONORS AND RETIREMENT

1. CVC, "Changes in Type of Contagious Disease," p. 5.

2. CVC, quoted in "Tributes to Dr. Biggs from Some of his Colleagues," *Health News* (Bulletin of N.Y. State Department of Health), 38 (July 1923), 178–179.

3. See H. Emerson, "The Story of the American Epidemiological Society," pp. 1–7.

4. G. A. Blumer, quoted in *Providence Journal*, January 29, 1924.

5. The previous three quotations are from *Providence Journal*, January 29, 1924.

6. C.-E. A. Winslow to F. P. Gorham, January 29, 1924 (Scrapbook 17). Winslow did just this in his book, *The Conquest of Epidemic Disease* (Princeton, 1943), ch. XVIII.

7. A. Newsholme to F. P. Gorham, February 2, 1924 (Scrapbook 17). See also A. Newsholme, "The Fever Chart of Progress," *Survey Graphic*, VIII, no. 2 (November 1925), 28.

8. W. H. Welch to D. L. Richardson, January 22, 1924; and Welch to CVC, January 27, 1924 (Scrapbook 17).

9. L. Frankel to Richardson, January 25, 1924; G. Goler to Richardson,

January 16, 1924; A. J. Chesley to C. Scamman, January 15, 1924; H. Emerson to Richardson, January 20, 1924; H. W. Hill to Gorham, January 21, 1924; and H. P. Walcott to Scamman, February 2, 1924 (all in Scrapbook 17, RIMSL).

10. W. H. Frost to CVC, January 27, 1924 (Scrapbook 17). Frost evidently refers here to Dr. Henry R. Carter, the teacher and investigator of yellow fever.

11. H. DeWolf, "Address by the President," *RIMJ*, IX (July 1926).

12. See CVC, "Health of the Family" (unpublished outline of lecture ms., 1926, RIMSL); and CVC, "Brown University and the Health of the Community" (unpublished lecture ms., November 11, 1926, Chapin mss., John Hay Library).

13. CVC, H. DeWolf, and J. Peters, "Obituary of Dr. James H. Davenport," *RIMJ*, XII (March 1929), 45–46.

14. G. E. Vincent, "Address," *RIMJ*, X (March 1927), 4, 33–47 *passim.*

15. M. Kacprzak to CVC, April 22, 1927 (Scrapbook 17); and M. Kacprzak to CVC, June 22, 1925 (Chapin mss., John Hay Library).

16. See "A Providence Health School," editorial in *Providence Journal*, May 27, 1926. See also Clifford Wells to CVC, May 7, 1924 (Chapin mss., John Hay Library), and various items in the Providence papers of the period.

17. See the comments of Donald Fleming, *Science and Technology in Providence*, pp. 44–46.

18. W. A. Macdonald, "League of Nations Lauds Rhode Island Man," *Boston Evening Transcript*, December 2, 1925. "New President," editorial in *AJPHealth*, XVI (November 1926), 1127–1128; and incident related to me by Dr. Edgar J. Staff of the Rhode Island State Board of Health and other former associates.

19. CVC and Anna Augusta Chapin, *A History of Rhode Island Ferries, 1643–1923* (Providence, 1925).

20. See CVC, "Of What Use Are Our Health Officials?," editorial in *AJPHealth*, XVIII (March 1928), 342–346.

21. The only previous recipients of this award since its establishment in 1913 were William C. Gorgas, George W. Goethels, Herbert Hoover, Gifford Pinchot, Charles W. Stiles, Samuel W. Stratton, and Cleveland Abbe.

22. H. S. Cumming, quoted in *Providence Journal*, April 16, 1930.

23. "An Unusual Record," editorial in *The American City*, March 1929.

24. H. DeWolf to CVC, November 3, 1931 (Scrapbook 21). See also, "Concerning Dr. Chapin," editorial in *RIMJ*, XIV (December 1931).

25. CVC to C.-E. A. Winslow, November 18, 1932 (Winslow papers, Yale).

26. CVC to A. T. McCormack, January 2, 1932 (Chapin mss., John Hay Library).

27. CVC to H. D. Glaisher, April 14, 1932 (Chapin mss., John Hay Library).

28. CVC to G. Goler, October 14, 1933 (Chapin mss., John Hay Library).

29. C.-E. A. Winslow to CVC, December 24, 1930 (Scrapbook 18).

30. *Providence Journal*, December 7, 1930.

31. CVC, quoted in *Providence Journal*, January 18, 1938.

32. CVC to Winslow, December 31, 1931 (Winslow papers, Yale).

33. These few included, between 1900 and 1945, only Billings, Biggs, and Gorgas.

34. A. Newsholme to CVC, September 18, 1935 (at RIMSL, pasted inside the cover of Chapin's copy of Newsholme's *Fifty Years in Public Health*, London, 1935).

35. H. Emerson to CVC, April 16, 1935 (Chapin mss., John Hay Library).

36. Related by Dr. Alton S. Pope in a letter to me.

37. Wells's experiments showed that the smaller viruses *could* carry a good deal further through the air than the average arm's length that bacterial infection carried in droplet spray. They also indicated that these particles could remain suspended in the air for far longer periods than had been thought possible. By the 1940's, public health leaders generally were substantially convinced that these experiments were conclusive and that their acceptance required certain changes in that part of Chapin's work which dealt with air transmission of disease. Continued experiment, however, although it confirmed the theoretical possibilities revealed by Wells and others, failed to show on a quantitative basis that there was much more risk from this form of infection than Chapin had believed. In any event, as Langmuir has pointed out, the pendulum of scientific belief, which after 1935 swung away from Chapin, by 1955 had returned to a point that was far closer to Chapin's view of 1910 than to Wells's view. See C.-E. A. Winslow, *Conquest of Epidemic Disease*, pp. 376–380; W. F. Wells, "Air-Borne Infection," *JAMA*, 107 (1936), 1698–1703, 1805–1809; A. D. Langmuir, "Air-Borne Infection," in K. F. Maxcy, ed., *Rosenau: Preventive Medicine and Public Health*, 8th ed. (New York, 1956), pp. 152–167; and J. E. Gordon and T. H. Ingalls, "Contact and Air Transmission of Infectious Agents," *American Journal of Medical Sciences*, 223 (March 1957), 334–357.

38. Of the names cited here but not referred to previously, Kenneth Maxcy, L. S. Reed, and Abel Wolman were or are all long associated with the Johns Hopkins School of Hygiene and Public Health.

EPILOGUE

1. René Dubos, "Medical Utopias," pp. 418–424.

2. CVC, "Science and Public Health," p. 1115.

INDEX

Abbe, Cleveland, 290
Abbott, Alexander C., 166
Abbott, Samuel, 75, 85, 86
Adams, Samuel Hopkins, 166
Addams, Jane, 140
Adenoids, 133, 134
Adulteration. *See* Drugs; Food
Agassiz, Louis, 13
Ainslie-Walker, J. T., 117
Air, 44, 138, 214; and diseases, 63, 111; fresh air campaign, 129, 222; CVC and, 206
Air infection, 22, 118–121, 159, 236, 291(n.37)
Alabama, 196
Alcohol, 37, 47, 214, 265
Alpha Delta Phi, 12
American Academy of Arts and Sciences, 235
American Academy of Medicine, 140
American Association for Labor Legislators, 175
American Association for the Study and Prevention of Infant Mortality, 141
American Child Health Association, 203
American Epidemiological Society, 211, 235, 236
American Hospital Association, 121
American Journal of Public Health, 86, 87, 199

American Medical Association, 81, 115, 169, 173, 195–200
American Medicine, 116
American Public Health Association, 38, 59, 67, 84, 179, 191; leaders of, 83, 164, 235, 282(n.67); CVC and, 83–84, 179–180, 226, 230–231; committees of, 84, 144–145, 147, 191, 202–203, 232, 233; manual on *The Control of Communicable Diseases*, 160; Epidemiological Section, 211; Report on the Costs of Medical Care, 234; and garbage disposal, 237(n.18)
American Society for the Control of Cancer, 174
Anatomy, 28, 35
Ancestors, 5, 120, 156
Andover Seminary, 6
Andral, Gabriel, 6
Aneurism, 20
Animal diseases, 39, 49–50, 52, 127. See also *names of specific diseases*
Animas, Las, Hospital (Havana), 95
Anthrax, 21, 38, 67
Antiseptic surgery, 22–23, 26, 115, 160
Antitoxin, 50, 71–72, 73, 83, 90, 197
Antivivisection bill, 81
Appleton, John, 13, 34
Arizona, 284(n.7)
Arkansas, 196, 284(n.7)